EXPERT

What the medical experts are saying about Protect Your Breasts:

Every woman will find the Protect Your Breasts program useful. Many patients are passive and wait for the doctor to tell them what to do. This program is for the motivated woman who wants to achieve mastery of her health. This program is for any woman who feels overwhelmed by too much information from many different sources. I will give this program to my three daughters.

With this program, there is a modest amount of work to protect breast health and it will pay off. We have no guides for breast health—only a confusing maze of bits and pieces of information. This program is the road to sanity and health.

—Dr. Max Chorowski, MD, FACOG,
Assistant Clinical Professor of OB-GYN and Psychiatry at Tufts University School of Medicine and Medical Director, Counseling & Gynecology Group, Longmeadow MA

~

The Protect Your Breasts program does a comprehensive job of directing women to healthful choices—it answers many questions and it doesn't leave holes.

The strategies outlined in this book and program are very important. Women are confused. They are not told the truth. There is much confusing information on safe estrogen metabolism. Women are misled on how to properly protect themselves from breast disease.

This book talks all about products and alternatives and provides a good selection of healthy products. The Protect Your Breasts program helps women find answers. This book is definitely the most comprehensive program available to improve a woman's health. In fact, it will bring health to the entire family.

There is nothing like the PBW program/Protect Your Breasts available for patients and professionals currently.

When Protect Your Breasts and the Proactive Breast Wellness program is published, I would like to see this program available nationally to all the compounding pharmacists and information regarding the program into the International Journal of Compounding Pharmacists.

—James E. Paoletti, RPh, FAAFM, FIACP, FACA,
Previous Director of Provider Education at ZRT Laboratory, Portland OR. Vice President/Director of Continuing Education for Professional Compounding Centers of America, Inc. (PCCA), Board of Directors at International Academy of Compounding Pharmacists

~

Protect Your Breasts presents a comprehensive overview of breast healthcare, including a Proactive Breast Wellness program that outlines multiple strategies to reduce the risk of breast cancer and its recurrence. The book also provides an excellent discussion of cryoablation or tumor freezing as a minimally-invasive alternative to surgery for the treatment of breast cancer. Furthermore, "The Early Freeze Protocol" proposes a novel strategy for facilitating the early diagnosis and treatment of breast cancer while also reducing the physical and emotional burden that typically accompanies diagnosis and treatment. In the context of Patient Centered Care, Protect Your Breasts is a worthy read!

—Dennis R. Holmes, M.D., F.A.C.S.,
Breast Surgeon and Researcher in Los Angeles, Cryoablation Expert and Advocate

~

Our current medical system has been designed to take our hands and give us direction when disease has become evident, but it has left us sadly wanting when it comes to prevention. Finding and accessing the information necessary to prevent disease is difficult and time consuming. And, even if we do find it, interpreting it and understanding it may take some help.

Thankfully, a comprehensive compilation of what we currently know about keeping our breasts free from disease, including breast cancer, is available as an engaging multimedia presentation offered by Ingrid Edstrom, FNP, M.Ed., CTT. Her new book and eBook, Protect Your Breasts and The Proactive Breast Wellness Program is her Magnus Opus and a labor of love.

—**Carol Petersen, RPh, CNP,**
Women's International Pharmacy

READER REVIEWS

ALL Breast Cancer Patients need to have this knowledge on Cryoablation. EVERYONE.

Ingrid's book and instructions on how to get Cryoablation therapy needs to be shared worldwide. Any woman with breast cancer or fibroadenomas should have this choice for treatment. Even PubMed and NCBI tout the incredible successes of this procedure. Ingrid is a pioneer in this field and is determined to save as many lives as possible while preserving our womanly anatomy. Who doesn't want an alternative to brutal mastectomies and lumpectomies? READ THIS BOOK, I promise, it is worth the small investment to gain this knowledge and could very well save your life.

—**Melanie N.,** Cryo Patient Advocate

Breast Cancer Cryoablation Disclosed!

This book offers a wealth of information, as does Ingrid herself if you have the opportunity to use her services at Infrared Breast Health, LLC. I especially appreciate her knowledge of and recommendation for breast cancer cryoablation, a procedure I never knew existed for breast cancer before I came to see her. I chose this option for myself in lieu of surgery and was amazed by the procedure.

The issue of insurance coverage is discussed. If men can have their prostate cancers frozen with liquid nitrogen and the insurance companies pay for this accepted standard of care, then women should be able to have their breast cancers frozen and save their breasts. More women should be insisting that this procedure be made available to them.

Read Ingrid's book and learn for yourself about this impressive option for treatment of many breast cancers. Thank you, Ingrid!

—**Jan Jaskilka**, Breast Cancer Thriver

THE guide

This book is THE guide for improving breast health. All my questions and points of confusion have been answered and I have greatly improved my breast health as well as reduced my risk factors for developing breast cancer.

—**Rosa Jimenez**, Professor at Lane Community College

Very valuable information for women

This book contains state-of-the-art information and education to avoid breast cancer. Every woman should have it in their medical library.

—**Janet Meyers**

Following the information in this book will change your life

I have been seeing Ingrid for 9-10 years and have been following her Breast-Wellness protocol. She not only helped me with my breast inflammation but also with my thyroid, cholesterol levels and improved my thermography scan. I will be 75 and have much more energy now than when I was 62.

Following the information in this book will change your life.

—**Rose C.**, Retired Nurse

I am extremely impressed with all the information

I am extremely impressed with all the information I have been given by Ingrid, both with the book and in person. I am 2 years post breast cancer. I have been given many helpful tools to help decrease the chances of the cancer returning by Ms. Edstrom. Ingrid has put her heart and soul into this book, I feel blessed to have met Ingrid and have thermography. The Protect Your Breasts book is full of information to decrease your chances of getting cancer in the first place, as well as preventing cancer from returning. I really appreciate Ingrid Edstrom.

—**Michele Fountain**, Breast Cancer Thriver

I can't recommend this book highly enough

There is a lot of information out there, and Ingrid Edstrom distills and clarifies the latest science into a simple, understandable, and most importantly DOABLE format. If you are fortunate enough to live in Oregon and can schedule an office visit, I encourage you to do so!

—**L. Buck**

Easy to understand

Ingrid's well-written comprehensive book is a must for every woman who wants to know the menu of options available for breast health and breast cancer prevention, treatment and recovery. I find it dense yet easy to understand, and it seems to merge the best of both allopathic and complementary modalities. I highly recommend this book by a fierce advocate of choice in least invasive breast-health treatments!

—Kira S.

Incredibly informative book and testing support from Ingrid Edstrom

Last winter I found a lump in my breast and went into shock as to what it was about. A friend referred me to Ingrid Edstrom FNP, M.Ed. for help. She is the kindest, dearest most understanding informative person I have ever met in the medical field. Because I was particularly vulnerable due to previous medical issues it was only by the understanding of Ingrid that I was comfortably tested and supported in the many steps that followed my initial visit with her. She is a wise compassionate being with grace and humor most appreciated. Her book includes her audio download, Waves of Serenity, which was extremely helpful and informative. Her gift of a soothing, guiding voice on "Waves" as a download or also as a CD/ DVD puts one immediately at ease. I would and do refer her services, her wondrous book and CD tools she has masterfully created to anyone seeking support, help, encouragement and enlightenment with breast health. Thank you Ingrid for your service to us all!

—Christine Anderson

Comprehensive Breast Prevention Guide

After many years of hearing about Thermography, I decided to have the procedure. It is far easier and more comfortable than mammography and yields information many years before things can be seen on other testing modalities. Ingrid is thorough in her explanations of historic breast care, how diet and lifestyle affect breast health and treatment options that are becoming more and more accessible. Knowledge is power, and this book provides such a complete overview of testing, preventive protocols and upcoming newer and more effective and less invasive therapies. I left her office feeling much less fearful and empowered with a wonderful arsenal of self care information. This book is a summary of what Ingrid shares in her consultations. She is a pioneer and forerunner in this competitive and economically driven area of health care. Her goal is to provide us with tools to prevent or better treat any breast abnormality.

—Legend Lin

Protect Your Breasts

Freeze and Cure Your Breast Cancer with Cryoablation

Reduce Your Risk of Breast Cancer or its Reoccurrence with the *Proactive Breast Wellness* Program

Ingrid Edstrom, FNP, M.Ed.

Protect Your Breasts: Freeze and Cure Your Breast Cancer with Cryoablation, Reduce Your Risk of Breast Cancer or Its Reoccurrence with the Proactive Breast Wellness Program

Printed in the United States of America

Cover Design by Matt Bennett and Claire Flint Last

Luminare Press
442 Charnelton St.
Eugene, OR 97401
www.luminarepress.com

LCCN: 2017945966
ISBN: 978-1-944733-28-5

www.ProtectYourBreasts.com

MEDICAL DISCLAIMER

The contents of *Protect Your Breasts* and the *Proactive Breast Wellness* (PBW) program and website are for informational purposes only and are not a substitute for professional medical advice, diagnosis, or treatment. Always seek the advice of your physician or other qualified health care provider with any questions you have regarding a medical condition, and before undertaking any diet, dietary supplement, exercise, or other health program.

Protect Your Breasts and the *Proactive Breast Wellness* program and protocol is not a substitute for working with your own primary care physician. If you do have cancer, it is important that you work closely with your oncologist. Having a close relationship with your medical care provider is of great benefit in meeting your medical challenges over time.

This protocol was created to improve a woman's general health and cardiac health, as well as her breast health. Our cancer patients utilize this protocol as well as other supplements not listed in the standard PBW Nutritional Suggestions for immune support. PBW recommends a customized nutritional support program for women who are also working with their physician teams.

The *Proactive Breast Wellness* program is an educational tool to help you explore options and research that you may not be aware of to assist you on your journey towards health.

The *Protect Your Breasts* and the PBW programs are directed towards health promotion with a disease prevention focus.

For my daughter Kristin Edstrom
It is a privilege to know you and to be
your mother.
You have tirelessly encouraged me over the
decades with wisdom and grace.

For my father, John E. Large, who believed in
my vision.

Lastly, *Protect Your Breasts* is dedicated to the
thousands of women whom I have imaged with
my infrared camera IRIS.

For the women who shared their stories of
breast cancer and of hope.

Remember – Prevention IS the Cure!

CONTENTS

INTRODUCTION

Welcome and Congratulations!

You have gained access to *Protect Your Breasts* and the *Proactive Breast Wellness* program to empower you to minimize your risk of developing breast cancer or reduce the chance of its reoccurrence. The *Proactive Breast Wellness* program is a comprehensive program. Along with this book, you can get the free resource digital download or free resource data disc (CD) so you can follow along more easily and research in greater depth. It includes over 1,000 pages of medically indexed materials that may be of interest. The resource digital download or data disc can be used as an index for the book and eBook version. Since we had already gathered 1,028 pages of medically indexed material for the first edition audio version of PBW, it seemed a duplication to have an index in the book version.

I have also included many lists and worksheets in the Getting Started section at the end of the book. The resource materials have dietary suggestions, supplement lists, and checklists for your pantry and kitchen to help make health transitions and shopping easier.

You can also access the free 45-minute *Waves of Serenity* progressive muscle relaxation/guided beach imagery digital download, CD or DVD. The mind/body connection is important in improving your health with more restful sleep and decreased stress! I suggest you receive these free items before you start the PBW program so you will have all the materials ready to go and have lists ready to refer to as part of your study guide!

To access your free gifts, go to my website Store at www.ProtectYourBreasts.com, click on Free Resources for your PBW book/eBook, and enter the password code **PBWBOOK (all capitals and no spaces)** to receive *Waves of Serenity* and the resource material as a free digital download. If you prefer to have these sent to you as physical CDs, click on **PBW MAIL DISCS**.

My name is Ingrid Edstrom and I will be your guide for the *Protect Your Breasts* book and the *Proactive Breast Wellness* program and narrator for the audio CD/digital download version of *Waves of Serenity*. PBW is an educational program I have developed to reduce your risk of breast cancer or the chance of its reoccurrence. This third edition is also available as a soft cover book and eBook.

To further protect your health and the health of your whole family, **you can receive 20% off all your supplements!** This will save you a lot of money on many brand name supplements that you may already be taking. Visit the website at www.ProtectYourBreasts.com and go to the Supplement section to sign up for your discounted supplement products.

Are You Worried About Breast Cancer?

Every middle-aged and mature woman that I know is concerned about breast cancer. It does not affect only women, it affects families: our mothers, our partners, our children, our sisters, aunts, and grandmothers. Just think about the people you know who have been touched by this medical crisis. Many younger women worry, knowing how this cancer has struck older female relatives, and they wait, hoping they will not become a statistic themselves. Scientists have been working for years to find links between genetics and the risk of developing breast cancer, and some links have been found. However, some of the research suggests that our environment – what we eat, how we live, the chemicals and radiation we receive from the natural surroundings of our environment – may have greater impact, perhaps as much as 91-93%, on our future health than our genetics, which contributes only 7-9% to our risk of developing breast cancer.

This information is heartening because it means we can make dietary, lifestyle, and environmental changes that will reduce our chances of developing breast disease or decrease reoccurrence rates, thus altering current statistical projections.

So far the medical community has not discovered a comprehensive approach that will prevent breast cancer. The *Proactive Breast Wellness* program will help you decrease your risks and improve the health of your whole family. The PBW program is also heart-healthy and women usually notice 15 to 30 pounds of weight loss and improvement in their lipid and thyroid panels. Women who follow my protocol usually improve their vitamin D3 levels and achieve hormone balancing, improved libido, better sleep, and decreased stress.

One of our professional medical experts, Dr. Max Chorowski, Assistant Clinical Professor of OB GYN at Tufts Medical School, who reviewed the PBW program states, "There are other books on the market; but they just are not as good as yours." There are more endorsements from expert reviewers on the website in the "What the Experts Are Saying" section.

Breast Cancer Statistics

Our fear of breast cancer is not unwarranted. According to

the National Cancer Institute, breast cancer incident rates have increased more than 40% from 1973 to 1998 in the US. Oregon, where I currently practice, consistently ranks in the top five states for breast cancer incidence, and reported the third highest per capita incidence in 2001. It appears that in 2007, Oregon moved to being the second highest per capita. Washington State was number one in the nation. The incidence of breast cancer in the US has risen during the past 30 years from one in thirty to one in seven women. Agencies that track these statistics are concerned that in the next 10 years it may be one in five. It would not be overstating the case to describe this as an epidemic.

According to Dr. John Lee's book, *What Your Doctor May Not Tell You About Breast Cancer And How Hormone Balance Can Save Your Life*, published in October, 2002, your risk of surviving malignant breast cancer is just about the same as it was 50 years ago, when the only treatments were a mastectomy. In other words, despite millions of dollars in research and hugely expensive and risky treatments, the conventional medical approach to breast cancer isn't working, and talk of prevention is virtually nonexistent.

One might wonder what could be the cause of such a statistical growth rate in such a short time? I believe there is sufficient evidence to show that we are being continually exposed to chemicals in our environment that increase our risk for breast and other cancers. These chemicals act like estrogens in our bodies and they easily bind to our estrogen receptor sites. These compounds are also called estrogen mimickers, or xeno-estrogens, and are found in many common products. Have you noticed that girls are developing breasts as early as 8 years old or four years before the standard age of 12, and their periods are starting as early as nine and ten years of age? These little girls are exposed to many more chemicals than our grandmothers were. In fact, the American Pediatric Association is now considering changing their growth charts to say that the norm now is to have breast development at eight and periods starting at nine or ten years of age! This has never been the case in all of human history!

These chemicals also affect our teenage boys. Sperm counts have been dropping, leading to infertility issues when they are ready to start a family. Have you also noticed that many adult males are growing "man boobs" and are carrying a lot of extra inches around their midriffs?

Making changes by following the PBW program will help everyone in your family. What you learn here will impact future generations. Knowledge is empowering!

What Are These Xeno-Estrogens and Estrogen Mimickers?

Prominent sources of these xeno-estrogens that promote cancer include pesticides, herbicides, bovine growth hormones in our non-organic meat and dairy, plastics, and a score of other sources that contribute to the estrogenic soup in our environment. Here in Oregon, herbicides containing xeno-estrogens are routinely used by the timber industry in clear cuts, in weed-suppression along country roads, and by well-meaning gardeners and farmers who collectively spray vast quantities of these chemicals. Brand names may include: 2-4-D Dioxin and Agent Orange-type compounds include Roundup and CrossBow. Atrazine is also being used on the urban, suburban, and rural landscapes.

Risk to human health is exacerbated by other miracles of modern chemistry. These include parabens, used as preservatives in cosmetics, food, shampoos, and sunscreen. Bovine growth hormone (BGH), is added to the feed of non-organic meat and dairy animals. Farmers use it to add three pounds a day to the weight of beef animals prior to slaughter and to increase the milk volume in dairy animals. It is then found in non-organic food products such as meat, milk, cheese, yogurt, and butter. There are real and troubling health consequences to these compounds finding their way into the human food chain.

Though legal in the United States, these estrogen-like products have been linked to breast cancer, prostate cancer, miscarriages, infertility, arthritis-like symptoms, gastro-esophageal reflux, multiple sclerosis, malaise, ADD, ADHD, and other symptoms and diseases. Well-meaning producers of these products have been unwittingly poisoning us. Canada and European countries have begun restricting the use of herbicides and pesticides because of their risks. The United States has not yet done so, and remains an exporter of herbicide and pesticide products to third-world countries, some of which export their exposed food products back to us. I strongly believe that restricting exposure to these chemicals in our day-to-day living will save lives and improve our health, as well as the health of future generations. The *Proactive Breast Wellness* program includes more information about these chemicals, as well as practical, easy-to-follow suggestions on how to rid these products that contain these chemicals from your lives and homes.

To learn more, please review my website in the "Protect Your Breasts" section, as well as the sections on The Dangers of GMOs and Herbicide Use. There are also a number of links in the Take Action section to connect with other organizations that have been active in trying to protect the health of citizens. While you are in that section, listen to the video clip on Genetic Roulette. It will change the way you look at your food supply.

Breast Cancer Patients Have a Profile. Could This Be You?

It appears that breast cancer patients have a profile. The following lab tests are often high: estrogen levels, free testosterone, DHEA and night-time cortisol from elevated stress levels and lack of sleep. The following tests are usually low: progesterone, iodine, and vitamin D3 levels. Cancer patients are typically hypothyroid, with abnormal or low normal thyroid test values and a morning temperature usually less than 97.8 degrees Fahrenheit when taken under their arm because their thyroid is not functioning well.

Consequently, it is extremely important to have some baseline laboratory testing done so you can find out if you are at higher risk to develop breast cancer or have it return. You can monitor your health with labs taken again after six months and following up on the checklist / work sheets once you have started to make changes on the PBW program to see how you are progressing. It is empowering and informative to be able to compare your current status with the baseline labs.

The *Proactive Breast Wellness* program assists you in learning how to achieve a balance in your hormones and to make dietary, lifestyle, and environmental changes that will improve your health and empower you. It also includes a protocol of dietary supplements that has been successful in reducing breast inflammation in six to twelve months, as well as reducing excess estrogen.

If you are curious about another way women have monitored their improvement on the PBW protocol, you can review the PYB website and watch the slides at Save Your Breasts in the "Protect Your Breasts" section on the website. Viewing these slides is important because you can see how an organic diet and xeno-estrogen exposure actually change the breast tissue metabolically and physiologically. There are also some before-and-after infrared images in the same section. This should give you some encouragement that the PBW program works because you can literally see the difference.

Women just like you who followed the PBW protocol improved their labs and infrared scans about 65% of the time in a six to 12 month period. This is why I have become so passionate about this PBW program. I have had my infrared camera since early 2006 and I have imaged over 10,000 breasts. Seeing the health of my clients improve has been extremely gratifying.

Many of the PBW recommendations will also enhance other aspects of general well-being, reducing perimenopausal and menopausal symptoms, promoting loss of unwanted weight, improving libido, decreasing fibrocystic breast issues, increasing bone health, supporting immune system function, and improving thyroid function. I have included the *Waves of Serenity* 45-minute relaxation program as a Digital Download, CD / DVD to decrease stress and insomnia and improve your cortisol levels, which supports your immune system. People who have listened to the *Waves of Serenity* program on a daily basis have dropped their systolic blood pressure about 20 points in six weeks. I have also used *Waves* for people with chronic pain. Together, these changes will reduce your risk of developing breast cancer or its reoccurrence and improve your heart health and immune system.

Ingrid Edstrom's Background

Let me tell you a little bit about my background. I am the founder and president of Infrared Breast Health, LLC, and the creator of the *Proactive Breast Wellness* program. I currently have a private medical practice in Eugene, Oregon. In my wellness coaching, I strive to empower people to take responsibility for their own health and to make lifestyle changes. I have been a nationally certified Family Nurse Practitioner since 1978, with a Masters in Health Education from Boston University in 1981. As a Nurse Practitioner, I have delivered extensive patient teaching about medical issues, diseases, and prevention. Lifestyle and nutritional counseling have been a focus of my practice. I started my academic career as a nutrition major prior to receiving my Bachelors in Nursing from the University of Rhode Island in 1974. I worked in some of the larger teaching hospitals in Boston, as well as for a large HMO for twelve years. I worked with four general surgeons who did a lot of breast cancer surgery. I scrubbed into cases in the operating room and did a lot of pre-op and post-op counseling and care at this HMO.

I soon became frustrated with the corporate need to push patients through medical care on a conveyor belt system with a certain number of minutes allotted to see and treat patients without addressing stress management or the nutritional teaching needs of clients. I also became aware that just handing out prescriptions was not getting to the cause of why people were ill. The medications only treated symptoms. They did not get to the source of the problem. The focus was on disease management not health promotion or disease prevention.

The Mind/Body Connection

A turning point for my career involved meeting a Korean Buddhist monk in the late 1980's when I began exploring suffering from a Buddhist perspective and started a meditation practice. This fostered an understanding of the connection between people's thoughts and perceptions of their reality and their health, profoundly affecting my views and my role as a healer.

I then enrolled in the *Behavior Modification Relaxation Response* course for medical providers at the Harvard Medical School in 1990. This program was run by Dr. Herbert Benson at the Mind Body Medical Institute in Boston, Massachusetts. I became certified to teach stress management programs in school systems, as well as the *Prepare For Surgery/Heal Faster* mind / body guided imagery workshops. My practice subsequently expanded to include stress and pain management, and natural menopausal management using bioidentical hormone replacement, dietary, and nutritional supplements.

I have worked with chronic pain clients and with those whose symptomatology benefits from a mind / body approach to treatment, including trauma, insomnia, irritable bowel, migraines, fibromyalgia, high blood pressure, ulcers, panic attacks, depression and cancer. I have also worked with hospice clients.

During this time I created a six-hour program called Chill Out Naturally, a stress management program that I provided to six high schools in Western Massachusetts to assist in improving test scores and reducing stress. My program was found to help reduce negative lifestyle choices regarding smoking, drinking and driving, and drug use among the high school youth.

I then created a 45-minute progressive muscle relaxation/ guided imagery CD / DVD entitled *Waves of Serenity*, currently being used in day-surgery centers, oncology suites, and by people recovering from hospitalizations at home. *Waves* has also been used by military veterans returning with post-traumatic stress disorders. This guided imagery was designed to help reduce stress and pain, and to decrease insomnia or just to help you relax.

The *Waves of Serenity* CD and DVD are available on the website as a part of the *Proactive Breast Wellness* program. It is also available as a download. As part of the *Protect Your*

Breasts eBook and the soft-cover book version, you will also receive a free copy of the *Waves of Serenity*. Please access your copy of *Waves* now if you have not done so. Use the password code **PBWBOOK** in my website Store to receive your free digital download of *Waves*.

In 2005, I became one of those frightened women with a thickened area in my own breast. I obtained an infrared breast scan, an adjunctive technique for visualizing physiological / metabolic changes in breast tissue. My thermography was borderline abnormal. I was at once terrified and energized to take action. I researched and started an early version of what has become the *Proactive Breast Wellness* program that includes an anti-estrogenic diet. I began eating organically, and got rid of bottled water and plastics for storing food. I took supplements to help take the extra estrogen out of my system. I evaluated my hormone levels, balanced my hormones, and started a course of bioidentical progesterone. Additionally, I made a number of other dietary and lifestyle changes. Thankfully, results were almost immediate. Within several months, I was able to eliminate the thickened area. I confirmed my medical progress by consulting a breast surgeon and having a mammogram and ultrasound done. I reversed all the inflammation as seen on the infrared scan in the course of just four months!

To see some of the before and after images of women who have been on the *Proactive Breast Wellness* program or to see the effects on breast tissue of toxic levels of xenoestrogens from herbicides and pesticides and bovine growth hormone, please go to the website at www.ProtectYourBreasts.com and view the images in the "Protect Your Breasts" section.

Following my own medical ordeal, I felt that if I was able to reverse these conditions once I knew I had a problem, then other women might also benefit. The *Proactive Breast Wellness* program took me seven years to research and create to help you protect your own health or the heath of a loved one. Since breast cancer is an inflammatory problem, and breast cancers take 10 to 12 years to grow, the sooner one discovers a thermal change or evidence of early inflammation, the better the chances are for survival. I came to believe that thermal assessment through modern high-resolution infrared imaging may well offer the best assessment tool available to detect or monitor changes in the breast. In fact, it may detect these changes three to eight years earlier than mammograms are able to. Now a major portion of my medical practice is infrared thermal imaging. With this tool, I am able not only to identify women who need surgical evaluation, but also to monitor women's progress in reversing their inflammatory changes and decreasing the vascularity in their breasts.

The *Proactive Breast Wellness* program is the protocol I use to decrease my clients' risks. I frequently see reversal of their inflammatory thermal patterns within six to 12 months. Breast cancer survivors also come in for thermo-mammography / infrared thermography to follow their progress through treatment. The Cleveland Clinic uses IR (infrared) in their medical oncology department to monitor women's status and progress. I am currently conducting a clinical study to document these positive results. I believe I am the only one in the country currently using thermography to evaluate metabolic activity and body burden of estrogen mimickers and their effects on breast tissue.

The military-grade infrared camera that I use has a 97% sensitivity. MRI's have a 98% sensitivity. I use the IR camera to monitor metabolic reactions to hormone replacement therapy and to follow breast cancer survivors to monitor their progress. Please view the "Protect Your Breasts" section on the website to actually see the difference the PBW protocol makes.

For many years, I have been concerned about breast cancer and worried along with all women. To put it another way, racing for the cure is great but I'm more interested in a preventative approach to this problem. Many of the women who come to see me for an evaluation are frustrated and frightened when they are told they have a questionable mammogram or ultrasound, and are simply told to return in six months for another one. The medical community does not tell women what to do about reducing their risks while awaiting the next mammogram or ultrasound. This seems problematic to me.

As a Nurse Practitioner and health educator, I am passionate about making a difference in the dreadful cancer statistics because these statistics only represent the sanitized version of real people's extreme suffering. Is this preventable? The *Proactive Breast Wellness* program and *Protect Your Breasts* are my offerings to women to empower them in their quest to reduce their breast cancer risk with a preventative focus.

In the following chapters, you will be educated about the topics mentioned earlier, with greater detail and specific recommendations. These chapters are accompanied by a free data disc or a free resource download that can be obtained from the website to supplement your learning and health exploration. Also remember that the resource guide contains the medical source materials and research articles upon which my book is based. If you wish to further your research, you can read the sections that you are interested in. There are over 1,000 pages of abstracts and articles divided by chapters.

Your password code is **PBWBOOK**. Obtain your free materials now to use and refer to them as needed. Also included on the www.ProtectYourBreasts.com website is a free gift of the *Waves of Serenity*. The guided visualization may also lessen your cancer risk and improve your immune system health. Practice daily with *Waves* and see the difference in your health and mood.

Congratulations again on taking the first step on your path to improved health and well-being and protecting the health of your children and your whole family.

Remember – Prevention IS the Cure!

CHAPTER 1

The Anti-Estrogenic Diet and Other Dietary Recommendations

As we go through the following educational chapters, please remember that there is an accompanying free data disc / resource download to refer to as needed for details mentioned in each chapter, plus additional resources, references and worksheets to expand your personal health research in the Getting Started section.

These free gifts are obtained at www.ProtectYourBreasts.com from the website Store. Use the password code **PBWBOOK**. As another option, you can have them mailed to you as a CD.

Women usually loose 15 to 30 pounds in six to 12 months on the PBW program, decreasing that stubborn belly fat and gain more energy. They usually decrease insomnia and stress, improve libido, and attain improved hormone balance. Vitamin D3 levels and thyroid function are optimized. The PBW protocol is a heart-healthy program reducing cholesterol levels and improving our good cholesterol or HDL levels. Making these healthy changes for your breast health will improve the health of your whole family as a side benefit.

Our grandmothers in the 1940s and 1950s ate simpler foods. They had a cleaner diet with less estrogen dominance. They cooked with ingredients from scratch; nothing was pre-processed. Many had organic gardens. They also were less exposed to plastics, and did not have to deal with as many chemicals in the environment. There were no synthetic hormone replacement therapies or birth control pills. The breast cancer rate back then was one in 28 in the United States. Pakistan, as an example of a third-world non-industrial country, had a one in 35 breast cancer rate. Currently in the United States, one in eight women will get breast cancer during their lifetimes. The American Cancer Society is projecting a future increase to perhaps one woman in five. This is an epidemic. We can benefit from the valuable wisdom of a simpler lifestyle and diet.

Breast cancer is for the most part an estrogen-dominant problem. Since we live in an estrogenic soup, whatever we can do to decrease our hidden estrogen load will improve our health. Environmental and dietary estrogen has also increased prostate cancer in men, and early breast development in girls. Many men are developing breast tissue and gaining more abdominal weight. Estrogen receptors are fat-bound. Making changes in your environment, diet and learning about supplements, will improve your whole family's health!

When dealing with the estrogen-dominant problem, there are two aspects to consider in reducing our intake of hidden estrogen in foods: the specific foods that we eat, as well as the way the foods are processed and stored.

First I'll talk about the foods we eat. Estrogens and estrogen mimickers are found in foods both naturally and as the result of chemical manipulation. High levels of estrogen affect many diseases including fibrocystic breast disease, ovarian cysts, and pre-menopausal symptoms or PMS, in addition to breast cancer.

The liver is important in metabolizing estrogen into an almost totally unharmful form. It also converts estrogen into compounds that can be excreted from the body through the urine and bile. The purpose of the *Proactive Breast Wellness* diet is to support the liver, reduce intake of estrogen, and support other glands such as the adrenal glands and the thyroid gland that influence estrogen levels in the body.

Do You Know What is In Your Food? The Hazards of Bovine Growth Hormone (BGH) and Genetically Modified Organisms (GMOs)

The two primary sources of estrogen in the diet come from non-organically raised meat and dairy products. Bovine growth hormone is fed to dairy animals to increase milk supply, and is also injected and fed to stockyard animals to increase their bulk prior to slaughter. These stockyard animals are not raised humanely and due to overcrowding and disease they are also given antibiotics.

Many people have developed resistance to antibiotic therapy, which in part has developed from consuming these second hand antibiotics from our conventionally raised meat and dairy diet. These are compelling reasons not to eat conventionally raised meat and dairy. To learn more about these practices, see the videos Food Inc. and The Real Dirt on Farmer John.

Additionally, research indicates that genetically modified organisms or GMO grains and the mutated molds and bacteria on such grains disrupt the liver's ability to detoxify normally.

These mutants also affect the gut wall lining allowing harmful compounds to slip past into the blood stream directly affecting sensitive tissues throughout the body and over activating immune response; damaging what otherwise was healthy tissue before. Conventionally raised animals are fed GMO grains. Moreover, a shocking 83% of all food items in grocery stores are genetically modified or have GMO products in them. This is, by the way, why labeling initiatives are so important to your health so you know what you are feeding your family!

Human genome research has begun to explore how mutated and genetically altered substances act as triggers for cancers. It will be some time before conclusive studies are completed.

The PBW program encourages you to lobby your local markets to label GMO foods so you and your family know what you are eating and to avoid GMO-containing products to protect your health. (The free data disc/resource download has links in the Take Action section to more information about this threat to your health.)

Environmental Sources of Estrogen Mimickers

The other sources of estrogen are primarily environmental xeno-estrogens from pesticides, herbicides, plastics, and other chemicals in our environment. These estrogen mimickers resemble natural estrogens and are bound at women's estrogen receptor sites, creating the effect of excess estrogen. Many of these receptor sites are found in fatty tissues, where estrogen can also be stored. This is why it is so very important for individuals to reduce their white body fat ratio and replace it with lean muscle mass. White fat is the giggly fat found under the skin. Brown adipose fat found in the core of the body is beneficial, cancer protective, and necessary.

A later chapter will go into more detail regarding xenoestrogens.

Organic foods are purposely produced without exposure to

pesticides, herbicides, petrochemical fertilizers, preservative waxes, and other potential estrogen mimicker chemicals. But be aware, there remain FDA-approved chemicals used on commercial organic crops, and ground water contamination remains an issue. While, as a general rule, organic foods have lower levels of chemical contamination – they are not chemical free. Your best bet is to purchase from reliable and ethical local farmers whom you can query about their chemical use and farming practices.

Eating organically is the Most Important Thing You Can Do to Reduce Breast Cancer

Eating organic foods is the most important single dietary practice you can follow to reduce your risk of breast cancer or its reoccurrence, and is the first *Proactive Breast Wellness* program recommendation. If possible, have as much of your food be organic as your budget allows. You may discover that as you start cooking more beautiful meals, you will reduce your take-out and going-out-to-eat meals, so you will have more funds for your organic fare. If you cannot eat completely organically, eat the organic items that you are able to, bless your food, and have positive thoughts about the way that you have now chosen to nurture and nourish yourself and your family.

It is sometimes overwhelming to try to change all your habits at once, so take baby steps, and make the changes with a positive intent. As you eliminate some things from your pantry and bring in new foods, you can do so in small increments. I have provided a pantry and kitchen checklist to help you get started in making these healthy changes. The worksheet checklist is located on the free data disc or free resource download or in the Putting It All Together and Getting Started section at the end of the book.

Select one change every four weeks to allow yourself to develop lasting habits. This will reduce the feeling of being overwhelmed, allowing you the opportunity to create positive movement towards your health goals. Some individuals may be able to immediately transition to new dietary practices. If you are one of those, please do not feel restricted to making slow changes.

Labels: What Is the Difference Between "Organic" and "Natural"?

When buying organic foods, one must understand what the various labels mean. The strictest compliance with organic production is indicated by the term "Certified Organic". The producers of these products have maintained their organic practices for more than three years, are independently inspected, and have paid fees to obtain this designation. At the time of this writing, the term "organic" alone on a product does not necessarily mean that organic practices have been stringently followed and confirmed. Often the terms "natural", "hormone free", "antibiotic free", and "pesticide free" are used, but may not indicate stringently organic practices.

According to the USDA National Organic Standards Board (NOSB), the term "organic" is defined by law, as opposed to the terms "natural" and "eco-friendly," which may imply that some organic methods were used in the production of the foodstuff, but with no guarantee of complete adherence to organic practices. Most "natural" products do not contain synthetic products but conventional food or feed that included synthetic chemicals may have been used in their production (as in "natural" beef). Non-organic meats in the US are fed estrogens in the stockyard to fatten them. Beware of labels that say, "natural meat." There may be fine print that claims that the animals were not fed antibiotics or hormones within 80 days prior to slaughter. These chemicals are fat-soluble and they remain in the tissues.

You may also find some foods labeled as "transitional organic," indicating that the producers are in the process of converting to fully organic methods, but have not yet met certification standards. So, your best protection is to look for the "100% certified organic" labeled foods, and, as a second choice, those labeled as "organic."

How To Avoid "The Dirty Dozen"

If you do have to include in your diet some foods that are not organically produced, some are safer than others. Some fruits and vegetables retain higher levels of pesticides or are sprayed more often than others. I call these the dirty dozen. This list is excerpted from the 2017 Environmental Working Group report, or *Shopper's Guide to Pesticides and Produce*. This report and many others are available at www.ewg.org, and you can find the list on the data disc/resource download and at the end of the book in the worksheet sections.

The non-organic fruits and vegetables that have been found to carry the heaviest pesticide load are strawberries, apples, and blueberries (these three consistently show the highest amount), bell peppers (usually from US or Mexico), spinach and cherries from the US, peaches, Mexican cantaloupes, celery, apricots, green beans, grapes from Chile, red raspberries, and cucumbers. Among the produce that has the fewest pesticides are avocadoes, onions, sweet potatoes, cauliflower, Brussels sprouts, bananas, plums, green onions, watermelon, and broccoli.

There are many major hazards in eating GMO foods. More information about GMOs is listed in Chapter 6 of the PBW program and in the Take Action section of our website. There is a fabulous video clip on our website entitled Genetic Roulette by Gary Smith. I encourage you and your family to watch the whole video to get a better understanding of how GMOs negatively affect your health and cause many diseases. I was able to meet and speak with Gary Smith several years ago and his video has changed the way I look at food and understand how GMOs are negatively impacting the health of my patients.

Pass Some Agent Orange With Your Corn, Please

The certified organic label represents that the seed used was not genetically modified (GMO) and the crop was raised using organic practices without chemicals. Our food sources are currently involved in a worldwide crisis related to who controls the seed for crops, which may have sinister consequences. In the future, if legislation is not put into effect promptly, people will no longer have a choice about the nature of the seeds used to produce the food they eat. Monsanto and other companies have been purchasing seed growers and creating GMO or genetically modified seeds. These seeds are altered so they can be ready for Roundup, 2-4-D Dioxin, or Agent Orange-like chemicals. The intent is to grow fields of crops that can be sprayed with herbicides to kill the weeds but not the crop. There has been news released about farmers wanting to be able to use even more powerful, currently banned chemicals due to weeds becoming resistant to Roundup. These chemicals will then increase in your food supply. Corn, wheat, canola, cotton, cotton seed oil, sugar from sugar beets, and soy are now about 98% GMO if not designated organically grown. Corn and soy are in a myriad of products and these GMO-produced grains are also fed to conventionally-raised animals. Other seeds are altered so that they will only grow one crop and farmers cannot save their own seeds to replant the following year.

The U.S. and Canada both prohibit 100% certified organic food from containing GMO ingredients. However, contamination of crops may cause organic feed to contain some percentage of GMO ingredients. Basically, the problem is that GMO crops spew pollen into the air, as all crops do. This pollen then cross-breeds with organic crops, which pollutes and corrupts the organic farms. I encourage you to go to my website links and resource section to take action, and send letters and vote against GMO practices before our whole food industry is destroyed.

You can also be aware of the seasonal cycles of fruits and vegetables. Out of season produce coming from third-world countries will more likely be pesticide exposed. For instance, eating domestic strawberries and cantaloupe in season may be safer than Mexican fruit out of season. However, unless designated organic, domestic products may still include pesticide residue. Some pesticides and herbicides that have already been outlawed in the United States are still being used in other countries, and their products are still being imported to the United States. Some of these outlawed pesticides are actually still produced in the United States for export only.

When eating away from home, the challenges of limiting your exposure to conventional and non organic food increase. Choosing an eatery that specifically indicates they use only organic produce and meat is the easiest solution. If that is not possible, you can quiz your server as to which items on the menu are wild caught, organic, or not. I recommend that you avoid the fast food arena because of the presence of bovine growth hormone and antibiotics in conventional meat and dairy, as well as the deep frying methods often used, which may involve GMO produced cooking oils.

It is more than just the deep fry methods. All the flour and corn, and the cooking oils made from corn, canola, and soy contained in commercial foods will contain chemicals like hexane, a dry cleaning chemical and GMO. In addition, according to food industry journals, synthetic proteins, algae, and modified yeast are increasingly in use. The best rule is to avoid all fast food or chain eateries. Whenever possible, select local bistros, cafes, and restaurants or locate an organic food store, farm stand, farmer's co-op, or sustainable agriculture vendor and make a picnic for your travel meals.

Food Storage, Preparation and the Dangers of Plastics

The second food-related exposure to xenoestrogens is related to how our foods are prepared and stored. The risk has to do primarily with food contact with plastics. All plastics may leach estrogen mimickers into food. Heat as low as 87°F encourages the release of these chemicals. Ideally, plastics are best not used at all for food preparation and storage.

Modern plastic storage containers are numbered one through seven to denote the types of plastic. I recommend that you avoid all of these when possible. However, some of the plastics are known to be more dangerous than others, especially plastics numbered seven, six, and three. The worst, and the most important to avoid, are those containing Bisphenol A, also known as BPA. This is found primarily in the number seven plastics, usually polycarbonate. Number seven items are frequently labeled as microwaveable, or as eating utensils, linings for metal food and beverage containers, and baby bottles. Many countries have banned polycarbonate dishes and cutlery, and newer replacement plastic items are often labeled as BPA free. However, BPA free does not mean safe and I would not use them.

The next plastics highest on the dangerous list are numbers six and three. Polystyrene number six is found in foam or Styrofoam containers and cups, as well as clear, disposable take-out containers. Styrene is a human carcinogen and leaches out when in contact with heat, fat, or alcohol.

Plastic number three is polyvinyl chloride, known as PVC. This type contains plasticizers called Adipates and Phthalates. This type is found in plastic wrapping materials for foods like cheese and meat, and in plastic oil containers.

If they must be used, the safer plastics are numbers one, two, four, and five. For more information on types of plastics, please refer to the data disc/resource download. The following practical suggestions may assist you in making changes in your kitchen.

Your Plastic Kitchen Utensils and Microwave May Increase Your Cancer Risk

The greatest risk of exposure from plastics results from contact with food at high temperatures. To reduce or prevent exposure may require you to change cookware and food preparation routines. Do not microwave in Tupperware, plastic containers, or on plastic plates. In fact, I would stop using your microwave altogether. Avoid pouring hot sauces or liquids into plastic. Do not use plastic cookware, colanders, spoons, or spatulas. Avoid nonstick cookware because of the plastic coatings. Use metal or wooden utensils when cooking. Use glass or ceramic plates and cups for serving, not plasticware. Stainless steel and cast iron cookware are the safest. Make sure your cast iron is from the United States or France – do not use cast iron made anywhere else. Aluminum cookware is not the best choice because of a possible relationship with Alzheimer's disease. It is not known if anodized aluminum is safer than other aluminum.

Get Rid Of Your Tupperware and Plastic Storage Containers

Exposure of foods to plastic during storage may not be as serious a risk as heated plastics, but should be avoided as much as possible. Store leftovers in stainless steel or glass containers. Lead-free ceramic, porcelain, and enamel-covered cast iron are also good options. If the containers have plastic lids, avoid having the food touch the lids and let the food cool first before putting on the lid. Otherwise, steam will condense on the plastic lid and fall back into your food.

You might consider using wax paper instead of plastic wraps. Some of the old-fashioned brown waxed papers use waxes that are vegetable-based, not petrochemically based. If you are uncertain, a phone call to the manufacturer can confirm. Glad Wrap is a different polymer product that may be a better choice than Saran Plastic Wrap. Avoid using plastic storage bags, when possible. If you must use them, try putting waxed paper inside the bag so that your food is not in contact with the plastic. Some health food stores carry unbleached cardboard vegetable-waxed food storage boxes that can be used in freezers with a protective wrap of freezer paper, freezer tape, or an external plastic bag. When buying meat or fish, have the butcher wrap it in regular butcher paper. In this way, you will avoid the Styrofoam trays, plastic absorbent pillows, and outer shrink-wrap. You don't know how long the meat has been in contact with these plastic materials.

Bring things home and store them in glass or stainless containers. You can freeze food in glass jars with straight sides as long as you leave about an inch or an inch and a half of air space above the food to allow for expansion. Tighten the lids securely after they are frozen. Freezing in plastic containers is equally a risk for petro-chemical release.

Buy Food in Glass Not In Plastic or in Cans

Cheeses and other items purchased in shrink-wrap can be removed from the plastic at home and stored in a safe container. To be even safer, you can trim off the portion of the product that was in contact with the plastic wrap. If you have a choice of fruit juice or other foods in plastic versus glass bottles, go for the glass containers. Realize also that canned foods may be in contact with a plastic coating inside the cans. Many manufacturers are now putting BPA free labels on their cans. Although challenging, you may be able to find similar products packed in glass, or make it from scratch. Buy fruits and vegetables that have not been waxed with petrochemicals. These waxes are not noted on produce labels or stickers. There again, you may want to be cautious. Check the apples and cucumbers next time. If you are purchasing organically, they will not be waxed with petrochemical waxes.

Get Rid of Your Plastic Drinking Bottles

Plastic water and beverage containers are common sources of xenoestrogen or estrogen-mimicker exposure. Additionally, they cause harmful environmental impact by ending up in landfills. The plastic exposure is completely unnecessary. Consider not purchasing any food or water in plastic bottles or containers. Using a high-quality solid carbon water filter or reverse osmosis water purification system in your home will produce a healthier product. You might consider getting a MultiPure solid carbon water filter for your kitchen and shower that removes about 99.8% of all the chlorine and fluoride, and a long list of other chemicals including many herbicides and pesticides that might be getting into your water supply. We all know that no water filter available gets everything out of the water supply, including many of the prescription medications that also include birth control pills and other estrogens. Filters grab the largest molecules first, which will be chlorine, lead, then fluoride. If these are in the highest concentrations, your filter will let pass many of the petrochemicals. All the chemicals are easily vaporized in a shower situation so you should always use a solid carbon filter on showerheads.

It is a bit of an investment to get a water filter for your home, but the water tastes a lot better. The MultiPure can be found through the links section on the website, or at www.multipure.com. Other solid carbon filter brands are readily available. Some of the lower cost filters, such as Britta, do not use an adequate solid carbon filter and store the filtered water in a plastic container. If you create healthy filtered water at home, do not store it in plastic containers.

If you must purchase water products in plastic containers, you can reduce your risk in various ways. Don't use water stored in plastic bottles left in your automobile because of the heat trapped in the vehicle. Remember, some plastics leach chemicals at just 87°F. Check the dates on the bottles to see how long the water has been sitting in the container. Unfortunately, we cannot know to what temperature the bottles were heated when transported during delivery. Transfer water purchased in plastic containers to stainless steel thermoses or glass bottles. I prefer US-made stainless steel because there are regulations and controls on what is being used in the product.

Use paper cups, the metal top of your thermoses, stainless steel or ceramic containers for beverages, especially if they are hot. Don't use Styrofoam or plastic cups. Watch out for those convenient plastic cup toppers. The heat from your tea or coffee will release the harmful chemicals in the lid into your beverage. Also do not stir your coffee or tea with a plastic stirring stick or straw. Look for a wooden stirrer or a clean metal spoon. If you have to use plastic on occasion such as for camping, be sure to choose BPA free plastics that are also numbered one, two, or five.

Other Dietary Recommendations

Besides dietary changes to reduce xenoestrogen exposure, there are other general health recommendations that may indirectly reduce breast cancer risk or its reoccurrence. Most of these recommendations have to do with avoiding unnecessary dietary chemicals, and achieving a more alkaline diet. This may, in turn, result in decreasing excessive body weight, which is a risk factor because of the role fat plays in estrogen storage, and may also help with diabetic and cardiac issues. The role of foods containing natural plant estrogens, called phytoestrogens, is a subject of continued research and confusion with respect to reducing breast cancer risk.

Food Additives & Other Nasty Things You Can Identify and Avoid

Although not estrogen mimickers, there are food additives that may be dangerous as a result of other mechanisms. Nitrites have been found to be carcinogenic, and are found in processed meats such as sausages and hot dogs. Colorings and other additives are under some suspicion as contributors to ill health. Fungicides are known to disrupt bowel flora.

Parabens, preservatives found in some foods as well as cosmetics, have been found in breast cancer tumor tissue. Soda beverages are discouraged because they have no nutritional value, most come in plastic containers, some contain bromine, they are very acidic, and their phosphates leach calcium from bones. Artificial sweeteners have been suspect for causing multiple maladies. These include aspartame, under brand names of Nutrasweet and Equal. Splenda is a brand name for sucralose. Sucralose does not seem to be produced by genetic modification but by a process of chlorination, so this is not a good choice. Aspartame is frequently found in diet soda. If it is stored above 86 degrees Fahrenheit it converts to formaldehyde and formic acid. Both are potent carcinogens.

Thirty years ago iodine was used in the bread-making process and in recent years it has been replaced with brominated flour. Two decades ago the breast cancer rate was one in 20, now the rate is one in eight. This coincidence should not be a direct breast cancer causality factor but I do feel that it has a direct correlation to thyroid function. Bromine blocks thyroid function and may interfere with the anti-cancer effect of iodine on the breast. My recommendation is to avoid brominated flour as much as possible. This will require careful reading of ingredient labels.

What May Be Making Your Lumpy Breasts Worse?

Although fibrocystic breasts are not a cause of cancer, they make evaluation and diagnosis of breast cancer more difficult. Methyl-xan-thines from all sources are known to increase lumps and tenderness associated with fibrocystic breasts. Caffeine is the primary substance in foods that contain methyl-xan-thine, found in coffee, black tea, chocolate, sodas, and other foods and beverages. Some studies have shown that if women who have dense fibrocystic breasts stop consuming caffeine, they experience a significant reversal of thickening within less than six months. This could have a huge positive impact for those of you who have lumpy or tender breasts before your menstrual cycles.

Organic green teas or organic white teas are relatively benign since they contain only a third of the amount of caffeine as black tea, and they also contain polyphenols that decrease inflammation and cancer risk. You can easily decaffeinate tea by pouring boiling water over the loose tea and discarding the first water before putting the rinsed leaves in the teapot. Two cups a day are necessary for the benefits of the polyphenols.

While we are discussing polyphenols, check out Upton Tea Imports (www.uptontea.com) they provide over 260 varieties of teas, including organic green and organic white teas. They also provide an educational newsletter about tea. Tea is a crop that is heavily sprayed when not organically grown. The following four teas are recommended in the *Proactive Breast Wellness* program to reverse breast inflammation: Wuyan Ruikang, Ceylon Green, Shou Mei White, Young Hyson. After sampling some of these organic teas, you'll never go back to standard name brands. You can also try herbal teas like peppermint, rose hip, and chamomile that are non-caffeinated. People with hay fever and asthma are advised to avoid chamomile.

Don't Bite White

A few thoughts about diet. Remember "Don't bite white". Eliminate sugar, white flour, white rice, and refined or processed foods. Unsweetened grape juice, stevia, rice syrup, and honey are fine in moderation. Try whole grain organic unbleached, unbromated wheat, rye, pumpernickel, or oatmeal flours and breads sparingly. Decreasing your carbohydrate intake from white bread while increasing your complex carbohydrates from vegetables and whole grains, preferably organic, will be beneficial. Brown or wild rice, lentils, beans, quinoa, and other whole grains are flavorful, filling, and very wholesome. Beans and rice together make a complete balanced meal without meat, if prepared properly with the right ratios. You can also add some steamed or stir fried vegetables cooked with organic oils (extra virgin olive oil, coconut oil, grape seed oil, hazelnut oil, avocado oil) with some spices. Increase sulfur-rich foods which appear to decrease cancer risk. These include onion, garlic, seeds and nuts.

What To Drink and Quit the Soda

Try iced organic green tea, or some juice, perhaps diluted with water instead of sodas. Cold water with a twist of lime or lemon is also very refreshing and alkalines your system if consumed prior to meals. Lemon stimulates bile production that then increases the release of enzymes for the breakdown of foods. Secondly, it increases stomach acid to facilitate digestion and the release of minerals. Without sufficient acid we cannot absorb minerals. A small amount of organic apple cider vinegar added to water a couple times a day will also help. I enjoy Braggs Organic Apple Cider Vinegar that is naturally fermented and increases your probiotics also.

Solid carbon filtered water is necessary to keep yourself hydrated and to flush out toxins. Avoid candy, since it increases your acidity. Candy and sugar increase insulin that then drives inflammation. Insulin also interferes with the utilization of other hormones, for example in the condition of polycystic ovarian syndrome and syndrome X or morbid obesity. Since estrogen is stored in fatty tissue, the benefits of decreasing sugars and losing weight will also help you.

Try Gluten-Free for Two Weeks and Watch the Belly Fat Melt Away

Try cutting out gluten, wheat, bread, pastry, and pasta for two to three weeks and you may discover that you begin to drop the pounds without trying to lose weight. In addition, as the "wheat belly" decreases, gas and bloating and bowel irregularities also decrease. If you have joint pain, this will improve as well. Gluten may make auto-immune problems worse, increasing leaky gut syndrome and affecting a host of other problems like allergies, asthma, rashes, fibromyalgia, and osteoarthritis. Try being off gluten for a few weeks and see how much better you start to feel. This information ties into the next section on acidic foods.

Avoid Foods that Make You Acidic. Try the Alkaline Diet

Foods that cause an acidic state in the body are termed acidic foods. This is not directly related to the actual pH of the food, but rather how the body responds to the food. These acidic foods cause inflammation, and cancer is an inflammatory process. Changing to an alkaline diet to decrease the acidic state may decrease your cancer risk. When following an alkaline diet, numerous other health benefits follow as well, including loss of excess fat, decreased osteoporosis, decreased arthritis, and decreased insulin resistance in pre-diabetics. The complementary medicine community has used this approach for many years, and now allopathic Western medicine practitioners are embracing it as well, especially with respect to treatment of insulin resistance and diabetes. The highlights of an alkaline diet include use of whole organic grain products, vegetables, seeds, and nuts; and the avoidance of red meats, dairy products, sugar, refined carbohydrates, white flour bleached with bromine, gluten, and alcohol. Fresh juices of carrots, celery, apple, and beets are beneficial.

It is not always easy to predict which dietary items best fit in an alkaline diet, so lists of appropriate foods have been prepared. There is a sample list available on the data disc/ resource download and in the Getting Started section at the end of the book.

Two excellent books that review the alkaline diet extensively are *The pH Miracle: Balance Your Diet, Reclaim Your Health,* by Robert Young, Ph.D. and Shelly Redford-Young, and *The Acid Alkaline Diet for Optimum Health: Restore Your Health By Changing pH Balance In Your Diet,* by Christopher Vasey, naturopathic physician. These books and many other source books are available in the Resource section on our website to help you easily browse through books that I recommend to improve your health.

The following are some general recommendations for an alkaline diet. Limit red meat due to its acidifying tendencies. If you do eat some red meat, make it organic, grass fed, which will avoid antibiotics and hormones and the use of GMO grain to fatten the animals. Organically-raised grass fed meat has more healthy fat than conventionally raised meat since toxins accumulate in the fat layer. It is very difficult to find organically raised pork these days. Organically raised fowl is fine in moderation, but remove the skin to decrease your fat intake if you are trying to lose weight and lower your cholesterol level. Wild caught fish is even less acidifying than fowl.

Oils and Healthy Fats

Use unsaturated fats such as those found in cold pressed or expeller pressed organic virgin olive oil or organic coconut oil, your best choices in oils. Of the olive oils available, the healthiest is the first cold pressed virgin olive oil. Oils produced from later pressings, the less expensive oils, often include added hexane, a dry cleaning chemical used to get more oil from the pulp during extraction. Hexane is used in the dry cleaning industry and should be avoided. (Because it takes over two weeks for hexane to air out of garments, after dry cleaning, they should be left in the garage, not in the house, to avoid polluting the indoor air).

Do not use margarine, commercial mayonnaise, or other salad dressings. Try vinaigrettes made with organic olive oil, balsamic vinegar, a garlic clove, drops of fermented soy sauce, a pinch of coriander, cumin, and perhaps rosemary. Do not use products that include hydrogenated fats, frequently found in crackers and cookies, and avoid deep fried foods. Use light olive oil for baking rather than Crisco or conventional lard. I would rather you use butter from a healthy organic grass-fed cow than to ever use margarine or canola oil, which are sources of GMOs.

The Dangers of Trans Fatty Acid

I would like to provide some information about trans fatty acids, which is an important topic for your health. I am quoting from a wonderful resource book entitled *What You Must Know About Vitamins, Minerals, Herbs & More* by Pamela Wartian Smith, MD. This book has become one of my favorite source books, and I recommend you get a copy. You can review this book on my website in the Resources section. Dr. Wartian Smith is a leader in the functional medicine/anti-aging physician fellowship training program.

The following is an excerpt from Dr. Wartian Smith's book:

> *"Trans fatty acids do not occur naturally in nature. They were developed by the food industry to help food stay*

fresh longer. They have been shown to increase LDL or Low-density Lipoproteins, decrease HDL or High-Density Lipoproteins or (good cholesterol), increase triglycerides, increase lipoprotein (a), and make platelets stickier, which increases blood clots. Furthermore, trans fatty acids cause your cell membranes to leak, disrupting cellular metabolism and allowing toxins to enter your cells. All processed oils contain trans fatty acids. Consequently do not use processed oils. The more solid the oil, the more trans fatty acids are included in it. Liquid vegetable oils contain up to six percent trans fats and margarines and shortening up to 58 percent trans fatty acids. Anything that says hydrogenated or partially hydrogenated contains trans fatty acids. Trans fatty acids will increase your risk of heart disease. Furthermore, trans fatty acids interfere with your body's ability to make its own DHA. Trans fatty acids occur in: boxed foods, breads, candies, chocolate, frozen dinners, processed meats, French fries, potato chips, corn chips, tortilla chips, donuts, pastries, margarine and mayonnaise."

What About Dairy?

My next recommendation is to eliminate or reduce non-organic dairy products such as milk, cheese, cream cheese, and ice cream. Doing this will help optimize thyroid function and reduce unnecessary calories. If you must have some dairy, occasional use of small amounts of organic yogurt, kefir, or organic cottage cheese is the best choice. Occasional organic butter use is a better choice than margarine or other spreads that are made from chemicals you will have difficulty pronouncing. The fewer additives you consume, the better. Eating large amounts of dairy tends to be acidic for the system and hence may cause increased inflammation. People with arthritis, asthma, and fibromyalgia may notice a difference in their symptoms when they decrease their dietary intake of dairy and gluten.

Goat milk or milk from "the tan" old world genetic cows like Guernsey and Jersey has proteins that are easier to digest than the more common milk from the black and white Holstein cows. Again, always choose products that are free of bovine growth hormone and antibiotics and find sources of milk from cows that just eat grass and no GMO grains.

OMEGA-3 FATTY ACIDS – Where Your Ancestors Came From Matters

Omega-3 fatty acids have numerous beneficial effects and are uniformly recommended by both complementary and allopathic practitioners for improving health. They can decrease inflammation, lower cholesterol, decrease joint pain, and improve mood and reduce depression. Omega-3 fatty acids are found especially in fish. However, fish oil may be a problem for those of Native American, Welsh, English, or Scotch ancestry. Human genome studies have found large sections of these populations do not have the ability to convert omegas properly. If you find you are experiencing an increase in cravings, inflammation, or cholesterol and triglyceride levels, switch to a GLA oil supplement. Another issue is guarding against rancid fish oil or fish oil with toxins or heavy metals. Check the supplement suggestion section on my website for brands that check every batch for impurities. I store my fish oil in the refrigerator as well.

The *Proactive Breast Wellness* program recommends that you increase your consumption of wild cold-water fish such as wild salmon, Atlantic sourced kippers, sardines, cod, and herring. These fish contain a lot of omega-3 fatty acids.

Avoid these foods if you have a family history of gout or kidney disease. Due to the high purines found in these foods, uric acid build up may result leading to kidney stones as well as joint pain.

Avoid shark, swordfish and mackerel due to their high mercury content. Eating smaller wild fish helps because they have not lived as long to accumulate toxins in their bodies. There is added concern about Asian or Pacific fish following the Japanese nuclear accident. Buy wild-caught fish to avoid the additives in farmed fish diets. In a recent report, over 80% of farmed fish is not from the US.

If you go to the Take Action section at www.ProtectYourBreasts.com, near the bottom under Other Organizations, you will find a link to Got Mercury. This is an excellent place to find out how much mercury you might be ingesting based on your weight and fish consumption. Fish oil supplements from Iceland and Norway are an alternative to natural fish in the diet. These supplements are discussed in detail in Chapter 2.

The Controversy Over Flax and Soy – They are Estrogenic

Flax seed and flax seed oil are also good sources for omega-3 fatty acids including alpha linolenic acid or ALA, but I do not recommend that you use flax. I would rather suggest instead that you use chia seeds or a handful of organic raw walnuts daily, particularly if you follow a vegetarian or vegan diet. I discuss my bias against flax and also non-fermented soy in Chapter 2 of the PBW program and later in this chapter.

The beneficial properties of flax that were noted in older research will be included here for a more complete understanding of the topic, though I am not suggesting their use at the current time.

The following is what the literature has offered regarding flax: Flax seed oil can be used as an alternative to fish oil for vegans, women intolerant of fish oil products, and women known to not be estrogen dominant. The PBW program usually suggests that you avoid flax due to its estrogenic effects and suggests instead using a handful of raw organic walnuts or chia seeds daily. Ground flax seed is an excellent fiber and has been associated with lower levels of ovarian, bowel, and uterine cancers, and also lowers cholesterol levels. However, I would prefer if you used non-estrogenic fiber sources found in chia seeds or Psyllium husks. Typical amounts of organic flax used are one tablespoon of ground flax seed or one teaspoon flax seed oil. If used, flax seed oil and ground flax seeds should be refrigerated. Whole seeds need not be refrigerated and are best ground just prior to eating. I recommend that pre-ground flax seeds not be purchased unless stored frozen. Ground flax becomes rancid quickly and loses its beneficial properties shortly after being ground.

However, there are additional hormonal issues with the use of flax seed products as well as non-fermented soy because of their estrogenic actions and I recommend you limit their use altogether.

Another consideration concerning flax is that the human conversion of ALA or alpha linolenic acid to EPA or DHA is unreliable and variable among individuals and can be inhibited by conditions such as fast foods, baked goods, alcohol intake, vitamin and mineral deficiencies of B3, B6, C, zinc, and magnesium.

A good quality fish oil is a direct source of EPA and DHA.

Phytoestrogens/Plant Estrogens & Estrogen Dominance

Some natural products have estrogen-like properties. These items are called phytoestrogens. Phytoestrogens are plant-derived xenoestrogens functioning as the primary female sex hormone. They include non-fermented soy, flax, hops in beer, black cohosh, dong quai, and red clover. In general, the *Proactive Breast Wellness* program recommends caution in using these products, especially for women who are estrogen dominant. Estrogen dominance is determined by infrared breast scanning or laboratory testing, and is discussed in the chapter on hormone balancing later in the book. More information is also available in Chapter 2 in the nutritional supplement section. The following is a discussion concerning these plant estrogenic foods.

Soy products have been an area of mixed research results and controversy because of their mild phytoestrogen/plant estrogen properties. Studies on Asian women seem to show protective effects for breast cancer from eating miso and tempeh. However, there are concerns that excessive use of soy products may be harmful. American diets have tended toward large quantities of soy hidden in our foods plus trendy soy power bars and energy drinks. The Asian diets usually include smaller quantities of soy, about a quarter of a cup per day total. The traditional Asian diet has not included processed soy bars and power drinks, or genetically modified soy products. Remember that about 97% of all soy is now GMO, which carries other dangers. Asian populations also use more fermented soy products such as miso, tempeh and soysauce that appear safer than non-fermented products.

The non-fermented products include tofu, soy protein or soy isolates, soy cheese, soy energy drinks, soy milk, soy bars, and processed foods with lots of soy in them. Tempeh and fermented soy products have less phytoestrogen than tofu. If you are being treated for cancer and have an estrogen sensitive tumor, check with your oncologist regarding what place soy should have in your diet, since at this time there aren't any straightforward answers to this soy question. Soy products have also been shown to down regulate thyroid function.

My recommendation is to avoid soy products in general, especially if you are hypothyroid. If you wish to continue eating soy, choose organic and non-GMO, or non-genetically modified soy products, eat smaller portions, a quarter cup or less, and use miso and tempeh rather than tofu. If you drink a lot of soy milk, you might try rice, goat, coconut, almond, oat, or hazelnut milk for a change. Choose organic brands when possible.

My concern regarding the use of soy and flax seed and other plant estrogen products has been heightened by my experience with infrared breast scanning. This technique can show breast vascular patterns consistent with increased estrogenic activity metabolically. In my experience of over ten years, these vascular patterns increase drastically when dietary intake of soy or flax seed increases. The *Proactive Breast Wellness* program recommends that flax seed and soy products be used with caution, preferably with hormonal monitoring by your clinician. If your clinician has determined that you are estrogen dominant or at high risk of breast cancer, the *Proactive Breast Wellness* program recommends that soy and flax seed products be avoided altogether.

If removing flax seed creates a problem with respect to loss of dietary fiber and you are becoming a bit constipated, try rice bran, oat bran, chia seed, psylium husks and increase your magnesium intake. If you are gluten sensitive, then I would also avoid wheat and oat bran. Acacia fiber is a far better fiber choice for those with diverticulitis, celiac disease, IBS, or thyroid problems. Anyone who is on pain medication for cancer treatments or injury would benefit from Acacia fiber to prevent constipation or increase your magnesium dosage. Several of these products are listed on my website Virtual Dispensary.

The soy and flax phytoestrogen content becomes a complex issue for vegans avoiding all animal products. For more information, refer to the portion in the supplement section Chapter 2 for more on phytoestrogens. Chia seed or a handful of raw organic walnuts will provide the fiber and the omega-3 fatty acids that you need. You can also get omega-3 from an algae source.

Think Garlic

Garlic has antiviral, antibacterial, antifungal, and anti-carcinogenic properties. It's also a blood thinner, supports the immune system, and lowers cholesterol levels. In spite of garlic being mildly estrogenic, it is highly beneficial and I recommend you increase your consumption of raw garlic, onions, leeks, and chives, which have similar properties. Garlic powder, garlic capsules, and garlic salt are not as beneficial and do not have the health benefits of raw, freshly chopped garlic. Cooking of garlic removes some of its beneficial properties, so adding it at the end of cooking is best. Pre-processed garlic in a jar has many preservatives and is best avoided. If you have upcoming surgery, you should stop eating garlic a few days prior to the procedure because it delays blood clotting. At the first sign of a scratchy throat, many people now use or chew a clove of raw garlic two to three times a day with boosted vitamin C in divided dosages to bowel tolerance. Take the garlic with some food so it is not taken on an empty stomach. Also, increase your vitamin D3 intake to 15,000 IUs for about three days. These measures often prevent the cold from getting started.

Explore Organic Mushrooms for Your Immune System

Organic shitake, maitake and reishi mushrooms are also thought by some to be beneficial, purchased fresh and then lightly cooked, or in a dried form, or in extract solution. These mushrooms are raised on sawdust rather than in manure as are button mushrooms, which are heavily sprayed with fungicides. Some practitioners believe they may help support the immune system in cancer patients. This is an area of controversy, and I recommend you consult with your health care provider regarding their therapeutic usage. The Proactive Breast program has included these mushrooms in the protocol for immune support. However, be sure you are not allergic to funguses before using these foods. Rain Forest Mushrooms in Oregon can ship fresh organic medicinal mushrooms or large bags of dehydrated mushrooms to your door. Dried mushrooms are less expensive and last a long time in your pantry. All you have to do is throw a handful into boiling water and let them soak a few minutes to rehydrate and then chop them up and make stews or soups with them. Delicious!

Iodine an Essential Mineral in Your Anti-Estrogenic Diet

Increasing your iodine intake is beneficial because low levels of iodine have been associated with increased incidence of breast cancer and thyroid dysfunction.

There is additional information in Chapter 2 for you to review. Use caution if you think you have an iodine allergy.

This is probably more related to people who have had dye studies using iodine, but it was probably another additive in the IV iodine solution that caused the allergic reaction, not the iodine itself.

At the time of publishing my third edition, I have decreased my previous recommendations for iodine supplement dosage requirements. I have lowered the amount I had suggested previously in my earlier books. In part I base this on Dr. Pamela Wartian Smith's second edition in 2020 of *"What You Must Know about Vitamins Minerals Herbs and So Much More"* and Jeffrey Bland's *"Clinical Nutrition: A Functional Approach."* The recommendation is for adults who are not pregnant: 150 micrograms daily or .150 milligrams. For pregnant women the recommendation is 220 micrograms daily or .220 milligrams. I have met Dr. Wartian Smith at conferences a couple times. My patients love her book which I provide in my clinic since it has an abundance of practical food sourcing and dosage suggestions. I also reduced my iodine recommendations for my patients after speaking with Dr. Deborah McKay who is a Naturopathic Endocrinologist in Portland, Oregon. You may discover that you may be able to get the iodine that you need from food sources. I had previously been suggesting 12 to 24 milligrams daily but I no longer make that suggestion to women because I feel that is much too high a dose to take.

I highly recommend that you evaluate your iodine levels before starting iodine supplementation. 90% of Americans are iodine deficient. A deficiency increases your breast cancer risk. Ensure that your sea salt is iodine fortified, such as the Celtic brand sea salt. An alternate product is Herbimare Original, a sea salt with herbs. Sea salts are recommended over refined salts because of the additional trace minerals that are included, and the absence of chemical processing.

However, salt alone/ sodium chloride, cannot provide sufficient iodine for optimal health.

With respect to diet, this is most easily done by adding 1/8 to 1/4 teaspoon of Atlantic seaweed daily or eating wild caught seafood two to three times a week. Seaweed may be added to soups or stews easily or eaten as a snack. The www.LoveSeaWeed.com website for Rising Tide Sea Vegetables or Maine Coast Sea Vegetables at www.SeaVeg.com are excellent resources for seaweed supplements and foods. They harvest their seaweed off the less populated coasts of northern California and Maine, contrasted with oriental varieties that may be harvested from more polluted waters. Mountain Rose Herbs in Eugene, Oregon, also has seaweed from Iceland and does a large mail order business.

After the nuclear accident in Japan, Atlantic sourcing of these products locally is even more important, with the added benefits of decreasing the carbon foot print, U.S. job creation, and supporting the eat local movement.

Varieties of seaweed include kelp, arame, nori, wakame, kombu, and dulse. Each has a unique flavor and texture. Powdered dulse is available from Sea Seasonings of Maine Coast Sea Vegetables. It contains only 22 mg of sodium per teaspoon. Seaweed can be used whole or can be ground in a coffee grinder, then sprinkled into salad dressings, scrambled eggs, soups, brown rice, quinoa, or stir fries. One-quarter teaspoon of powdered Atlantic seaweed equals about three mg of iodine, and you can easily use less. Non-food iodine supplements are discussed in the next chapter if you feel it may be difficult to eat seaweed daily or if you do not eat wild caught ocean fish.

Make Gradual Changes to Diet and Lifestyle and Decrease Your Stress

Dietary and food changes can be very challenging. If what you are doing with your food is stressing you out, stop. Food is meant to be enjoyed, and to be nourishing and satisfying. If you develop bad or negative food relationships, it won't matter if your food is organic. The stress will do more damage.

I recommend that your changes be gradual. It is better to make small consistent and permanent changes than to try too much and then feel overwhelmed or quit. This is an education process, and a matter of also changing your lifestyle and eating habits, with a focus on your breast health. You may discover other health benefits such as weight loss, improved cholesterol levels and heart health, decreased joint pain, decreased irritable bowel symptoms, less insomnia, and less stress.

Remember to get your free gift of a digital download of *Waves of Serenity*, the 45-minute progressive muscle relaxation / guided beach imagery program to reduce stress. Go to my website Store and click on Free Ressources for your book / eBook. When asked for a password code, use **PBWBOOK** to get this stress management tool and resource download.

We also have *Waves* available as a CD or DVD for a small additional shipping charge if you prefer that format or wish to give someone a Gift of Health / Relaxation Program. You can listen and view the video clip on the home page of my website. Besides great food and dietary changes that the PBW program will help you with, I have included this wonderful *Waves of Serenity* 45-minute relaxation program to help your mind, mood, sleep and stress. The DVD I created are scenes from Moonstone Beach in Rhode Island. This was my favorite beach to roam when I was an undergraduate nursing student.

I have used my *Waves of Serenity* CD and DVD in many of my stress management classes that I provided to groups and patients over the years. Decreasing stress and improving your immune system is essential for protecting your health in many ways. Have a listen and close your eyes and imagine wiggling your toes in the sand on a perfect summer day!

Great mystics throughout the world caution about bad eating habits and the dangers to digestion and health from stress, poor sleep, and emotional unrest. Making the changes offered in the *Proactive Breast Wellness* program will improve the health of your whole family! Advocating for other women and helping to guide your children or grandchildren will help to protect the health of future generations.

Congratulate yourself on making changes to benefit your health. The *Proactive Breast Wellness* program will guide you towards a more fit and healthy mind and body!

This is my "Gift of Health" for you or a loved one.

Remember – Prevention IS the Cure!

CHAPTER 2

Nutritional Supplement Protocol and Suggestions for Decreasing Breast Inflammation

Nutritional supplements can decrease your risk of developing breast cancer or its reoccurrence. Several nutritional deficiencies have been found to be associated with higher rates of breast cancer, including low vitamin D and low iodine. Improving these deficiencies through dietary supplements has been associated with a decreased rate of breast cancer. In addition, some other dietary supplements have been shown to decrease inflammation, improve general health, improve adrenal function, or to fill gaps in nutrients that are not typically found in American diets. I have developed a protocol of recommended supplements that optimize breast health. This was done with information from various academic contributors including Dr. David Zava, PhD, from ZRT Lab, along with material by the late Dr. John Lee, MD, who previously worked with Dr. Zava, and co-authored *What Your Doctor May Not Tell You About Breast Cancer*. You can review this book and many others on my website in the Resources section. I have also included excerpts, from one of the many publications by Dr. Pamela

Wartian Smith, MD, MPH, that I feel is an essential text entitled *What You Must Know About Vitamins, Minerals, Herbs and More.* Dr. Smith is the Founder and Director of the Fellowship in Metabolic, Anti-Aging, and Functional Medicine.

I have compiled over 90 book resources that I have used in creating the *Proactive Breast Wellness* nutritional protocol and program. It took me seven years to research these areas of study in order to provide you a comprehensive educational program all in one place. I have broken down the program into segments so you may easily embrace these changes and improve your health. I have listed all these books conveniently on my website under Resources so that you too can expand your knowledge base and find trusted books that will assist you in improving your health and vitality. Please take a few moments to familiarize yourself with these resources.

In general, the *Proactive Breast Wellness* supplement protocol includes multivitamins, calcium, magnesium, binders of estrogen, vitamin D3, vitamin C, iodine, omega-3 fatty acids, and linoleic acid supplements. These will be detailed below with reference lists on the data disk/resource download, including shopping aids. Printing these lists or referring to the worksheets at the end of this book will make it easier to follow the information presented.

This chapter will deal only with nonprescription supplements. The initial products and dosages listed are for general breast cancer prevention and breast health. Some practitioners recommend more aggressive dosages for women who are breast cancer survivors or who are currently being evaluated for suspected pathology or planning breast surgery. Specific recommendations for these high-risk women will be listed at the end of this chapter.

In later chapters, I will discuss how to easily test your own hormone levels at home with ZRT and Dutch Lab Kits. In another chapter, I will discuss hormone balancing preparations, an additional aspect of the *Proactive Breast Wellness* program protocol.

The *Waves of Serenity* CD / DVD and downloads are available on the website Store to help you relieve stress and insomnia to improve your health. Use password code **PBWBOOK** to receive your free *Waves* and resource download. PBW is a comprehensive breast wellness program that also combines mind-body medicine with supplements, and lifestyle and dietary changes to improve your health.

Multivitamins

First, let me state that multivitamins as a whole have problems with effectiveness. There are a multitude of issues with fillers, binders, and absorption. However, we understand that life sometimes gets in the way of eating well. This is why a multivitamin has become a cornerstone in the PBW program. Adding organic green juices and smoothies will also greatly benefit your health if you can consume them daily or several times a week.

When selecting a high-quality multivitamin in pill, capsule, powder, or liquid, first look at the "Other Ingredients" label. If you see this list is longer than the supplement list or contains words like propolean glycol, titanium, zinc oxide, or artificial colors and sweeteners put it back on the shelf and walk away.

Look for whole food nutritionals that list a wide selection of natural foods, herbs, trace minerals that are microencapsulated and include enzymes and probiotics.

While it is challenging to find a totally organic nutritional product, there are more manufactures today utilizing as many organic products as possible. Look for Kosher and Parv ratings, as well as products free of gluten, soy, corn, sugar, and coloring-free statements on the label.

Remember multivitamins do not take the place of healthy food choices; they only serve as a backup plan.

Multivitamin preparations with minerals are the first component of the *Proactive Breast Wellness* supplement protocol. Many of the foods that are being grown today are depleted of their nutrient value compared to those of a century ago when organic farming methods rather than synthetic fertilizers were used. Although multivitamins per se have not been proven to decrease breast cancer risk, multivitamins have many nutritional benefits for general good health. Some individual micronutrients found in high quality multivitamins have been found to have anti-cancer properties. These include: vitamin A, the B vitamins, vitamin C, vitamin E, folic acid, magnesium, selenium, zinc, alpha lipoic acid, coenzyme Q10, and lycopene. A multivitamin that also includes herbs like curcumin/turmeric is also an excellent choice. A good multivitamin can enhance your body's ability to function at its best. Unfortunately, many common vitamin and mineral supplements have inadequate quantities of the ingredients and many are in forms that are not well absorbed. Many of the minerals compete with each other when naturally present in our diet or when we supplement them. For example, large amounts of calcium can reduce absorption of magnesium, phosphorus, zinc, and manganese. Zinc can reduce iron, copper, and phosphorus absorption, while phosphorus when taken in excess can interfere with absorption of a great many minerals.

As a reference to help you decide what multivitamin and mineral product to use, I refer you to the article on the data disc/resource download called *Take Your Multivitamins* from Dr. Lee and Dr. Zava's book, *What Your Doctor May Not Tell You About Breast Cancer*. You can compare your current multivitamin with those recommendations. You can also compare it to the products I have chosen to recommend for the *Proactive Breast Wellness* protocol, which can also be accessed through the Virtual Dispensary on our website. Ingredients for the products are also listed on the data disk/resource download. These products were chosen after consulting with several holistic MD's, naturopaths, and nutritionists. They have ingredients that I recommend. We also chose products with less fillers or no fillers, avoiding colorings, sugars, soy, corn, and gluten so that they are more easily tolerated by those with irritable bowel and gastric problems. All soy and corn, unless identified as organic, are now genetically modified, which leads to another Pandora's box of health and environmental problems. Explore the data/resource section to learn a lot more about how to protect your family and to make better food choices. Remember this is free as a download when you buy my book or eBook.

We are also recommending many whole food supplements made from organic fruits, vegetables, and herbs. These products are scrupulously tested for impurities. They have food-grade glaze and are vegan friendly.

We are offering a 20% discount available on the Protect Your Breasts website Virtual Dispensary. You may also call Emerson Ecologics and tell them that you would like a 20% discount as a client of Ingrid Edstrom, and that you are following the *Protect Your Breasts/ Proactive Breast Wellness* program. Money can also be saved by sharing orders and shipping charges with friends and neighbors. Emerson carries products from over 385 different manufacturers. You may certainly choose a different product if you find one that satisfies the recommended criteria and still receive 20% off.

To make supplement decisions easier, go to the Virtual Dispensary section on my website where you can click on the product photo to see what it contains and then compare with your current supplements to save you money and better protect your health. You may also find supplements that your doctor or naturopath has suggested. These will also be 20% off through my website www.ProtectYourBreasts.com.

Vitamin D

Vitamin D3 or calcidiol is the second essential supplement in the *Proactive Breast Wellness* supplement protocol. The *Proactive Breast Wellness* protocol recommends a dietary supplement of vitamin D3.

First get your vitamin D3 tested either at your own lab or with a ZRT home test kit so you will know exactly how much you should be taking. Sometimes the lab test is listed as Vitamin D3 25-OH. Do not guess. You probably will be incorrect.

It is important for individuals to have their vitamin D routinely checked at least yearly or every six months if you have had low levels and are now trying to bring up your levels with higher amounts of vitamin D supplementation.

Vitamin D controls the level of calcium in the blood, and is significantly involved in immunity, osteoporosis, hormone production, glucose tolerance, and bone production. Deficiency of vitamin D has been found to be associated with an increased risk of breast cancer. Research from Great Britain shows Caucasian women, particularly those with ancestry from Northern Europe or Scandinavia, have a high likelihood of not being able to store vitamin D properly due to a gene mutation. Switching from a pill form to sublingual vitamin D3 drops frequently helps in bringing up your vitamin D levels.

Vitamin D, which in reality is a hormone, can be produced in the body by exposing the skin to sunlight where cholesterol is converted to the vitamin. Depending on the type of skin you have, it takes from 10 to 20 minutes of midday summer sun at the equator in a bikini for adequate vitamin D production. However, this length of exposure in the United States is frequently not sufficient to generate optimal amounts of vitamin D. Above the latitude of 45 degrees, it's not possible to get enough sunshine during six to eight months of the year. In the Pacific Northwest region, where cloudy and rainy weather prevail, vitamin D deficiency is found in more than 75% of the population when tested. Even at lower latitudes, less than 30 degrees, it is very unlikely that you will get adequate levels of vitamin D from sunshine unless you are a farmer, a lifeguard, or a regular sun worshipper. Ultraviolet type B light is the kind that stimulates vitamin D production. UV-B is present predominantly during midday at higher latitudes because it does not pass through the atmosphere when the sun is shining at an angle. Also, UV-B does not penetrate fog, clouds, or smog, and only about five percent goes through glass. In Oregon, UV-A will cause burning before you get enough UV-B to supply adequate amounts of vitamin D. Besides inadequate sun exposure, other conditions that make vitamin D deficiency more likely include aging, having darkly pigmented skin, using sun screen, bowel mal-absorption syndromes, and some medications such as prednisone and dilantin.

Because sunlight-produced vitamin D is so often inadequate, for optimal health, you must obtain vitamin D from your food sources or supplements. Very few foods contain vitamin D in sufficient amounts to make a difference, and none of the food sources are acceptable for vegan use. Depending on individual preferences, calcicalciferal from lanolin will not work either if you are a vegan due to it coming from an animal source.

Societies living on traditional native foods had an abundance of vitamin D-rich foods in their diets. These were foods such as intestines, organ meat, and fat from certain land animals, shellfish, oily fish, and insects, all of which are not part of most western diets. For the most part, we have been advised by the cardiac experts to avoid lard, butter, whole milk, whole eggs, kippers, tripe, chitlings, and other vitamin D-rich foods. Most milk products are fortified with some vitamin D. Perhaps this information needs to be reconsidered and some of these foods added back into our diet.

I have come to support the health benefits of a more Weston Price-based diet with healthy organic grass-fed butter, milk, meat, and eggs. The Weston Price diet also promotes fermented foods and probiotics. I included their cookbook in the Resources section. Check out the photographs taken by Dr. Weston Price of children on their traditional native diets and then several years later after missionaries had brought western foods to these indigenous people. The results are striking!

Farm-raised salmon are a poor source of vitamin D because they are fed predominantly on GMO soy and corn pellets. Wild salmon feed on small fish such as sardines and krill. They are not vegetarian. Wild-caught salmon should come from Alaska or the Northern Pacific. Check the origin of the fish on the packaging. If labeled Atlantic salmon, salmon from New Zealand, or any other locations, they are probably farm-raised. Catfish, trout and tiliapia are also frequently farmed fish and frequently imported from Asia.

Of the supplements available, vitamin D3, also called cholecalciferol, is better absorbed and stays in the tissue longer than vitamin D2. The proactive protocol for adults suggests that after laboratory testing, an initial supplement of at least 5000 IU (international units) per day of vitamin D3 as a maintenance amount if your levels are 60 to 80 ng/ml. The Vitamin D Council estimates vitamin D deficiency is the most common medical condition in the world. It is becoming known that vitamin B12 may also be deficient in the world's population. The Vitamin D Council recommendation from October, 2011, is to get your levels into the 50 to 80 ng/ml range, at a minimum. The Vitamin D Council recommendations suggest that recent evidence reveals beneficial effects of vitamin D3 serum levels around 50 to 55 or higher, which may indicate a need for upward revision of the deficiency reference. Based on this data, if the vitamin D3 deficiency threshold was raised to a level of 50 then 90 percent or more of the world's population would be deficient.

For adults and children, your lab level may vary due to where you live, your skin color, and the amount of time you spend outside in the sun without sunscreen. Another factor is whether or not you have a problem with absorption in your intestines due to lactose or gluten intolerance as well as Crohn's Disease, IBS (Irritable Bowel Syndrome), ulcerative colitis, diverticulitis, bypass surgery, or damage from adjunct cancer and chemotherapies. If you have any of these problems you will not be able to absorb vitamin D3 properly.

Many physicians are recommending 1,000 to 4,000 international units a day to begin with, which may be too low based on current research. If your levels are lower than 70 it is advised to start with 5,000 to 6,000 units per day. In the Pacific NW where it's rainy for months, my new recommendation is 8000 IU daily if you are already in the optimal range so you can maintain the 55 to 75 level. Vitamin D3 is a fat-bound vitamin, so if you are taking over 10,000 IU's a day, it is best to have your blood levels checked every three to four months because it can build up in fatty tissue. You should also take for vitamin D3 supplement with food that has some good fat in it, like olive oil, coconut oil etc to improve absorption. Depending upon the lab, current normal ranges seem to be 30 to 100 or 32 to 80. More information is being gathered regarding desirable blood levels.

In the past, levels as low as 30 were termed adequate or normal. We now know that levels over 50 are desirable and that 70 to 75 may be optimal to protect your breast health. Women with concerns about breast cancer and who are headed toward a biopsy or surgery, or who have had breast cancer and are trying to prevent a reoccurrence may wish to aim for labs in the 75 to 80 range. If you were a patient of mine, had a low vitamin D3 level (in the teens to low 30s range), and you were about to go for a needle or surgical biopsy, I would place you on a high clinical strength vitamin D3 supplement protocol of 20,000 IU or perhaps 25,000 IU two to three times a week prior to your surgical date. A woman's survival rate increases by 65% if their vitamin D level is optimal prior to surgery! These dosages are outlined in depth on my supplement protocol list of Nutritional Supplement Suggestions for Breast Cancer Prevention with adjusted dosage based on recent lab work that you may have had done. Refer to the worksheet section at the end of this book.

Levels over 125 are potentially toxic. It is actually difficult to get into the toxic range and you probably would have had to have made the mistake of taking 40,000 IU daily for three months to get to a toxic level. The risk of toxicity with supplements of 6,000 to 8,000 international units per day or less is remote. Sometimes larger doses are used with careful clinician monitoring. Vitamin D levels are best measured after a supplement has been used for two months. You want to measure your steady state baseline, so you will know if you should adjust your dose up or down.

In addition to increasing the risk of breast cancer, vitamin D deficiency can be associated with, and supplementation can sometimes be shown to correct the following: osteoporosis, diabetes, senile cataracts, polycystic ovarian symptoms, auto-immune disorders, melanoma, leukemia, fibromyalgia, chronic fatigue, infertility, peripheral neuropathy, PMS, cancer of the prostate and colon, and depression. People with higher vitamin D levels at the time of their cancer diagnosis have nearly twice the survival rate of those at the lowest levels. Vitamin D also decreases calcification in the arteries, joints, and perhaps even the brain, and lowers high blood pressure. Research has suggested that a high calcium intake with a vitamin D deficiency can lead to the deposition of calcium in your arteries.

Absorption and utilization of vitamin D3 is essential, and is associated with the type of fat we eat. Polyunsaturated fats decrease the binding of vitamin D to proteins. These are commonly known as vegetable fats. It is especially important to avoid Canola Oil as it is a GMO product and detrimental to heart health. Canola is genetically engineered rape seed oil. This is another reason to increase your consumption of healthy organic animal fats, organic coconut oil, organic olive oil, or avocados.

Vitamin D may not be absorbed if the intestinal mucosa integrity is damaged. This can be caused by allergies, bacteria, yeast, chemicals, chronic stress, or parasites. The use of sublingual drops may provide better absorption when there are gastro-intestinal issues. We have included sources of these products at our website's Virtual Dispensary where you will also be able to save 20% on all your supplements.

Probiotics and Digestive Enzymes

New research suggests that your immune system plays a key role in helping you recover from cancer or chronic disease, and also in preventing these problems from occurring in the first place. We all have experienced becoming run down, not eating or sleeping well, suffering too much stress, etc., and suddenly coming down with a cold or flu. Our modern diet has drifted away from whole raw foods and fermented foods. Processed foods have additives, preservatives, fungicides, coloring agents, and chemicals added that are difficult to pronounce. Conventional meat contains bovine growth hormone and antibiotics to prevent disease in overcrowded conditions in feed lots. The antibiotics and additives negatively impact and kill off friendly bacteria in our intestines. Research shows that three quarters of our immune system activity takes place in our gut. If you eat fast foods and heavily processed foods, you place your immune system at risk. It is your immune system that is on the front line of defense against chronic illness or diseases.

High quality enzymes do more than improve your digestion; they also reduce scar tissue and have been shown in research to reduce tumor sizes. Several forms of enzymes are especially good at thinning the blood, reducing the chance of stroke and blood clots.The PBW program strongly suggests that you add a high quality probiotic and digestive enzyme to your diet and start eating more fermented foods like raw sauerkraut, kimchee, kombucha, or kefir. You can make all of these products yourself or find a local source in the refrigerated section of your grocery store in glass jars. The Weston Price Foundation is a wonderful source of information and recipes. We have added a probiotic with 14 different strains and 50 billion organisms and also a digestive enzyme to the PBW Virtual Dispensary. You may also add organic ginger root, organic pineapple, and organic papaya to your diet. They also contain digestive enzymes in a food-based source.

CoQ10

The protocol also has 50 mg of Ubiquinal CoQ10, which is a recommended anti-cancer and heart health supplement.

If there is a cancer concern, then you might increase your CoQ10 to 100 mg daily. Ubiquinal forms of CoQ10 are much more absorbable and cellular-active in the prevention and recovery from disease.

Estrogen Binders

The next section of the protocol addresses estrogen binders. These are all supplements derived from the cruciferous or cabbage and broccoli family. These substances bind with excess estrogen in the body, allowing it to be excreted in your bowel movements. They are also anti-oxidants and inhibit the formation of free radicals. The naturally present sulfur compounds found in the cruciferous family keep cell walls soft and permeable. This action is critical to keeping aberrant cancer cells in check by the immune system. These compounds help prevent the development of estrogen enhanced cancers such as prostate, breast, cervical, and uterine cancers. Some doctors also feel they may prevent cancers caused by pesticides and other toxins. Using these binders helps to eliminate extra estrogen from environmental sources, as well as bovine growth hormone from non-organic meat and dairy, and xeno-estrogens or estrogen mimickers. Commonly performed estrogen testing cannot assess all of these estrogen compounds. Even if someone's blood or saliva test for estrogen is low, there may be other estrogen compounds activating the breast tissue. At the current time, we do not have blood or saliva testing for bovine growth hormone that you are ingesting in your drive-through burger or for Atrazine or Roundup that is being sprayed over your backyard. By helping remove these substances from the body, the estrogen dominant risk factor can be reduced. The *Proactive Breast Wellness* program protocol recommendations and dosages are listed on the data disk / resource download

Getting Started section of this book and on the website Virtual Dispensary.

Use Trans Resveritrol, an anti oxidant that comes from organic grape skins, or organic grape juice or grapeseed oil, or you can also add either Indole-3-Carbinol or DIM complex, also known as Din-dolyl-methane. If you use Indole-3-Carbinol as an estrogen binder, the recommended dosage is 400 mg per day. The alternate choice is DIM complex at 100 to 120 mg a day. DIM is a derivative of Indole-3-Carbinol. Some clinicians suspect DIM may be more protective, but it has also been reported to cause gastrointestinal issues on occasion.

If you want a whole food approach, I strongly recommend growing your own estrogen binders by sprouting organic broccoli seeds. New research suggests that broccoli and pomegranate are the two most cancer-protecting foods but you would need to eat 20 to 25 heads of broccoli per week to ingest a sufficient amount of estrogen binder. Now consider organic broccoli sprouts where each seedling has the DNA to create a whole plant making several heads of broccoli. Get organic seeds in bulk. Sources are in the resource section.

Cancer clinics in Europe are using a substance called Sulforaphane made from broccoli sprouts, as a natural chemotherapy treatment, since it appears to kill breast cancer stem cells. Traditional chemotherapy does not kill breast cancer stem cells. My personal favorite is to eat about an inch of broccoli sprouts or about 25 seedlings a day raw. You can throw them into smoothies, put them on the side of your plate as a condiment, or add to salads. Raw broccoli sprouts do not negatively impact thyroid function if you are being treated for hypothyroidism. You can receive an amazing amount of cancer protection daily by eating these delightful and tasty sprouts!

Calcium and Magnesium

The next ingredients on the protocol are calcium and magnesium for general bone support, especially important in perimenopausal and menopausal women. Some versions of calcium are difficult to absorb and should be avoided, such as calcium carbonate found in the form of Tums antacid. The *Proactive Breast Wellness* program protocol recommends calcium citrate, calcium malate, or hydroxyl apatite at dosages ranging from 400 to 600 mg of these varieties for adult women. Earlier recommendations for calcium were 1,200 to 1,800 mg per day but newer research conducted in 2011 showed that doses of calcium above 1,000 mg was causing cardio vascular plaque in the arteries and micro-calcifications in the breast, which is very unfavorable. Since 2012, some researchers are now suggesting taking 500 mg calcium but not from clam shell / calcium carbonate or bone sources but from diet sources instead.

I suggest women avoid taking more than 500 mg of calcium in supplement form, but find calcium in food sources like dark green leafy vegetables instead. This is when I go to one of my favorite books in Resources on my website by Dr. Pamela Wartian Smith, *What You Must Know about Vitamins, Minerals, Herbs and More*. There are in-depth lists of food sources for vitamins and minerals, so you can find a food source for what you need and possibly avoid taking more capsules. It is always better to find a food source to enhance your diet and health.

Many good sources of calcium exist, including seaweeds such as kelp, wakame, and hijiki (Make sure they are from the Atlantic Ocean), nuts and seeds (like almonds, hazelnuts, sesame, and pistachio), blackstrap molasses, beans, figs, quinoa, okra, rutabaga, broccoli. Dandelion leaves, kale, and fortified products such as orange juice all contain calcium.

Numerous vegetables, notably spinach, chard, and rhubarb have a high calcium content, but they may also contain varying amounts of oxalic acid that binds calcium and reduces its absorption. The same problem may to a degree affect the absorption of calcium from amaranth, collard greens, and chicory greens. This response in the body may also be related to the generation of calcium oxalate.

An overlooked source of calcium is eggshell, which can be ground into a powder and mixed into food or a glass of water. The calcium content of most foods can be found in the USDA National Nutrient Database.

Calcium is best taken in divided doses throughout the day. Absorption is enhanced by 100% when taken with vitamin C. For more information on microcrystalline hydroxyl apatite used as a bone-building supplement, please refer to the data disc/resource download.

Non-organic or conventional dairy products contain bovine growth hormone and are, for this reason, not the best source of calcium because of possible repercussions with respect to acid/base balance and vascular changes in the breast from the estrogens in the bovine growth hormone. Eating acidic foods like milk actually increases your bone loss. Some research from the China Study suggests eliminating most dairy from your diet.

Use only pharmaceutical grade supplements because lower grade products are sometimes contaminated with lead, mercury, or aluminum. There have been issues with some Asian imports. Another reason to use my Virtual Dispensary and Emerson sites where you will find high-grade supplements that have been tested for impurities.

Magnesium supplementation is recommended and believed by many nutrition experts to be more important than calcium due to its anti-inflammatory, and cardiovascular supportive properties. Magnesium works as a smooth muscle relaxant among other things. Magnesium, along with trace minerals and calcium, is necessary for bone health and over 300 other body functions as an enzyme cofactor. It also counteracts the constipation that can result from calcium supplements, poor thyroid function, and pain medications.

Magnesium decreases hot flashes and palpitations caused by hormonal fluctuations, and helps leg cramping and restless leg syndrome. The *Proactive Breast Wellness* protocol recommends magnesium 500 to 750 mg daily if tolerated. Magnesium citrate is used most commonly for constipation and other forms of magnesium reduce the likelihood of diarrhea in some individuals. Work up to this dosage slowly increasing dosages each day in divided dosages. Do not take 500 to 750 mg all at once. Magnesium can make some individuals feel light-headed or have stomach upset. The best solution to this is to increase water consumption and take magnesium with food. If symptoms persist, lower the dosage or change the type of magnesium. Higher dosages over 600 mg may cause diarrhea. A minimum desired dosage is 500 mg daily. Better-absorbed products include magnesium citrate, magnesium glycinate, magnesium gluconate, magnesium lactate, and magnesium aspartate. Magnesium oxide is not as well absorbed.

When I work with patients, I first find out their thyroid status by lab testing for a thyroid panel and have them review the Professional Compounding Pharmacy Association (PCCA) questionnaire and complete a temperature journal. These forms are in the Getting Started section at the end of the book, as well as in the data / resource downloads. If they are hypothyroid, they usually are constipated unless they are a vegetarian with a high-fiber diet. It is normal to have one to two or possibly three soft-formed bowel movements a day. If you only have a bowel movement that is firm daily or, worse, a bowel movement every two to three days, magnesium will become your best friend!

If you are constipated and perhaps hypothyroid, then try magnesium citrate gradually in divided dosages throughout the day since it softens the bowel movements, which is an advantage if you are tending towards constipation. Types and dosages are also on the PBW Nutritional Supplement Suggestions list for further guidance. This list is located in the worksheet section at the end of the book.

If you are not constipated, then try magnesium glycinate, which is less loosening.

My own current regimen is to take magnesium glycinate (two capsules, which equal 250 mg total) at breakfast. I take my shower, dry myself off, and then spray magnesium chloride oil or also called Magnesium Oil, five to six sprays, on my abdomen and thighs and rub it in topically. Avoid getting it into your eyes or where you may have scratched yourself. It will sting. One spray equals 18 mg. When you use it topically, it does not loosen your bowels and you can add some extra magnesium without bowel effects. I will take more magnesium glycinate (250 mg) in the late afternoon and maybe another 125 mg at bedtime. I am trying to get to the 600 to 750 mg range on a daily basis.

The other magnesium I use that does not loosen you up so you can easily add some extra magnesium on a daily basis is a product called Hylands Mag Phos 6#, which is a magnesium homeopathic. You can put two to four pellets under your tongue at the first sign of any muscle leg cramps, palpitations, or cardiac flutters that many women feel that seem like butterflies in your chest. The homeopathic magnesium works in about 20 seconds so I carry it in my purse all the time and have a bottle next to my bed.

Essential Fatty Acids

Essential fatty acids are required nutrients that have been found to enhance health in many ways, including their anti-inflammatory effects. They cannot be produced by the body, so they must be consumed in foods or supplements. It is impossible to get therapeutic amounts of these substances in a normal diet, so supplementation is recommended.

Two branches of these nutrients are the omega-3 fatty acid, and the omega-6 fatty acids. American diets tend to be high in omega-6 fatty acids that can cause chronic inflammation if not counteracted by omega-3 fatty acids. Interestingly, the linoleic acids, a subfamily of both the omega-6 and omega-3 fatty acids, have been found to decrease breast tenderness and fibrocystic changes, and to generally enhance breast health. The *Proactive Breast Wellness* protocol recommends a balancing of these fatty acids with the use of both omega-3 fatty acid supplements, as well as some supplements from the linoleic acid family.

For the omega-3 portion of fatty acid balancing, the *Proactive Breast Wellness* protocol recommends fish or krill oil or a vegetarian choice of chia seeds, walnuts, or astaxanthin from algae as a first choice. Fish oil is recommended at 4,000 mg per day in the capsule form, or 1 teaspoon of cod-liver oil or 1 tablespoon of certified mercury-free cold water fish oil per day of the liquid formulations. Indigestion and fish-burps can be an issue for some people with the liquid formulations, and can be minimized with the use of capsules, especially if they are swallowed when frozen or have lemon added in the capsule. Krill oil appears to cause fewer digestive issues and is well-tolerated by many people. Another recent option is astaxanthin at a 4 mg dosage. In the wild, this compound makes salmon and krill pink. It can be grown commercially from water algae and it is vegetarian.

Besides fish oil and krill oil, omega-3 fatty acids are also contained in flax seed and some soy products. About 97% of soy is now genetically modified. Flax seed oil has been used as an alternative for vegans, and for women intolerant of fish oil products. However, flax seed and soy products contain alpha linolenic acid (sometimes called ALA) that has been found to estrogenize the breast tissue due to their phyto-estrogenic or plant estrogen properties. These are estrogen-like compounds from natural plant sources. Other examples besides flax and soy that have estrogen-like effects include red clover, dong quai, black cohosh, hops (in beer), and hemp seeds. These all should be avoided due to their plant estrogen body burden

The omega-3 fatty acids called DHA and EPA, found in fish, lamb, and some nuts including walnuts and Brazil nuts, do not have estrogenic properties. If you are vegan or vegetarian, try organic walnut oil or eat a handful of organic walnuts or add a tablespoon of chia seeds daily to get omega-3 fatty acids.

Caution With These Fatty Acids Before Surgery

Omega-3 fatty acid supplements should also be stopped two weeks before and one week after elective surgeries or as directed by your surgeon to avoid excessive bleeding. A person using other blood thinners such as Coumadin should discuss this with their clinician before consuming these oils. Fish oils increase the slipperiness of blood fibrogen, allowing it to move through vessels more efficiently. Other items to avoid two weeks prior to surgery and one week after surgery include garlic, ginkgo biloba, vitamin C, Vitamin E, Saint John's wort, and cayenne pepper.

Linoleic Acid Supplements

The second portion of the essential fatty acid balancing is done with the linoleic acid family of supplements. These include organic black currant seed oil, borage oil, and evening primrose oil. All contain linoleic acid, alpha linoleic acid, and gamma linoleic acid. If choosing black currant seed oil, a typical dose is two capsules a day. Please check the protocol or the Virtual Dispensary on my website to get exact milligram suggestions. The other alternatives are evening primrose oil and borage oil, of which only one supplement is needed and you can alternate them. Check the data disk/resource download or Virtual Dispensary for exact dosages for these products. Additional benefits include improvement of fibrocystic breasts, dry eyes, eczema, and hair quality, and softening of the skin. The black currant seed oil is especially good for dry eyes, sometimes improving the condition within three to four days of usage by enhancing the oily lubricating function of tears. In choosing between these, black currant seed oil may be more expensive, but the borage oil capsules are larger and may be more difficult to swallow, but you can chew them up and then swallow them if that seems easier.

Estrogen dominance is determined by infrared breast scanning or laboratory testing and is discussed in the chapter on hormone balancing later in the program.

I recommend that you should avoid flax and non-fermented soy products after seeing too many infrared scans of clients over the past twelve years who have become more vascular on flax or non-fermented soy. The infrared scans improve after four to six months if the woman goes off the phytoestrogens/plant estrogens, stops eating conventional meat and dairy that contain bovine growth hormone and antibiotics, and follows the rest of the supplement protocol. All of these foods increase estrogen dominance and vascularization in the breast tissue. Since there has been such an increase in our lives over the past 30 to 50 years of environmental estrogens like food additives, plastics, herbicides, pesticides, etc., we should not further increase our body burden of these chemicals and estrogens by adding them to our diets.

In fact, 65% of the women who embrace the PBW protocol and diet and lifestyle changes greatly improve their infrared scans and other aspects of their health in six to 12 months. PBW is also heart-healthy, which supports thyroid function and improves hormone balancing. Another plus is those women usually loose 15 to 30 pounds of weight, which delights my patients.

Vitamin C

Vitamin C is another compound that our bodies do not produce; it must be obtained through food or supplements. Vitamin C helps the body in many ways, including boosting immune system function, modulating adrenal steroid production, and preventing the formation of cancer-causing nitrosamines. It is an anti-oxidant and is necessary for progesterone production, and adrenal and immune system support. The *Proactive Breast Wellness* program recommends a Vitamin C supplement of at least 600 mg to 2500 mg per day. I would suggest trying 2,000 mg a day to begin with and increasing further to bowel tolerance, to protect you against cardiovascular disease. Dosages are also based on the type of Vitamin C used but do not use an ascorbic acid form as this is manufactured in the same fashion as high fructose corn sweetener, which is made from corn that is now usually genetically modified and contains harmful molds and heavy metals.

Higher doses of Vitamin C are sometimes recommended during times of illness or stress. Mineral ascorbates, such as calcium ascorbate crystals, or ester-C are good choices because they are buffered, helping to prevent stomach lining irritation and diarrhea. Powders can be mixed with foods or liquids. Higher amounts should be taken in divided doses. Dosages over 5,000 mg may cause diarrhea, so decrease the amount if that occurs. Do not continue a dosage amount that causes persistent diarrhea, stomach burning, or nausea.

There is new research showing that Vitamin C is essential for preventing plaque in the arteries. If you are not consuming enough Vitamin C, your body can't produce enough collagen that lines your blood vessels. When the collagen breaks down, your body responds by depositing cholesterol plaque to patch the area. If this continues, you end up with hardening of the arteries or atherosclerosis. If the plaque breaks off, it can result in stroke and heart attack. To promote breast and heart health, we suggest increasing your Vitamin C to bowel tolerance in divided dosages. This will be individually based on how dry a person's stool is, medications, fiber intake, and transit time. The Linnus Pauling Institute website has an abundance of information on this topic. I suggest you visit this website.

What I have tried is to increase my Vitamin C to bowel tolerance in divided doses every hour until my stomach starts to grumble then I cut back. That marks my daily dose. I use the Innate brand of Vitamin C powder from the website because it is produced from fruits and tastes like orange juice and it does not upset my stomach. If I am coming down with a cold, I start adding a half scoop (500 mg) Vitamin C powder to water every two hours, throw in one quarter teaspoon of baking soda or one half to one teaspoon of Bragg's apple cider vinegar to alkalize my system, and start eating some raw garlic. Usually I am able to prevent the cold symptoms from taking hold.

Iodine and Thyroid Function

As mentioned in the introduction, most women who develop breast cancer are hypothyroid, are not getting enough vitamin B complex, and have low iodine levels. Two-thirds of the body's iodine is stored in the thyroid, and most of the rest is stored in breast tissue. The body needs the building blocks of vitamin B complex and iodine to assist the thyroid gland in producing thyroid hormone. If these key nutrients are absent, your thyroid gland cannot produce the hormones that your body requires and hence puts you at greater risk of developing breast cancer.

We are seeing an epidemic of low iodine levels associated with breast cancer. Much of the hypothyroidism found is related to low iodine levels. It can be safely estimated that greater than 45 to 65 percent of menopausal women in industrialized countries have hypothyroid symptoms. The World Health Organization has stated that up to 72% of the world's population is affected by an iodine deficiency disorder.

It's estimated that 90% of Americans are iodine deficient. Much of the worsening of iodine deficiency may be related to decreased use of salt for women who were following a no salt or low salt dietary program. In the United States, we began commercially adding iodine to salt in 1900. Salt has been the primary dietary source of iodine for many people. In attempting to decrease their sodium intake, they have inadvertently decreased their iodine intake. In addition, many commercial salt brands actually have taken the iodine out of the product. Check the label of the salt that you are using to see if there is iodine listed on the label and how much. There is quite a variation.

Research prior to the Japanese nuclear disaster had focused on the diets of Japanese women, with their high intake of iodine-rich seaweed products and seafood. They ingest an average of 13.8 milligrams per day, which is almost 100 times the current RDA and 50 times greater than the amount consumed by most North Americans. These Japanese women had remarkably low levels of breast, endometrial, and ovarian cancers prior to their nuclear accident. At the time of publication, I do not have any Japanese cancer statistics after their nuclear disaster. They also had a significantly lower incidence of fibrocystic breasts prior to their nuclear accident. One third of U.S. women have fibrocystic breasts. The U.S. recommended daily allowance, or RDA, of 1.5 milligrams per day of iodine was for optimal health.

A Word of Caution on Iodine Dosing

I want to add a word of caution to this section on optimal dosing of iodine. For several years I was recommending that women take 6 mg to 12 mg of iodine daily in my clinical practice. I have now changed my viewpoint. My altered views are based in part on a consultation before this third book edition that I had with Dr. Debra McKay, a Naturopathic Endocrinologist who works in Portland, Oregon. In addition she provides phone support to MDs across the country who have complicated patients calling the ZRT Lab Helpdesk. Dr. McKay lectures on thyroid disease management at Anti-Aging / Functional Medicine Conferences. Her concern is that in the past couple decades holistic practitioners have jumped on the band wagon of high dose iodine supplementation which she feels evidence based medicine research does not bear out.

Dr. McKay states that the human body only requires 200 mcg/micrograms or 0.2 mg/milligrams of iodine a day for optimal functioning. This aligns with Dr. Pamela Wartian Smith and Jeffrey Bland's research and books where that range was more in the 150 mcg to 200 mcg range as well.

Some of these holistic practitioners were promoting iodine supplementation in the 12 mg to 50 mg range of iodine daily. People will urinate out the iodine in a 24-hour period but she is concerned about these higher dosages since she feels that your optimal intake should only be 200 mcg or 0.2 mg.

Then Dr. McKay pointed out an interesting concept that takes into account the region of the country that you live in and how much wild caught ocean fish that you consume. She said since I live in Eugene, Oregon, which is west of the Cascade Mountain Range that I do not need any extra iodine. She states that everyone in this belt that is west of the mountains do not need any additional supplementation with any iodine. The premise is that the ocean air coming east from the Pacific drops the iodine on to the land when it rains. The fruits and vegetables plus dairy cows and meat animals eat the iodine rich vegetation. Also if I eat wild caught ocean fish two to three times a week or consume some seaweed, then I will be consuming my optimal amount of iodine of 200 mcg or 0.2 mg through food sources. So with this better researched information, I am decreasing my iodine recommendations. If you live in Iowa where the last ice age came through and removed the iodine rich top soil and you do not have sea air blowing over your part of the country then you need to consider supplementation, but only in the 150 mcg to 200 mcg/microgram range daily. If you are pregnant then intake should be 220 mcg/micrograms daily.

Later in this chapter I will address other forms of iodine supplementation in case you happen to live far from the ocean or you are a vegetarian and will not eat fish, then you may need to consider augmenting your iodine to the 150 mcg–200mcg or 0.2 mg range which is all that you require.

Ways to Increase Your Iodine

The *Proactive Breast Wellness* program recommends ensuring increased iodine intake through the use of iodine fortified sea salts, sea weed products, wild caught sea food two to three times a week or low dose iodine supplements.

Some salt is necessary for cooking. Ensure that your sea salt is iodine fortified. One source is the Celtic brand sea salt. Compare several salts at the store to see which has the highest iodine. I use Celtic Sea Salt and Himalayan Salt that includes minerals.

Sea salts are recommended over refined salts because of the additional trace minerals that are included, and the absence of chemical processing. However, salt alone cannot provide sufficient iodine for optimal health.

Dietary seaweed is the easiest, most natural way to supplement iodine. Kelp or dulse is also loaded with magnesium, potassium and a bunch of other trace minerals, which is also a plus. Seaweed products come in capsules or, less expensively, in a powdered bulk form. There are many types of seaweed and they all have different flavors. You might wish to taste test several at your health food store to see which one you like the best. I have a cute little bowl with both powdered kelp and dulse on my dining table so I can sprinkle some on my food. I also frequently use the powdered version in stirfries, stews, and soups. Some people put it in their fruit or green smoothies to hide the seaweed taste.

Check your seaweed source and see if you can purchase product from Atlantic sources like Maine, Iceland, or Norway.

These locations have a less dense coastal population than many Asian Pacific sources, which may have more coastal pollution and Japan has a radioactive problem after their nuclear disaster a couple years ago.

Look at the amount of iodine listed in your seaweed product. Frequently it is listed in micrograms or mcg, where 1000 micrograms equals one milligram or mg. If the seaweed is in a capsule, say 1200 mcg, then that equals 1.2 mg. If you want to try seaweed in a powdered loose form then one-quarter teaspoon of powdered kelp provides approximately three milligrams of iodine, with only 16 mg of sodium. One-quarter teaspoon of iodized salt has 590 mg of sodium, but less than one mg of iodine. Since seaweeds have a salty flavor, they can be used in place of salt, decreasing your sodium load while getting your iodine. You can easily decrease the powdered seaweed to 1/8 teaspoon or less. Change the iodine dosage over a few days and see how you feel. You can also refer to the Worksheet section to do the Temperature Journal and the PCCA Symptom List to track your temperatures with your altered iodine intake to see what your body is needing.

An alternate method of ensuring optimal iodine intake is to use an iodine supplement. This might be necessary for those not eager to eat seaweed, or those who just want to make sure they are getting enough iodine. The *Proactive Breast Wellness* program recommends that you start to use an iodine supplement and there are several considerations to be made before you start supplementation as to what form may be the right one for you.

Iodine supplements are most commonly available as tablets or in liquid form. In general, it is important to start iodine supplementation very slowly and increase the amount over several weeks. The slow initiation of this product is recommended because the iodine supplement flushes some toxins out of the iodine receptor sites. These toxins include fluoride, bromine, and chlorine, which previously filled the iodine receptor sites if there was not enough iodine in the diet. If you start the iodine at too high a dose or too quickly, the flushing of these toxins can result in a few days of severe malaise, rashes, headaches, palpitations, and other side effects followed by a surge of energy as the toxic effects of the halogens leave your system and diminish, which may take three to four days. To prevent this from occurring, I suggest you start really low and slow and increase over several weeks. In this way, the toxins are bumped off the receptor sites gradually as they are replaced by the iodine and, in my experience, the side effects do not seem to occur. If you do experience any of these side effects, then decrease the amount of iodine you are taking for a few days.

James Paoletti, our compounding pharmacist consultant, wished to add a caution that starting iodine at even 6.25 mg daily may cause a toxic reaction from other bromides as these halogens are flung off the iodine receptor sites.

Please go to the Putting It All Together / Getting Started section at the end of PBW so you can review and print the directions for how to use liquid iodine, how to do an iodine Paint / Patch Test, as well as the PCCA (Professional Compounding Pharmacy Association) Hormone Symptom List and How To Do a Temperature Journal. Doing these exercises will really assist you and your provider to help determine a plan for improving your health. It is important that you print out or copy these forms and worksheets so you can follow along and date them so you can see your progress over time. Make several copies of the original symptom list so you can write on the copies.

Another way to start iodine slowly is to use liquid iodine Lugol's 2% (half-strength Lugol's) or Atlantic kelp capsules, which can be used at a lower daily dose so you can build up slowly. Please refer to the previous information on seaweed capsule strengths and how to start liquid iodine in the Getting Started section.

Using Lugol's 2% Topically for Breast Cysts and Tender Breasts

Please note that possibly five to eight percent of people may notice a slight stomach upset after using iodine in water. Taking it with food may help. I would strongly suggest to always dilute it and never just put it on your tongue. I think it has too strong a taste without diluting it. I personally have not had any issues taking the iodine by mouth when diluted. Another way to use Lugol's 2% liquid is to put one drop, which is 3 milligrams or 3000 mcg, directly on the breast and then moisturize with some organic coconut oil or apply some of your progesterone cream on top as a moisturizer if you find it drying. This does an amazing job of decreasing tender fibrocystic breasts and it absorbs well through the skin if you do not like the flavor when diluted in water or juice. Please note this suggestion is for a slightly higher dosage of 3 mg per drop than I previously recommended for optimal daily dosage is because in this instance we are using iodine as a treatment not just a daily dosage amount. If you are able to resolve your tender breast situation, you could consider decreasing the iodine amount. If something flairs up again, you can go back to topical application of the liquid iodine. If you discover that your breasts just feel softer and less "Lumpy" if you are using a bit more than 150–200 mcg or 0.2 mg iodine daily, then use a bit more. You will urinate out all the excess iodine every 24 hours so it does not build up.

One word of caution, this may slightly stain undergarments and the skin as it is first applied but it is absorbed and disappears rapidly if you are deficient. I would not apply iodine topically and then put on your best white silk blouse.

Please also review Chapter 7 on Breast Care. I have expanded my suggestions on using Lugol's 2% iodine topically in that section for breast massage, lymph drainage, and the care of tender breasts.

When women start using topical iodine and progesterone, amazing changes often occur in their breast tissue. Breasts should feel like good bread dough, soft and pliant. If you have dense, lumpy, bumpy fibrocystic breasts or tender breasts, this frequently helps. Several women that I have seen in my clinical practice who had large cystic one-inch breast masses that were tender, particularly with their cycles, were able to reduce the size of the cyst in two to three menstrual cycles, which decreased the need for a needle aspiration to drain the cyst.

Using Lugol's 2% in Water

Here are my suggestions for taking liquid iodine diluted by mouth in the form of Lugol's 2% (half-strength Lugol's) solution from J.Crows. You can find this product on my website Virtual Dispensary. Lugol's 2% iodine equals 3 milligrams per drop of iodine.

If you use Lugol's 2% solution, one drop equals three mg/milligrams of iodine (Do not use a dropperful, which would be way too much and a toxic dose). Also do not put the liquid iodine directly under your tongue. I think it will be too strong a taste.

I used to have people put one drop (three mg) in a glass of water and stir. Then divide the glass of water in half so you can drink the other half tomorrow. The half-glass mixture contains 1.5 mg/milligrams of iodine. Starting low and slow works the best. Then try the half-glass amount (1.5 mg) for five to six days. You can add my suggested Vitamin C powder by Innate from my website Virtual Dispensary and then it tastes like orange juice. You can take this mixture in the morning and swallow your other vitamins with this. I advise morning dosing, otherwise you may have a surge of energy at night when you should be winding down. The iodine encourages your thyroid to make more hormone and hence more energy.

Based on my new iodine recommendations in 2020 you could perhaps only use a half drop or 1.5 mg every other day or maybe three times a week and you could apply that directly to the breasts for tender areas.

If You Are Taking Thyroid Replacement Medication

If you have thyroid problems, which means if you are on thyroid replacement medications like Armor or Naturothyroid or Synthroid, etc., then just take 0.2 mg up to 3 mg of iodine total per day. Again if you are eating seaweed or you are consuming wild caught ocean fish two to three times a week you do not need extra iodine. If you take more iodine, it sometimes makes your thyroid create more thyroid hormone, but you are already replacing thyroid hormone with your prescription so your provider might need to rebalance your dosage to get you adjusted again and do more labs.

Another caution applies to women who are already hypothyroid and are being treated on thyroid replacement medications. They need to start at an even lower iodine dose of 150 mcg to 200 mcg / 0.2 mg per day with a gradual increase over a couple weeks to the three milligrams maximum per day total. It would be better to get by with less iodine if you can if you are already on thyroid medications.

Check your iodine level by doing the iodine paint / patch test, which may be printed from the Getting Started section at the end of the book. Getting an accurate serum / blood draw lab value for iodine is difficult since you urinate out the iodine rapidly within 24 hours. You are then only getting a snapshot in time by serum lab testing so it is probably a waste of money. However if you did a dried urine test through ZRT Lab or Dutch Labs, you would get a better lab result.

It is better to do the temperature journal every 4–6 weeks to start to see if your body temperature is rising and your symptoms are dissipating and you are feeling better. This is also free to do and gives a lot of clinical information.

If You Are Trying To Support Your Thyroid

If you are doing thyroid support, which means that your provider has not put you on a prescription thyroid medication yet, then you will be adding iodine and one vitamin B complex tablet twice a day. In this scenario, you probably have half to three-quarters of the hypothyroid symptoms on the PCCA list (to be printed out from the Getting Started section). If your morning axillary (under the arm pit) temperatures are lower than 97.8F, and your thyroid labs are probably all on the low normal range, your thyroid may need to be supported to function better. In this case, you could consider trying to give your poorly functioning thyroid some of the building blocks that it needs to make your own thyroid hormone in the form of vitamin B complex and iodine. Then you can slowly increase the iodine from 0.2 mg to 3 mg and see how you feel. If you feel revved up and like you had four cups of coffee, then decrease the iodine dose. It passes out through your urine quickly, within 24 hours. Japanese women, on average, eat a lot of seaweed and ocean fish and they average 13 mg of iodine intake a day. Prior to the nuclear accident, they had the lowest breast cancer rate internationally and many feel it is due in part to their iodine intake. They also usually do not eat as much meat or dairy that might have quantities of Bovine Growth Hormone.

Another form of iodine in tablet form is Iodoral, an iodine supplement, produced by Optimox as a 12.5 mg tablet containing iodine 5 mg and potassium iodide at 7.5 mg. This is a common combination in iodine supplements. You can cut the tablet in half but 6.25 mg may still be too much. Iodoral also comes in a 6.25 mg tablet. Remember I have cut my optimal iodine daily dosage suggestion down to 150 mcg to 200 mcg or 0.2 mg so I do not recommend Iodoral any longer but I am adding some guidance here for women who knowingly wish to take a higher dose of iodine or trying to use up some product that they currently have before they change to a more optimal dosage amount. I still suggest to first start with Atlantic seaweed or very small amounts of liquid iodine to build up more slowly.

There is another product called Prolamine Iodine, 3 mg tablet (by Standard Process). Again, these may be too high a dose for some people if you are to be taking thyroid replacement like Armor, WP Thyroid, Natur-Thyroid, Levothyroxin or Synthroid.

Some providers have their patients on even higher doses of iodine in the 12.5 to 25 mg range, but I would discuss this with your clinician. Ingesting higher dose iodine supplements may occasionally cause some unpleasant symptoms. If you experience any of the following, stop taking Iodine and contact your health care provider: an unpleasant brassy or metallic taste, frontal headaches, increased salivation, sneezing, a sense of fullness when swallowing over your thyroid or acne-like skin lesions. There is no anecdote for this, you just need to wait for the symptoms to go away that may take several days. I do not recommend these higher dosages of iodine any longer.

The Role of Iodine in the Event of a Nuclear Disaster

While I was researching this iodine section I came across the recommendations of the New York Department of Health for citizens and workers near its nuclear power plants. Hopefully none of us will be faced with a nuclear power plant accident or in the event of a nuclear war. You might wish to go to their website for more information and for iodine dosages for children in the event of a national disaster and save the information somewhere. This amount listed here is way too strong for a pediatric dose. The New York Department of Health suggests adults taking 65 mg to 130 mg of Potassium Iodide before or just after you are exposed to a radioactive iodine. They said you can take it three to four hours later but it may not be as helpful. The concept is that you flood your iodine receptors in the thyroid with natural iodine so it blocks the radioactive iodine from harming your thyroid gland. The excess iodine is eliminated by your kidneys through the urine over a few days.

Maybe better to think happier thoughts, but Potassium Iodide has a long shelf life. Check the New York Health Department website or the Life Extension site for their fact sheet for nuclear power plants and dosing for children.

Other Causes of Hypothyroidism and What to Do About Them

Hypothyroid symptoms include fatigue, menstrual irregularities, fibrocystic breasts, depression, dry skin, hair loss, weight gain, low body temperature, and a host of other symptoms.

Please check the resource section for symptoms related to hormone deficiencies provided by the PCCA compounding pharmacists on the forms in the Getting Started section.

Many contributors have been identified as causes of hypothyroidism. In addition to low iodine, remember that ingestion of large amounts of non-fermented soy products can also contribute to hypothyroidism. Other contributors include low levels of growth hormone, high cortisol from stress, as well as adrenal insufficiency. Finding out if these are problems for you then correcting the issue will greatly improve your health. So what do you do to start figuring out what is going on?

How To Do A Temperature Journal

An interesting and easy self-screening for hypothyroidism is to measure your axillary or under the arm temperature in the morning just before getting up, and again at four o'clock in the afternoon. The afternoon temperature will usually be your warmest temperature of the day. Record these values in a journal for about one week to see if you have consistently low temperatures. If you add up all the morning temperatures over the five to seven days that you took your temperature and divide that number by the times you took your temperature, this will give you an average morning temperature. Write down your temperatures and date them in your journal. If the temperatures are below 97.8 degrees on a regular basis, you may have a low thyroid condition. If an iodine deficient person starts iodine supplementation, they may notice improvement of hypothyroid symptoms. This might include noticing after a few weeks that they feel warmer in cold environments.

Rechecking the temperature journal a few weeks into supplementing iodine daily and a vitamin B complex twice a day may show an increase in body temperature. If your body temperature consistently remains low, or if you want thyroid screening before beginning iodine supplementation, this could be explored further with your clinician to evaluate your thyroid function or you can also easily have a hormone kit sent to your home from the ZRT Lab or Dutch Lab website. Contact them directly to have the easy home use kits mailed to you. There are choices of saliva, blood spot or dried urine testing. This is beneficial because they are easy to do and they are free hormone levels and you do not need to go to a lab or have a lab slip. If the iodine and vitamin B complex twice a day did not increase your temperatures or laboratory values over several months you may need to add more thyroid support.

Do You Want to Try a More Natural Thyroid Glandular Product?

Some of my patients are trying very hard to get their thyroid working better, but they are trying to avoid getting on a thyroid replacement medication available through Big Pharma. Levothyroxine was created in 1927 and Synthyroid came out in 1955. Before this time doctors used a lot of natural glandular products and herbal preparations to treat people with thyroid issues and other medical issues. Big Pharma is actually a very recent edition to medicine and even now more than three quarters of the world's population is using natural herbal remedies. In fact there was an amazing recent video out entitled "Remedy: Ancient Medicine for Modern Illness". Check it out!

Getting back to my thyroid patients, if they have tried the slow increase of daily iodine and vitamin B complex twice a day and three to four months have passed and they still have symptoms that need some improvement, there is something else to try in the form of thyroid glandulars and thyroid support products. Please check out Thyro Complex by Progressive Laboratories or Thyroid 65 by Priority One. There is also a product called Thyroid Response Complete Care by Innate. They are on my Protect Your Breasts website Virtual Dispensary where you can get 20% off all your supplements. You can also get anything else you or your family wants through the Wellevate/Emerson site at 20% off.

Thyro Complex is a powdered glandular bovine thyroid at 60 mg, plus spleen, pituitary, and adrenal product with less than one mg of iodine from kelp. This may not appeal to the vegans or vegetarians, but it works quite well by taking one to two capsules a day in the morning or split with one capsule in the AM and another at lunch time. I did personally discover something interesting about this Thyro Complex product. I had been taking it for several years, and I still take it, but I noticed that on my every six-month thyroid labs that I have done, I began to see that my Free T3/Thyroxine level had begun to float down into the insufficient range. I looked more closely on the label and discovered this glandular was "Thyroxine Free". To fix this I worked with my holistic MD to add a very small amount of T3/Thyroxine compounded in olive oil that I take under my tongue. My levels are now back in the optimal range with improved energy.

There is another product that contains 65 mg of glandular bovine thyroid without other glandular tissue. This product is Thyroid 65 by Priority One. Please note that Armour Thyroid contains 65 mg of pig or porcine thyroid. Also 1 grain of thyroid equals 65 mg of hormone. I am not fond of products made from pork since they usually are not organically raised. Bovine glandular products that are sourced from New Zealand or Denmark are free of Bovine Growth Hormones since these countries forbid the use of these chemicals in agriculture.

Thyroid Response Complete Care by Innate contains 150 mcg of iodine plus zinc, selenium, copper and some herbs that support thyroid function. This product does not have any glandular components.

I would still work on the thyroid support practices and possibly add a glandular product. If this does not improve your thyroid function, temperature journal and labs over a few months, you may need to consider getting on thyroid replacement Big Pharma with the assistance of your medical provider.

Thyroid Laboratory Testing

Unfortunately, there is controversy in the medical community regarding what testing to do for thyroid function, and just what laboratory results constitute a low thyroid condition. I recommend that if testing is done, the testing include not only TSH (Thyroid Stimulating Hormone) but also at least a TPO AB (Thyroid Peroxidase Antibody), a Thyroglobulin Antibody, Total T4, a Free T4 and Free T3 for the best profile.

Your clinician may also order tests for hematology and blood chemistry and possibly an advanced lipid panel to check out your cholesterol. Depending upon these results, as well as your examination and history, they may order a TPO Antibody test or a Thyroglobulin Antibody evaluation test and perhaps a thyroid ultrasound if they feel you have a thyroid nodule. Do not assume that your thyroid is fine by only doing a TSH (Thyroid Stimulating Hormone) test. It is important to find out if you might have an autoimmune thyroiditis, a thyroid cystic or a thyroid cancer. Doing this larger thyroid panel will give you a more complete idea of your thyroid health.

If you have completed the temperature journal and printed out the PCCA Hormone Symptom List and you bring these to your provider appointment, you can easily show them proof that you have most of the symptoms for being hypothyroid and may be able to convince your provider to do all the testing to find out what is going on with your health.

Vitamin D3 is important to thyroid receptor function, so the level should be checked and vitamin D3 dosed to maintain a level of at least 60ng/dl. I prefer that you get into the "Optimal" Vitamin D3 range, which is 70–75 on a 32 to 80 scale. If your lab uses a 30 to 100 range as normal, then I would like to see you at 80 to 85. I covered this earlier in the book and there are dosage suggestions on the "PBW Supplement Suggestion Sheet to Reduce Breast Cancer Risk or Reoccurrence" to assist you with how much you should be taking based on your laboratory testing.

Low ferritin levels cause hypometabolism. If your ferritin drops below 70, a woman's hair starts to fall out and they tend to have a lot of fatigue. Ferritin is related to your iron storage capacity. Red blood cells, hemoglobin, need iron to be able to carry oxygen to the cells. Ferritin levels should be checked and ferrous glycinate taken to raise levels as necessary if you are a cycling woman with heavy periods. Organic organ meats like liver or heart are rich in iron. Menopausal women should not be taking extra iron. If you discover that you are an older woman and anemic or have lower iron, you need to explore this further in much more detail as to what is going on with your primary care provider.

You can have most of these labs done through your provider or you can check out ZRT Lab or Dutch Lab for home test kits. There is also a dried urine test available by contacting DutchTest.com (Dried Urine Test for Comprehensive Hormones).

This lab is very interesting because it also gives valuable information regarding metabolites and how your particular body is able to metabolize. I created a large section on my website that is dedicated to hormone testing for further research.

Another option to mention here which is that there is a ZRT Medicare Kit that ZRT can bill Medicare for if you and your PCP send them the correct paperwork. ZRT can mail you a FREE Medicare EZ Kit. Your provider can send you home with a prescription stating they want ZRT to perform the blood spot hormone testing, which may be a Female Profile 2 or there are other panels that are available. The PCP needs to also put the ICD-10 Codes for why they want you to do testing. Menopause or hypothyroidism are usually good codes to use. I would make a copy of the prescription to keep and send the original prescription in the box when you mail it back. Another method is when you get the ZRT EZ Medicare Kit through the mail, you can also have your PCP sign and put the ICD-10 codes on the form inside the box. You can also call the ZRT Medicare EZ Kit office for any questions. There is also a lot of information on my website under FAQs for hormone testing to learn more.

How To Check On Your Thyroid Function Progress

It is important to realize that if you are already being treated with thyroid hormone for low thyroid function, the initiation of an iodine supplement may improve your underlying thyroid hormone production. This creates the potential for your thyroid hormone dosage to become excessive, requiring downward adjustment by your clinician.

The *Proactive Breast Wellness* program recommends that if you are already undergoing thyroid hormone replacement therapy when you start iodine supplementation, you should have your thyroid blood tests repeated six weeks after initiation of the iodine. If you are not on thyroid medication, a repeat of your thyroid blood tests is recommended in three months to six months after starting iodine. Symptoms of excess thyroid hormone could include palpitations, anxiety, increased sweating, and intolerance to heat. If these symptoms occur after starting iodine, you should contact your provider, even if it has been less than the follow-up periods mentioned earlier.

Many holistic practitioners are convinced that many people with hypothyroidism are under-diagnosed, and that many of their symptoms are related to iodine deficiency. These practitioners feel that many symptoms can be reversed with iodine supplementation, increasing seafood or seaweed and taking a Vitamin B Complex. Remember that all the women who develop breast cancer, that they all are all hypothyroid and Vitamin D 3 deficient. This is easy to fix if you are aware of your lab status.

Other anti-inflammatory supplements

There are several other herbal products that have anti-inflammatory properties and are helpful for chronic painful conditions that frequently improve on the PBW protocol. Since breast cancer is an inflammatory process, some of these may be beneficial for breast cancer reduction. I also find many of my clients have chronic painful conditions of various sorts and these supplements may be beneficial. For more information, the free data disk / resource download in the Getting Started section includes a reference sheet titled, "Anti-inflammatory Herbal Approaches for Pain Management and Decreasing Inflammation." Print the sheet if you feel this may benefit you.

Glucosamine Sulfate

Glucosamine sulfate helps rebuild the cartilage of joints, and is especially good for the knees, elbows, hips, and backs that have been aggravated and have joint issues. Glucosamine is an amino acid that occurs naturally in all body tissues, and is very important for the preservation of cartilage. Declining levels of glucosamine are theorized to be one of the contributors to osteoarthritis. I recommend one 500 mg tablet three times a day when there is a lot of pain or 1,000 mg daily for a joint pain maintenance program. Glucosamine supplements come from crab shells, so do not use if you are allergic to shellfish.

Bromelain

Bromelain is derived from pineapple and it has anti-inflammatory effects and also acts as a digestive enzyme. It can be obtained by eating organic fresh or dried organic pineapple or in capsule form. It has been used for pain in sports injuries, bruises, sinus infections, and bronchitis. An appropriate dosage is one to two 500 mg capsules a day with meals.

Ginger

Ginger is another anti-inflammatory herb. It helps to decrease morning stiffness, joint pain, morning sickness, motion sickness, and nausea from chemotherapy. It's wonderful as a tea. Grate an organic ginger root with a cheese grater, putting about a half to three quarters of a teaspoon in some boiling water. Let it steep for two to three minutes. You can add a little honey to sweeten it, if you wish. It also makes a delicious iced tea. You can use ginger to grate into stir-fries, salads, pancake batter, and other sorts of foods. You can freeze organic ginger root for up to six to eight months. Wrap it up in old-fashioned brown waxed paper first, and then place it in a Zip-Lock bag for freezer storage. If you're using ginger capsules, use 500 to 1000 mg a day with food. Crystalline ginger is available and can be chewed or minced into foods. This product may have sugar added. I prefer fresh or frozen organic ginger root.

Curcumin

Curcumin is a phytonutrient derived from turmeric. It has anti-inflammatory properties by enzyme inhibition within the inflammatory pathway, improves lipids, and may prove to have an anti-cancer effect. It helps maintain mental functioning, and helps inflammatory bowel diseases and ulcers. It is especially good as an anti-inflammatory for pain. Some research suggests that Curcumen may be able to shut off blood flow to tumors. This spice is used usually in curry, and you can take 400 to 600 mg per day. A dash of black pepper improves absorption

I sometimes sprinkle it into my salad dressings, on organic fried eggs, or put it into a stir-fry or soup. Raw organic turmeric root is also available and it can be frozen and grated as you would a ginger root. I have added a CurcuPro capsule to the Virtual Dispensary that is very bioavailable.

Cayenne pepper

Cayenne pepper, also known as capsaicin or red pepper, is an anti-inflammatory, antioxidant, and can reduce pain. It has been especially useful for pain from osteoarthritis and nerve pain. It can be used as a spice, as a supplement internally, or as a topical cream pain reliever. One of its pain relieving mechanisms is the depletion of the pain messenger to the brain called substance P. There is some theorizing that it may also have a role in modifying inflammation. As a supplement, it can be used in capsule form of 20 to 100 mg three times a day. Too high a dose can cause nausea or vomiting. As a topical cream applied to the region of pain, such as joints or nerve pain, it is usually used as a thin coat three to four times a day. After pain improves, the frequency of usage can sometimes be decreased to just twice a day, but needs to be used regularly to maintain effectiveness. There may be some initial burning or itching that usually subsides with continued use. Do not use the cream on broken skin, avoid contact with eyes and sensitive tissues, and be sure to wash hands after application. You can also get some non-latex exam gloves and cut off a glove finger to apply the cream to the area so it does not get all over your hands. Brand names include Capzasin-P, Zostrix and Sombra cream. It can also be formulated by a compounding pharmacist.

Cancer Immune Support Protocol

For women who are cancer survivors, we will soon have a custom protocol to support the immune system as part of my newsletter. Please sign up on our Newsletter link at the top of our website www.ProtectYourBreasts.com to receive our newsletter, providing new research and product suggestions to you by email.

Until the custom protocols are available, we have added some additional products for immune support on the website Virtual Dispensary and we will list them separately as well. We have included other source books on the website in Resources and on the data disc/resource download and in the Getting Started section for your review. Charting a course for your nutrition during your breast cancer recuperation can be daunting. We have added some of our favorites for you to review and to share with your oncologist or clinician.

If you are post-operative, going through radiation or chemo, all of these therapies tend to cause increased fatigue, anxiety, insomnia and leaves a woman worn out. Remember we are what we eat and improving your diet during this time is essential. Raw juicing or smoothies and raw probiotic foods are very important to help build your health back up. I encourage you to reach out to friends and family to help create and deliver the juices to you or other healthy meals if you are trying to recover and do not have much energy at first. They can make up meals and freeze them so all you have to do is heat them up in the oven or toaster oven. People care about you and many will be delighted that they can help if you ask them. Connecting to a breast cancer support group or a women's support group if you have one through a spiritual organization will help through the rough spots. Reach out and establish your own network of support folks.

Spend time in nature and get out and start walking even if it is for short distances at first. Exercising even for 20 minutes four to five times a week has shown to decrease risk of breast cancer by more than 65%. So grab a friend, family member or a dog and start a new exercise program! Sit in your garden or on your deck. Hang up a bird feeder. I love my hummingbird feeder! Get an African violet or pick some flowers and put them on your table when you dine. Light some candles for dinner time. Make it a healing experience even if it is leftovers. Play soothing music in the background when you are at home or in the car. Get an aroma therapy diffuser and use some organic essential oils to lift your mood. It does wonders to how you are feeling. Essential oils also help with sleep and stress. Watch funny movies, laugh, dance, make music and sing.

Try to keep your thoughts in the moment in the Present, because that is all we really have. The Past is past, you cannot change that. The Future is in front of you and that is an unknown, so being in fear or anxiety for something that has not happened yet is a waste of your essential health promoting and healing energy. You can control what you are thinking and you can stay in the Present moment and enjoy everything about you. Start focusing on three things you are grateful for right now in this instant. Explore these three things in your mind's eye to really sense this gratefulness and let this healing energy sink in and surround you. Give it a color or a texture. White or golden light, the feel of a soft pink polar fleece blanket that you can imagine yourself wrapped in. Find your own imagery that is calming and healing. Try journaling and write down your thoughts.

Your mental health and healing is as important as your physical healing right now. I have a little card near my desk that I look at daily. It says:

"I am Full of Love. I have Faith, Trust, Gratitude and Courage".

The following are other sources for cancer immune support.

My women's book group is now reading "Radical Remission" by Kelly Turner, which is awesome and it is wonderful for women who do not have cancer as well. There may still be a video series by the same name. It was really uplifting!

Another valuable information source is the documentary and review *The Truth About Cancer—A Global Quest* by Ty Bollinger. I found this nine-part documentary fascinating. It talks about how cancer clinics in other countries and holistic practitioners here have been successfully using approaches to treat cancer that the current allopathic community does not seem to be enlightened about yet. My feeling is that your immune system is the most important defense against cancer and chronic disease!

Another docu-series that came out in the spring of 2019 is now available on discs. The series was entitled *"Remedy~Ancient Medicine for Modern Illness."* This series was about the use of herbal medicine to treat and heal all sorts of medical conditions. Some of these herbs have been used for centuries. The presenters were clinical herbalists, oriental medicine practitioners and Anti-Aging/Functional Medicine MDs. They pointed out that about three-quarters of the world's population rely on herbal medicine with the wisdom passed down through the generations. The series pointed out that more than 20% of our current drugs are plant based. Another interesting concept is that medications and Big Pharma only came on the scene approximately after World War II. Plant medicine also has way fewer side effects.

If you also start taking care of the mind-body connection by learning and doing meditation, yoga, Tai Chi or other forms of relaxation and start an exercise program, this will help greatly!

Start listening to the *Waves of Serenity* CD/DVD or digital download one to two times daily to get a rush of endorphins that will last for eight hours, relaxing you and decreasing insomnia. Go to the website Store and use password code **PBWBOOK** to get your free download copy or we can mail you a disc. Having a positive outlook is very important to your healing and state of mind. I created this program for you!

SUMMARY

This concludes the nonprescription supplement recommendations for *Protect Your Breasts* and the *Proactive Breast Wellness* program. In summary, this includes the regular use of a high potency multivitamin, vitamin D3, calcium, magnesium, estrogen binders, fatty acids such as are found in black current seed oil, fish oil, krill, walnut oil or chia, vitamin C, immune support and iodine. Another crucial aspect of the *Proactive Breast Wellness* protocol is the use of bioidentical hormones under the supervision of your clinician. Most of the hormone replacements are prescription items but some are over-the-counter, and will be discussed in detail in the next chapters.

CHAPTER 3

The Acid/Alkaline Diet

We spoke briefly in Chapter 2 about the alkaline diet. In this chapter, I would like to discuss more about the physiology and importance of maintaining an alkaline balance in the body. More details about what I'm discussing can be found in the reference section of the free data disc/resource digital download obtained from the website to support your new health goals and further your exploration.

Our metabolism functions best when the acidity of the body's fluids is in a narrow range of pH that is actually alkaline: 7.35 to 7.45. A pH level of 7 is neutral, lower numbers are acidic, and higher numbers are alkaline. Our bodies generally do an excellent job of maintaining our pH in this range, and do so by buffering the fluids and adjusting urinary acid excretion.

Modern Processed Food Diets and Aging Creates an Acid Load

The typical modern American processed food diet results in an increased acid load compared to that of a more traditional diet with lots of whole grains, nuts, and vegetables. This typically results in acidic urine, which indicates the body is trying to rid itself of excess acid. In addition, natural aging results in gradual worsening of acidosis within the normal range, probably as the result of declining renal function. Some researchers believe that this combination of diet and aging is creating a relatively chronic low-grade metabolic acidosis that impairs ideal body functioning.

It is known that even mild acidosis causes impairment in endocrine function including hormone insensitivity, hypothyroidism, and elevated cortisol levels. Links have also been found to muscle wasting in the elderly. The calcium needed to buffer excess acid is stolen from the bones, resulting in increased osteopenia and osteoporosis. Magnesium can also be a buffer, but if you are depleted, your body will steal the magnesium from the muscles.

Cancer Cannot Grow in an Alkaline Environment

When population studies are done comparing cancer incidence, the rates are lower in societies that don't eat as many meats and processed foods, the same foods that result in acidic urine. It is commonly quoted that cancer cells cannot thrive in an alkaline environment. In one type of research, cancer cells were placed in both acidic and alkaline growth media in Petri dishes in various strengths. What was found was that the cancer cells grew profusely in the very acidic growth medium, and as the media became less acidic, or became more alkaline, the cancer colonies were less able to grow on the alkaline Petri dishes!

Chronic Inflammation Linked to Many Chronic Diseases

Another link still being researched is the relationship between increased body acidity and inflammation. It is known that inflammation levels as measured by a laboratory test called C-reactive protein, or CRP, and the CRP levels are greater in obesity. This is especially true when the obesity is abdominal. Higher levels of inflammation are related to increased risk of many harmful conditions, including arthritis, allergies, autoimmune diseases, diabetes, asthma, coronary artery disease, irritable bowel, gastritis, Crohn's disease, ulcerative colitis, Alzheimer's disease, as well as cancers of breast, lung, prostate, and stomach. It turns out that an alkaline diet is also a diet of low glycemic-index foods. These are foods that are less likely to increase blood sugar and stimulate insulin secretion. High blood sugar and higher insulin levels are associated with increased amounts of inflammation. Indirectly, it appears an alkaline diet will decrease inflammation.

You Can Decrease Inflammation With Exercise and Stress Management

Other things that can decrease inflammation include physical exercise and reducing chronic psychological stress. I have included *Waves of Serenity*, my 45-minute relaxation CD/DVD or digital download to help you reduce stress and cortisol levels, reduce pain and insomnia as part of the mind/body healing portion of the PBW program. Go to the website Store to receive your free gift of *Waves of Serenity* as a digital download when you use password code **PBWBOOK**. *Waves of Serenity* is also available as a CD or DVD, and as a gift of health for a loved one!

Becoming Alkaline Decreases Osteoporosis and Improves Athletic Performance

It is clear that there are many health benefits of a diet that results in alkaline urine. Research is still being conducted to see how many of these benefits are from the nutritional aspects of these foods, as opposed to the alkaline/acid aspect itself. In studies done with athletes, they were found to have a greater exercise capacity simply by using an alkalinizing supplement. A study by research scientist Robert Burns, PhD, showed less muscle fatigue, less muscle cramping, more rapid muscle recovery, and greater distance capacity in those competitive long-distance bicyclists using an alkalinizing supplement.

In women being treated for osteoporosis, a study has actually shown increasing bone mass in women using an alkalinizing or mineral agent, presumably by stopping the calcium leaching from the bones, allowing calcium supplements to be adding to the bone density. Some clinicians have therefore advised the regular use of an alkalinizing agent in addition to following the alkaline diet recommendations.

Frankly, the medical community doesn't know all the mechanisms in action when an alkaline diet is followed, or when an alkalinizing supplement is used or when organic raw apple cider vinegar or lemon juice is added to your water before meals. However, in my clients and myself, I have found these practices have resulted in significant improvements in day-to-day functioning. These have included loss of excess weight, as well as reduction in symptoms of arthritis, morning stiffness, irritable bowel, chronic pain, and fibromyalgia. I have reason to believe these methods decrease loss of calcium from the bones, and that they might result in general reductions in inflammation and cancer risk. For that reason, I am recommending an alkaline diet, as well as considering the use of an alkalinizing supplement or food agent like organic apple cider vinegar or lemon juice if diet alone is not resulting in an alkaline reading when you test your urine.

So How Do You Become More Alkaline and Decrease Inflammation?

It might be interesting to see where you are starting from on the acid / alkaline scale. It is simple to do by checking the acidity of your urine with some litmus paper, easily obtained without a prescription at most pharmacies. Get litmus paper that at least shows a range from pH 6 to 8. (pH 6 is acid, pH 8 is alkaline, and pH 7 is neutral). See if you can find litmus paper with smaller increments like: 7.0, 7.2, 7.4, etc. for more accuracy. The pH of your urine can change from hour to hour depending mostly upon what you have been eating and the amount of exercise you have been doing. The best time to test is in the morning after not having eaten during the night. Simply dip the litmus paper into your urine stream and compare the resulting color to the color code. Ideally, your urine will be pH 7 or greater most of the time for best health. Even a modest change from more acid to less acid is an improvement. Checking your urine on occasion can give you some positive feedback regarding your dietary progress in attaining an alkaline inner environment.

In my own life, I have seen prompt increases in litmus paper acidity with use of wine, coffee, red meats, and pastries. This has been associated with more achy joints, which go away if I eat more alkaline foods or use an alkalinizing supplement. I have also noticed it is much easier for me to maintain my ideal body weight if I am following an alkaline diet. Some of the recommendations for an alkaline diet were mentioned in Chapter 1 with the anti-estrogenic diet. More specific food lists are provided on the free data disc / resource download.

Two books that might be helpful are *The pH Miracle: Balance Your Diet, Reclaim Your Health,* by Robert Young, PhD, and Shelly Redford-Young, and *The Acid Alkaline Diet for Opti-*

mum Health: Restore Your Health By Changing pH Balance In Your Diet, by Christopher Vasey, naturopathic physician.

Go to the Virtual Bookstore in Resources on the website to easily review these books and a selection of other books that I feel will greatly improve your health and become a reference for you on your journey towards improved health.

It takes time to change the way that you are eating, but I think that you will find it very beneficial. What I used to do in the late afternoon would be to have some cheese and crackers as a snack. Now I'm trying to shift to something a little more alkaline, so I might choose a few dates with some Atlantic seaweed, a few nuts, or Greens First or Hope Renewed Balanced Greens Products, an organic powdered vegetable mix added to some organic green tea. You can add a spoonful of chia seeds for extra protein and omega-3 fatty acids. I bit of fresh squeezed lemon is also lovely or add a sprinkle of cinnamon. The tea can be hot or cold. This type of snack is very substantial and fills me up in a way that does not increase my acidic levels.

If your partner wishes to have a nice organic grass-fed steak, you can limit the size of the organic red meat portion, put a twist of lemon in your water, and accompany the meal with more whole grains, Swiss chard, or an avocado. Check the lists in the references and start choosing foods that are more alkaline and less acidic. For instance, wild-caught fish, organic turkey and lamb are less acidic than veal, pork, and beef.

I'm sure you will find it relatively easy to change some items in your day-to-day diet that will greatly improve your health once you realize what could be a better choice. It will require review of the food lists that you can print out from your free download or print worksheets in the Getting Started section to see the best types of diet changes for you and your family. The changes are most easily done gradually over time, as you use up the older-style foods, and develop a pantry full of more alkaline choices.

Another way to enhance your efforts to become more alkaline is to use an alkalinizing supplement. I have tried several of the products available. There is a reference in The Lark Letter, a newsletter by Susan Lark, MD, that discusses alkaline balance and is referenced on the free resource download.

Alkaline agents are usually non-toxic mineral supplements containing calcium, magnesium, and potassium. Alkaline products may be available at your health foods store, or through the website in the Virtual Dispensary where you will get 20% off all your supplements when you are following the PBW protocol. This will also save you money through Emerson Ecologics. You will also be receiving higher quality products through the Virtual Dispensary. You may now be paying full price for the same supplements that you will find on my website.

Click on the product image in the Virtual Dispensary to see the ingredients so you can compare with what you may be using now. I will be offering the Greens First and Renewal Greens alkalizing powder through the website in the Virtual Dispensary. These alkalinizing agents can be used regularly, or at the time that you partake of more acid-producing foods.

Another simple way to alkalize your system is by adding a wedge of lemon to water and drinking the lemon water a half hour before meals. This may seem surprising since you may think that lemon juice is acidic. When consumed, lemon juice actually alkalizes your system. Or you can also add a half to one teaspoon of Bragg's organic raw apple cider vinegar to your water. This contains the fermented "mother" and is another way to add more fabulous probiotics to your daily regimen. The apple cider vinegar should have a cloudy appearance to have probiotics in the product.

Usage needs of an alkalizing supplement may be individualized to your life style, diet, and personal preferences. The litmus paper testing can assist you in determining proper dosages. These supplements are non-toxic, but do not use the agents excessively. A urine pH range of 6.8 to 7.2 is optimal. You do not need to target your pH higher with more supplements. You may notice even more alkaline urine just from diet alone when you start testing. That is also OK, and is frequently seen in vegetarians because of their plant-based diet and avoidance of meat.

Other Ways to Alkalinize

There are other alkalinizing agents available that use sodium bicarbonate or potassium bicarbonate. These are immediate alkalinizing agents, but are not always well-tolerated, perhaps because they diminish the functioning of stomach acids for digestion. If bicarbonates are used, a dose of one quarter to one half a teaspoon in water can be taken a half hour before or one and a half hours after a meal. Sodium bicarbonate can be an issue for some people trying to reduce their sodium intake.

Increasing your magnesium intake to 500 to 750 mg daily or consuming more magnesium-rich foods will also create a huge improvement in your health and make you more alkaline as well. Review the PBW Nutritional Supplement Suggestions in the printable protocol for more information on choosing the correct magnesium and dose for your body's specific needs.

This concludes the chapter about maintaining an alkaline diet and alkalinizing supplements.

CHAPTER 4

The Power of Progesterone

This chapter introduces the practice of using bio-identical hormones to decrease the symptoms of menopause, decrease breast cancer risk, and improve breast health. To assist you in exploring this area in greater depth, I have included a number of my favorite books on the website under Resources. You can click on the book to read a review.

Progesterone is an amazing hormone that can help decrease the estrogen dominance issues mentioned earlier. Some of this is referenced from *The Breast Cancer Prevention and Recovery Diet* by Suzannah Olivier, which is listed in the free resource material section.

How the Estrogen-Progesterone Symphony Works in Your Body

This book by Suzannah Olivier has practical and valuable advice from a breast cancer survivor and it gives a lot of information in a succinct way on how you can decrease your cancer risk. Here is her introduction, and I quote:

> *"While there are several types of estrogens which we produce naturally, there's only one progesterone. Women produce progesterone in the ovaries and in the adrenal glands and men produce a lesser amount in the testes. Progesterone is created from cholesterol, which converts to pregnenolone,*

which in turn converts to progesterone. Simply put, the main function of progesterone is to prolong gestation, hence it's name. When a fertilized egg starts its life, this hormone is responsible for ensuring that the appropriate conditions in the womb are optimal for the egg to implant, mature, and develop. During pregnancy, progesterone is produced by the corpus luteum of the ejected egg, and eventually by the placenta. However, if fertilization has not taken place, progesterone drops dramatically until triggered again half way through the next cycle. Following menopause the woman's progesterone production only takes place in the adrenal glands. This abrupt drop in levels has led to the idea that progesterone is not an important consideration after menopause.

A simplified explanation of progesterone's primary job fails to make clear its important function in breast cancer management. Progesterone is also critical for maintaining a woman's hormonal balance and it does this in two ways. Primarily, it is the first step on the ladder or precursor hormone for a number of other hormones that are made from progesterone. These daughter hormones include estrogen, testosterone, and the corticosteroid hormones. The second and hugely important job is to counter-balance excessive estrogen, which from the point of view of breast cancer management, this is of key interest. The general assumption is that progesterone drops at menopause because, apart from not being needed to promote pregnancy, there is a concurrent drop in estrogen levels to around 25% of full capacity, meaning that progesterone no longer has to work in opposition to estrogen in order to maintain a woman's health. But this was before there were hundreds of man-made chemicals in our environment that exert a damaging xenoestrogen or estrogen mimicking effect, and this thinking may now be outmoded.

Additionally, after the age of 35 women are statistically more likely to have more anovulatory cycles. These cycles are when everything appears to be functioning normally but she does not produce an egg. The implication of this is that women will continue to produce estrogen in ever increasing amounts in her cycle but will not produce any progesterone to counter-balance it. This leads to an increased estrogen load. The majority of breast cancers are detected post-menopausally, but you will recall that the average time that it takes for a breast cancer to be detectable is about 10 to 12 years. This means that a large number of breast cancers are probably initiated during this phase of high, unopposed estrogen levels prior to menopause.

Progesterone is of interest for women with breast cancer or with a risk of breast cancer because it has the opposite effect of estrogen on breast tissue in that is slows down cell division. The slower the cell division the more chance there is that the cells will be produced intact and undamaged. A study of over 1,000 women at John Hopkins University showed that women who had low levels of progesterone sufficient to interfere with fertility had over five times the normal risk of developing breast cancer. Even more alarming, there was a tenfold higher death rate from all malignancies.

Another interesting study in The International Journal of Cancer 1996, noted that women who were tracked for a 28 year period who had given birth to twins where 29% less likely to go on to develop breast cancer. The researchers suggest that the higher levels of hormone levels that occur with twin pregnancies may be responsible for this protection. The hormones that were being produced in a double dose from two placentas are progesterone and the breast-cancer protective estriol, or E3. Two genes are important in this process of apoptosis, or natural cell death, which occurs when normal healthy cells die in order to be replaced. The P53 gene prevents cancer by signaling that the cell is ready to die, and the P53 gene is turned on by progesterone. The BCL2 gene triggers cancer by preventing the cell from dying naturally and the BCL2 is turned on by the estrogens."

This previously mentioned material is a fabulous explanation of the way estrogen and progesterone affects the body by Suzannah Oliver in her book *The Breast Cancer Prevention and Recovery Diet*.

Now I would like to apply this information to the discussion of estrogen dominance. The situation of having excess natural estrogens, estrogens coming from bovine growth hormone (BGH) from meat and dairy products, combined with exposure to the highly-damaging environmental xenoestrogens, creates a condition termed estrogen dominance. John Lee, MD, author of many books on using natural progesterone and the multiple roles of this remarkable hormone, coined this terminology. Dr. Lee spent his entire career working with progesterone and observing its effects on the variety of predominantly female problems, including breast cancer. His books on the subject have revolutionized thinking in this area, and he was of the opinion that natural progesterone should be used by all patients that either now have or have had breast cancer, or are at risk for breast cancer. He taught that progesterone prevents breast cancer, prevents metastases, and prevents late re-occurrences of breast cancer. This is tremendously important for all the women reading this book!

Dr. Lee also cited the work of researcher and clinical biochemist Dr. David Zava, PhD, who has examined thousands of breast cancer tissue biopsies. He found that, without exception, estrogen dominance was present in biopsies positive for breast cancer.

Dr. Zava, who continues his hormonal research and runs ZRT Laboratory in Beaverton, Oregon, and several of his staff were kind enough to review portions of the PBW program and gave some input on this subject.

James Paoletti was the Director of Provider Education at ZRT Laboratory at the time and is the Vice President and Director of Continuing Education for Professional Compounding Centers of America. James Paoletti edited the entire *Proactive Breast Wellness* program and we are tremendously grateful for his input.

Women with Breast Cancer All Have This Hormone Profile

The connection between measured hormone lab levels, environmental estrogens which are not easily measured and estrogen dominance has a major impact on the woman's future risk of developing breast cancer. Dr. Zava and James Paoletti feel that there are hormone profiles that have been identified through the saliva and blood-spot testing at ZRT Lab that may be indicative that the woman has breast cancer even prior to the woman becoming biopsy proven.

This hormone profile includes the following: the women are high in estrogen and low in progesterone and are considered estrogen dominant; they have high testosterone levels and their night-time cortisol levels are elevated; they are low in vitamin D3, low in iodine, and are hypothyroid. Dr. Zava also feels strongly that there are clinical issues connected to elevated estrogen levels that include water retention, premenstrual mood problems, breast swelling and discomfort, fibrocystic breasts, blood sugar fluctuations, polycystic ovaries, uterine fibroids, increased incidence of breast, cervical, and endometrial cancers, and reduced thyroid hormone effectiveness. He and I agree that many of these clinical problems and breast cancer risk can be reduced with the use of progesterone within a program of hormone balancing, supplemented by dietary and life-style changes.

To delve further into this subject, go to the Resources section on my website and review the book *What Your Doctor May Not Tell You About Breast Cancer* by Dr. John Lee and Dr. David Zava. This is one of my favorite books and, if you are concerned about breast health, this book should be in your library.

Applying Progesterone to Your Breast Prior to Surgery May Improve Your Survival Rate by 65%

In another tribute to the power of progesterone, *Dr. Susan Love's Breast Book*, by the noted breast surgeon, researcher, and activist, cites retrospective studies that indicate that reoccurrence and survival rates of women undergoing breast surgery or biopsy are improved by 65% if the surgery is done during the later phase of the menstrual cycle when progesterone is highest. She suggests surgeons should schedule lumpectomies and mastectomies during days 13 to 24 in cycling women. Dr. Love suggests you avoid surgery just before and during the week of your menstrual flow due to your progesterone levels being the lowest during this time frame when you are having your period or just prior.

An alternative is to put menopausal women on topical over-the-counter bio-identical, paraben-free progesterone for at least a week or two, three weeks would be better, prior to their surgery. If you are cycling, you can get some over-the-counter bio-identical progesterone and use it day 11 through day 28. Breast cancer recurrence may be up to four times more likely if surgery is done during or around the time of menses, and twice as likely if the surgery is done during the first half of the menstrual cycle, rather than the later half.

In a study of 249 women, 84% were still alive after 10 years when their surgery was done during days 13 to 24, compared to 54% for those whose surgery was on day three to twelve of their cycle. For this reason, I advise my menopausal clients to use one quarter teaspoon compounded / bio-identical progesterone cream (which would be 20 mg per quarter teaspoon). This could also be over-the-counter, paraben-free topical progesterone to be used in the morning and at bedtime (40 to 50 mg total) for at least one and a half weeks to three weeks, applied to the affected breast prior to biopsy or surgery. You can apply any extra cream to other thin skin. Cycling women could use 20 mg a day or a bit more per day starting on day 11 to 28 and again avoid surgery during their menstrual flow cycle.

If you wish to learn more about the studies and research, remember to request your free data disc or free resource download from the webstore at www.ProtectYourBreasts.com to augment your book or eBook experience.

Artificial/Synthetic Progesterone or Progestins Cause Breast Cancer

Now I would like to discuss the role of artificial progesterone, also known as progestin; and how these substances are different from bio-identical progesterone. Bio-identical progesterone is chemically identical to a woman's own natural progesterone. *The Breast Cancer Prevention and Recovery Diet* by Suzannah Olivier has an excellent section on this subject. I quote from her book:

> *"Early on the pharmaceutical companies became aware of the impact that progesterone had upon unopposed estro-*

gens when their first attempts at producing estrogen-only contraceptive pills resulted in an alarming increase in complaints including thrombosis (blood clots) and hormone triggered cancers. The next strategy that was adopted was to add "Progestins" to the birth control pills and hormone replacement preparations. Progestins are artificially manufactured progesterone-like clones, and sure enough, the risks decreased somewhat but not as much as was hoped. One of the hormone replacement products that have been under recent scrutiny is made from pregnant mare's urine and known as the product Premarin. These unfortunate horses are kept tethered in stalls with urinary catheters and kept thirsty to increase the concentration of the estrogens in the urine. Progestins have been added in the attempt to balance off the effects of the estrogen. Progestins do not have the same advantages as the natural progesterone molecule and it actually enhances the risk of breast cancer from the hormone replacement therapy. Whereas, natural progesterone may have the opposite effect and reduces the risk from hormone replacement therapy."

If It Cannot Be Patented Because It Is from Nature, There Is a Low Profit Margin

There are many synthetic progestins, one of the more popular brands being Provera, or medroxyprogesterone acetate. I believe these are synthetically designed because the natural progesterones that can be found in nature cannot be patented, so they are of little interest to large pharmaceutical companies. The profit margins from the natural products are lamentably small for an industry used to higher profits. Progestins are patentable, and of course the birth control pills and hormone replacement therapies using artificial progestins are very big business. So the progestins are perhaps produced more for the benefit of the pharmaceutical industry than for the long-term benefit of the women taking them.

Side Effects of Synthetic Progestins

Synthetic progestins have many known side effects such as bloating, headache, and weight gain, and they increase PMS symptoms since they decrease the body's natural progesterone levels.

More and more clinicians are switching their prescribing practices to natural progesterone, as well as other bio-identical hormone replacements including estrogen and testosterone.

Natural Progesterone at Normal Physiological Doses Has No Serious Side Effects

Natural bio-identical progesterone has no serious side effects at normal physiological doses. It does not commonly cause the progestin problems of bloating, headache, weight gain, or any increase in PMS symptoms. Occasionally, the natural progesterone might cause mid-cycle spotting, or delay of onset of the menstrual period, but these symptoms usually resolve in a couple of months of continued usage. At very high doses, there have been some rare cases of dizziness or euphoria. Occasionally, women who are taking doses greater than 200 milligrams a day orally complain of being too sleepy, which might be a benefit if dosed at bedtime.

In a personal experiment, I tripled my usual 40 to 50 mg total dose per day, using 150 mg at bedtime once to see what would happen. I usually take 20 to 25 mg in the morning and the same dose again at bedtime. I slept very well on the 150 mg dose but felt extremely fatigued and sleepy for several hours upon awakening. The drugged feeling and drowsiness wore off by about 10:30 a.m., and I resolved to return to my more typical dosage of 20 to 25 mg twice per day. Actual dosages must be individually tailored and will be discussed later in this chapter.

Ways Progesterone Can Be Administered

Bio-identical progesterone can be used orally, sublingually, or vaginally by prescription, or with topical preparations available by prescription or over-the-counter. Again, avoid parabens added as a preservative to any of your products.

The dosages of progesterone are variable depending upon the purpose and situation, and are best determined in consultation with a clinician experienced in using bio-identical hormones. The following discussion has general guidelines for its use, as well as a discussion of other progesterone precursor products such as wild yam.

How Is Progesterone Used and How Much is Enough?

How is progesterone used or applied and how much is enough? I use the topical preparations more than oral or sublingual products. Natural bio-identical progesterone is available as a cream without prescription. It can be applied to areas of thin skin, rotating the sites of application. You can apply it to the neck, face, inner thighs, and inner arms. Applying progesterone to the abdomen should be avoided because progesterone can affect gastro-intestinal motility. It is absorbed into the fat under the skin and is taken up slowly by the blood. Many of my compounding pharmacy colleagues also suggest using it directly on the breast, particularly on the areas that may be tender or have thickening, or areas where there may be upcoming surgery.

If you are using Pro-Gest or another over-the-counter progesterone cream, then use one quarter to one half a teaspoon twice a day.

Most over the counter bio-identical progesterone products are dosed at 15 to 20 mg per one quarter teaspoon of cream. Check the dose prior to purchasing so you know what the dose is. You may receive 20% off all your products through my website.

I strongly recommend that you use only preparations that are paraben-free because parabens have been identified in the tissues of breast cancer tumors. Parabens are used as a preservative in many cosmetics, personal care products, and creams.

There is more information about parabens in the chapter on environmental toxins, as well as on the free data disc/free resource download that you can obtain from the website. The website also has a cosmetic link on the *Take Action* page that allows you to check the contents of your personal care products, giving a one to ten scale rating of product ingredient safety. You can then do a reverse search to find a safer group of products for you and your family.

Not All Over-the-Counter Progesterone is the Same – What to Check

A word of caution on over-the-counter progesterone creams. Not all products are of the same quality, and there is little effective regulation of over-the-counter hormone preparations. Independent testing of hormone products has shown that some over-the-counter progesterone creams contain little or no progesterone. Make sure the label says one or more of these words: USP (US pharmacy grade), micronized or bio-identical progesterone, and a dosage given per ¼ teaspoon. You will find a large selection of products through my Virtual Dispensary and Emerson Ecologics. They are a distribution center for hundreds of manufacturers.

Compounded Progesterone in an Oil Base Works Well

The progesterone can also be blended by compounding pharmacists into liquid drops applied to the skin. I usually order bio-identical progesterone compounded as 40 to 50 mg per eight drops in organic jojoba oil applied topically. Several of my compounding pharmacy colleagues have warned not to try to compound more than 50 mg per eight drops because the product gets too thick and becomes a paste. Other pharmacists feel that concentrations of more than 50 mg will not absorb well through the skin. I like having the compounding pharmacist mix the micronized progesterone in organic jojoba oil because the oil is not greasy and does not stain clothing. It absorbs well and does not need a preservative if used before 120 days when stored at room temperature. I usually order about 15 milliliters for a client to try a short trial of one to two months and then have them order a larger amount for the refill in the 30 to 35 ml range. Since the progesterone is in an oil suspension, rather than a solution, the progesterone powder settles to the bottom of the container, so you need to shake the bottle well.

There is a risk that as the oil is gradually used; some progesterone ends up sticking to the sides of the bottle where it is not accessible. If you have transferred the suspension to a wide mouth jar there is no waste. I suggest that you transfer a two-week portion of your large prescription supply to a very small one to two inch tall colored glass container with a wide mouth. Be sure to shake or stir the suspension well each time before transferring or using the oil.

The larger supply can be left in the refrigerator, or used when traveling. When you need to replenish your small bottle, allow the stock bottle to sit at room temperature for about 20 minutes to liquefy, and then shake before transferring. I also specify that the compounded product be in organic jojoba to avoid the unnecessary chemicals found in most other products, especially for my clients with environmental allergies. My clients apply four drops (5mg per drop) which is 20 milligrams, in the morning and again at night if they have breast complaints. If the woman is also on an estriol or estrogen preparation, I recommend at least 50 milligrams per day so there will be enough progesterone in her system so the estrogen is not unopposed

Caution: Some products use propylene glycol as a base for their topical drops or creams. Propylene glycol is a known sensitizing agent and should not be used for regularly repeated application to the skin. If you are working with a new provider or pharmacy, make sure to ask them what the base is for your new preparation and inquire what the preservative is if they have added a preservative. Vitamin E oil is perfectly safe as a preservative but if you use all the progesterone in oil within 120 days, you do not need a preservative in the first place. I don't have any preservatives in the prescriptions that I write. You can request your provider to leave preservatives out of their compounded prescriptions.

Progesterone for Non Cycling and Menopausal Women

For non-cycling and menopausal women, one recommendation is to use progesterone for three weeks of the month and then not use for the fourth week. You can start it at any time if you are menopausal. Some women decide to start on the first day of the month so they can keep track more easily. If PMS symptoms seem to return with complaints of mood swings, difficulty sleeping, being tearful, or feeling edgy when off the progesterone for more than four to five days, you can shorten the period that you are off the progesterone.

Another approach that I have come to prefer for menopausal women is to apply the progesterone topically twice a day, after your shower in the morning and at bedtime, Monday through Friday. You can be off progesterone on the weekends. This approach improves remembering to use the progesterone and decreases any edgy, PMS-like feelings.

Progesterone and Women Who are Still Cycling

For women who are still cycling or have irregular cycles you may want to increase the levels to match your body's normal rhythms. This would be to match the progesterone rise after the middle of the month when you ovulate. For women who are still cycling, they start the progesterone day 11 or 12 counting from the first day of bleeding of their cycle. They continue to use it until their period occurs and then stop.

If they are perimenopausal and cycles are becoming irregular, you can use progesterone to help regulate the cycles by discontinuing on day 28 to 32 depending on what your previous rhythm happened to be. This will work and help keep you more regular for awhile, until your body decides that you will not cycle any longer. Remember that the term menopause is the time in your life after you have had 12 missed menses in a row.

Avoid a Hysterectomy and Shrink Your Uterine Fibroids?

Many women have also used progesterone successfully to shrink uterine fibroids and decrease heavy bleeding, hence avoiding a hysterectomy. Higher progesterone dosages may be needed for this purpose. Fibroids tend to decrease in size after menopause, so fibroids may not be an issue once cycling ends. In addition to the use of progesterone, dietary changes that reduce estrogen levels may also help in the treatment of uterine fibroids. Women with this problem may do very well by first eliminating dairy foods for at least three months and staying on a low fat, high complex carbohydrate diet that reduces excessive circulating estrogens. This would be in the range of 30 grams of fat or less with 75% of calories from complex carbohydrates. Many premenopausal or perimenopausal women have found that if they follow a low-fat, high-fiber diet to treat their uterine fibroids, they may be able to eliminate or decrease the amount of progesterone needed over time.

Younger Women with Estrogen Dominance Symptoms and Migraines

For younger women who are not in the perimenopause stage yet but have other symptoms of estrogen dominance, I may use a lesser amount of progesterone, in the 10 to 15 milligram per day range, during days 12 to 28, along with the other dietary suggestions discussed in previous chapters. Natural progesterone also works well for women whose primary premenstrual complaint is a migraine-type headache, often times using the progesterone daily and not having any days off. I also use progesterone in the early stages of perimenopause when a client is having mild hot flushes or palpitations. Increasing magnesium and taking a substantial multivitamin with minerals may also help with these symptoms. Discounted, high-quality supplement product suggestions are listed on the website Virtual Dispensary.

What Is with the Black Box Warning You May See on Over-the-Counter Progesterone?

Before you think I am trying to poison you, I want to explain a warning on some of the Pro-Gest over-the-counter tubes of progesterone cream that states, "It has been found that in some laboratory studies in California that this product may cause cancer in rats." I found this statement alarming so I spoke with one of the chemists who produce this product. She said that the FDA lumped progestins or synthetic progesterone in with natural progesterone when they made this statement to protect their big pharma friends and the products they produce that have progestins in them. It has been shown that the progestins have been implicated in causing cancer in rats and in women, but the natural progesterone has not. At the moment, there is no differentiation in the labeling that would make this clearer. If you notice this warning on the over-the-counter natural bio-identical progesterone cream, you can better understand the origins of the label. If progesterone caused cancer, we probably would not have the number of pregnant women wandering about. These pregnant women in their third trimester are making more than 800 mg of progesterone per day while pregnant. In fact, progesterone levels have to be high to achieve a pregnancy.

While we are on the topic of over-the-counter progesterone cream, it is important to read the label to make sure there are no parabens in the product. These cancer causing preservatives may be listed as methyl paraben or ethyl paraben. Avoid the whole paraben family!

Trouble Sleeping? Oral or Sublingual Progesterone May Help

I seldom use the oral capsules or drops placed under the tongue of the bio-identical progesterone products. One exception is in the situation of sleep disturbance. I then would consider using a compounded slow-release oral preparation in the 100 to 200 milligram range. Some metabolites of progesterone that may aid sleep are produced as the progesterone is metabolized by the liver.

There is a pharmaceutical version of bio-identical progesterone called Prometrium, which comes in 100 and 200 milligram capsules in peanut oil. This may be slightly less expensive than a compounded product. However, since there are many women with peanut allergies, I do not use this product very often.

Also, Prometrium does not maintain the progesterone level the same as a compounded slow release preparation and therefore may not balance the estrogen throughout the day and night unless excessive dosing is used. Many women have complained of being too sleepy on doses of 100 mg to 200 mg a day in capsule form. You and your provider may need to do a bit of experimenting to see what dose and in what form is best for you. You could ask your provider to write for 10 pills of Prometrium 100 mg as a trial to see how you do. This would be the least expensive way to try this. A compounding pharmacist could also make up a lesser dose. If you have a peanut allergy, the pharmacist could make the progesterone up in a capsule without the peanut oil.

How are Natural Progesterone/Wild Yam Products Different from Bio-identical Progesterone?

When purchasing nonprescription progesterone creams, the terms "natural progesterone" and Mexican yam products create another area of confusion. The term "natural progesterone" can be misleading because the chemical is not technically natural; it is actually a manufactured product created in a laboratory from diosgenin, an extract of soy or the Mexican wild yam. Some Mexican yam products have this laboratory-created progesterone added to them, but it varies in strength. Diosgenin cannot be converted directly into progesterone by the body, so Mexican yam products that do not have the laboratory-derived progesterone added to them do not have significant health effects. There is also some concern that the yam products might have some mild phytoestrogenic properties.

Check the Label

Caution: Due to lack of good regulation of over-the-counter hormone products, there is no guarantee the product contains the ingredients listed on the label. I recommend that women only use nonprescription progesterone creams if they see these three words listed on the label: micronized, bio-identical, and pharmacy grade progesterone (USP) and only if there is a dosage listed in milligrams per application or ¼ teaspoon dose is also listed. If you do not find any of these words listed on the product, do not purchase that brand. You will just be wasting your money. Again, it is best to work with a health professional.

In summary, the use of bio-identical progesterone is an important aspect of the *Proactive Breast Wellness* program. Progesterone is used in combination with other bio-identical hormones, which will be discussed in the next section.

CHAPTER 5

Hormone Balancing and Laboratory Testing

There is a group of other hormones beyond progesterone that play important roles in a woman's hormone balancing and breast health. These include estrone, estradiol, estriol, testosterone, thyroid, cortisol, and DHEA. During the perimenopausal and menopausal period there are many fluctuations in these hormones. Therapeutic balancing of these hormones over time is an art form with a woman's changing body physiology.

The actual balancing of your hormone levels is beyond the scope of this program. There are many books available addressing the symptoms and hormone dosages, and there is a selection of these books listed on the free data download / disc or on my website under Resources for your review and to browse through my favorite titles. I suggest that you locate a medical practitioner in your area who works with bio-identical hormone replacement to assist you in customizing dosages that work for you. These amounts will change over time as your body changes.

To find a skilled medical practitioner knowledgeable in bio-identical hormone replacement therapy (BHRT) and hormone testing in your area with whom you may wish to work, I suggest you contact ZRT Lab or Women's International Pharmacy. They have practitioners listed by state and towns and would be an excellent resource for you. Practitioners who work with BHRT have probably been using ZRT Lab & Women's International Pharmacy for years. You could also ask the lab or compounding pharmacy how long the provider has had an account with them. That will give you an idea of how seasoned the practitioner is in this area of knowledge.

I would like to add one important note: Hormone dosages need to be individualized. Providing physiologic amounts of deficient hormones is highly beneficial, but both too little or too much hormone can have long-term effects that are detrimental to your overall health. Be sure to work with a practitioner who monitors your levels as well as your symptoms, by the use of saliva, capillary / blood spot or dried urine metabolite testing to ensure physiologic levels are achieved.

Bio-identical Hormones

Synthetic hormones, animal estrogen (Premarin), and synthetic progestin products have been used extensively in traditional allopathic medical practices, both for menopausal symptoms, as well as contraception and managing dysfunctional uterine bleeding. There has been a glaring omission in all the research in the exclusion of natural hormones in the prevention of and therapeutic approaches to breast cancer. Companies will not invest millions of dollars to obtain medical use approval for natural hormones that anyone can copy. Pharmaceutical company research on hormone replacement therapy and cancer is restricted to the development of cancer treatment drugs that can be patented.

Large population studies with hormonal contraceptives have produced mixed results and many of them have been funded by pharmaceutical companies. At least some of these studies have indicated an increased breast cancer risk after only a few years of use. Birth control pills contain only aggressive estrogens and they do not contain any estriol, which has been shown to have breast cancer protective benefits. Even with the progestin-only products such as DepoProvera and the Mirena IUD, it is known that these progestins or synthetic progesterone products have estrogenic effects as well as progesterone-like effects. When possible, I suggest women avoid hormonal contraceptive products altogether. For dysfunctional uterine bleeding, with bio-identical progesterone available, there is no need to use the synthetic progestins. Likewise, for perimenopausal and menopausal symptoms, the bio-identical hormones are far superior with respect to safety and limited adverse effects.

As a practitioner who uses infrared breast imaging as one of my tools, I have another window into the effects of hormones upon the breast tissue that is not available by any other means. Some of the radiologists to whom I have shown my scans say that the grey inverted scale is able to show neo-angiogenesis patterns or blood flow that is leading to a tumor which are somewhat similar on MRI scans. Estrogen dominance and hormone influence can easily be seen with infrared imaging, showing increased vascularity of the blood vessels in the breasts. This is of great importance in the instance where there may be pre-cancerous cells beginning to form into colonies, creating an active vascular system that is dilated due to the release of nitric oxide by the cancer cells. This increased vascularity is now available to meet the growing nutritional and oxygen needs of the cancer cells. This is one of the reasons that estrogen-sensitive breast cancer cells have a doubling rate of 80 to 90 days in women under the age of 50 when their estrogen levels are still high. If the vessels have dilated in this estrogen-dominant state, this does not bode well for breast cancer risk management, breast cancer reoccurrence, or the doubling rates of tumors.

With the infrared camera as a tool, I have found prominent large vessels and abnormal scans in women being treated with synthetic hormone replacement, birth control pills, and women being treated with excessive bio-identical hormone replacement using estradiol or estrone without progesterone.

I see similar patterns in women with known toxic exposures to herbicides and pesticides, plus soy, flax, hemp, and Marijuana products. I do not see these patterns as frequently in women eating only organic foods including meat and dairy without bovine growth hormone. The estrogen-dominant pattern is also diminished by the use of progesterone and iodine replacement therapy after a period of six months. I do not see these patterns when bio-identical estriol is used. For this reason, I recommend that estriol be the bio-identical estrogen of choice when possible, or have a larger amount of estriol than estradiol in your Bi-Est (a prescription of estradiol and estriol in one product) mixtures plus enough progesterone to balance them out.

Bi-Est comes in different ratios for example; 20/80 or 40/60 or perhaps 50/50. If the woman is estrogen dominant, usually the woman is receiving too much estradiol and perhaps too little progesterone or too little estriol. In this woman I might suggest backing off the estradiol and adding more estriol in perhaps a 10% to 90% ratio with estriol being the larger amount in the ratio. This may take some adjustments over time with your local provider to assist you. If you can get off the estradiol which is the stronger product all together and use the weaker estriol instead, that may be better to reduce the vascularity as seen on infrared. The trade off is whether or not you suddenly have an increase in menopausal symptoms, like hot flashes. This is where adjusting hormone replacement is a bit of an art form.

Herbicides, Pesticides, Environmental Estrogens that Negatively Influence Your Hormone Balancing

Here in Oregon, we have one of the highest breast cancer rates in the country per capita. I feel strongly that there is a direct correlation with the amount of herbicides and pesticides used in agriculture and especially by the timber industry in Oregon.

To document this unsettling and deadly trend, I posted a PowerPoint presentation on the website at www.ProtectYourBreasts.com in the "Protect Your Breasts / You Are At Risk" section. I encourage everyone who is reading this program to stop and go to the website to see what toxic levels of these estrogen-like chemicals do to breast tissue. You will better understand how too much estradiol without enough progesterone to balance your prescription, synthetic hormone replacement, bovine growth hormones from not eating organically, and these other estrogen-like compounds that are in herbicides and pesticides, and other estrogen-mimicking compounds effect your health. You can actually see how these chemicals and estrogen-like compounds affect the breast tissue and increase your risk of breast disease. There are also images of women before and after the PBW program. Share this PowerPoint and my website with all the people you know.

The infrared images shown on the PowerPoint slides were the main impetus that led me to create the *Proactive Breast Wellness* program and *Protect Your Breasts* to assist women to lessen their risk of developing breast cancer or reduce reoccurrence rates. It is reassuring that the changes and choices that you make actually have an effect and that these can be verified visually as well as physiologically, and by the woman herself as her moods, energy, and vitality improve. These improvements are also frequently mirrored in the improvement of her lab test results.

No Easily Available Testing for BGH/Bovine Growth Hormone and Environmental Estrogen Mimickers

The next significant challenge in the area of hormone testing is that there are no tests available currently for bovine growth hormone, 2-4-D Dioxin, Agent Orange, Roundup, or a plethora of other chemicals that are estrogen mimickers that current environmental research is beginning to link to various disease states and cancers. A woman's laboratory values for her hormone levels may look totally normal when she and her provider look at her estradiol, estrone, estriol, progesterone, and free testosterone levels. There may be other estrogen mimicker chemicals in her body or in her environment and they may currently be increasing the vascular patterns in her breast by activating her estrogen receptor sites. These chemicals cannot be easily monitored.

The danger is that she may have a group of abnormal cells developing and the increased estrogen-like effects of these chemicals can create an increased number of engorged vessels that will provide nutrition to a potential growing tumor. If her tissues are being activated by these environmental estrogens, her provider may unknowingly prescribe more estradiol for menopausal symptoms because her estradiol laboratory values appear low. Since there is no way currently to evaluate the estrogen-mimicking chemicals, bovine growth hormone, or the effects of eating too much flax or non-fermented soy products, or too much black cohosh or red clover, then the vascular patterns will worsen. Without availability of a local infrared thermography camera and clinic, a woman will not fully understand her personal physiological status. However, after doing several thousand infrared images, it has become apparent to me that the women who start trying to make environmental and dietary changes along with following the *Proactive Breast Wellness* protocol tend to see improvement in their images in about six months to a year in approximately 65% of the cases. Since we are all living in this estrogenic soup, anything we can do to lessen the impact will improve our health and the health of our families.

Could You Have a Thyroid Nodule Influencing Your Thyroid Hormones?

The infrared camera is also very accurate in identifying sub-clinical hypothyroidism and thyroid nodules. When I see a thermal asymmetry or shift over the thyroid poles, I start a work-up for hypothyroidism. If a small circular hyperthermic pattern is noted on the infrared image, then the work-up would expand to diagnose a thyroid nodule or a possible thyroid cancer. A thyroid ultrasound would be added if the lab values are abnormal. The thyroid testing would include a TSH, freeT3, freeT4, thyroid peroxidase or TPO test and a thyroglobulin antibody evaluation with a referral to an endocrinologist if the laboratory tests and the thyroid ultrasound are abnormal. There is additional information in regards to infrared thermography discussed in greater depth in the diagnostic imaging section.

The Estrogen Family: Estrone/Estradiol and Estriol

There are three natural estrogens made in the human body: estrone, estradiol, and estriol. These different estrogens have different effects in the body, and also have different potencies. Estradiol (abbreviated as E2) is the strongest, estrone (abbreviated as E1) is mid-potency, and estriol (abbreviated as E3) is the weakest. All three of these estrogens have been used in various strengths and combinations for various therapies, both by traditional practitioners and practitioners trained in using bio-identical products. Estrogen supplements are generally not used by women who are still cycling because they are still producing their own estrogens.

The following is a discussion of these estrogens provided by James Paoletti, pharmacist and Fellow of the American Academy of Anti-Aging, Regenerative, and Functional Medicine (FAARFM). James Paoletti formally was the Director of Education at ZRT Laboratory, working with Dr. David Zava. Paoletti was formerly (1995-2006) the Vice President and Director of Continuing Education for Professional Compounding Centers of America, Inc. (PCCA). James graciously reviewed the whole *Proactive Breast Wellness* program and he offered a number of articles, which have been medically indexed on the free resource download / data disc, which you can receive from the website. The following quotation is from Jim Paoletti, to assist you in understanding the important roles these estrogens play and the effects they have on breast tissue and breast cancer.

> *"The strength of a hormone is representative of how tightly it binds to its receptors. The tighter it binds the longer before it dissociates from the receptor and the ligand no longer exists. The commonly expressed comparison of estrogen strength is that estradiol is 12 times more potent than estrone and 80 times more potent than estriol. These relative strengths of the three bio-identical estrogens were determined by measuring effects on the uterus lining, but do not necessarily apply to all tissues in the body. Estradiol*

has been estimated to be 1000 times more potent than estriol in stimulating proliferation of breast tissue. Estriol is the most potent of the three estrogens on the vaginal estrogen receptors. Estriol is the only estrogen that has been shown to reverse symptoms of vaginal atrophy at doses that do not raise blood levels or induce systemic effects in most women. However, estradiol appears to be the strongest estrogen in general for overall effects throughout the body, much stronger than estriol. The result of any potential interaction of estrogens with the estrogen receptors depends not only on the relative strength of the estrogenic substances present, but their relative quantities as well. In most cases, estrogen receptors combine to form heterodimer receptors, so it takes two estrogenic molecules combined with the two receptors for formation of the ligand to begin translation of the message for genomic effects. If two stronger estrogenic molecules combine with the receptors, then they will produce the strongest genomic estrogenic effect. If a weaker estrogenic substance combines with one or both receptors, then the message will be comparatively short-lived, and a weaker estrogenic response will be affected. It therefore takes a greater quantity of a weaker estrogenic substance to produce similar results to a stronger estrogen because there has to be enough of the weaker substance to sustain the message over a longer period."

"Estriol's role in the body has not been completely determined, but evidence points to the fact that it may protect against the proliferative effects of the stronger estrogens estradiol and estrone. Early studies by Dr. Lemmon demonstrated less risk of breast cancer in women with a greater proportion of estriol relative to their levels of estradiol and estrone. Lemmon also showed that estriol limited the growth of breast tumors in rats. More recently, several studies have demonstrated that estriol administration

causes no increase in the risk of breast cancer."

"Being much weaker, estriol can block the interaction of the stronger estrogens with the receptors and reduce their genomic responses. The more estriol in the system, the greater the chance of blocking the effects of the stronger estrogens. In this sense, the estrogenic substance estriol could be considered an anti-estrogen when compared to estradiol and estrone. Similarly, Tamoxifen, a substance that has been shown to initially decrease then increase the chance of reoccurrence of breast cancer if used more than five years, is classified as an anti-estrogen, even though Tamoxifen is an estrogenic substance itself."

"The same receptor blocking effect occurs if too much of a phytoestrogen (plant estrogen) or xenoestrogen is introduced to the body. Although estrogenic in their effect, and much, much weaker than estradiol, sufficient quantities can decrease the effectiveness of estradiol."

In summary, when you are working with your medical provider, discuss your desire to emphasize the use of estriol over estradiol and estrone. Estriol's beneficial effects are greatest in the vaginal tissues, and appears to have less systemic effects. In my experience, estriol does not increase the estrogen-type vascular patterns in breast tissue, whereas estradiol, estrone, and synthetic estrogens and synthetic progestins do increase the vascular patterns in the breast, and in my opinion should be avoided. When switching from estradiol, estrone, or synthetic hormone replacements, it may be necessary to wean off these products as you increase your estriol. Once the older estrogens are out of your system, the dosage of estriol required may decrease. This will sometimes require careful monitoring by your health care provider to make such a transition. Estriol is not as strong at suppressing menopausal hot flashes, but these may be helped by other non-estrogen techniques. Estriol is prescribed by providers who use bio-identical hormones, as well as some other traditional medical providers.

Commonly, a combination of estradiol and estriol is used, adjusting the amounts of each to obtain normal physiologic levels of each of these estrogens. This provides the normal protective benefits of estrogens and minimizes risks associated with estrogen therapy.

Your local compounding pharmacist will be able to suggest providers who prescribe bio-identical hormones in your area.

Testosterone – It Is Not Just For Men

Testosterone is the male, androgen-type hormone. Both men and women naturally produce this substance, with men producing much higher levels. In women, there has been some evidence that high testosterone levels may increase the risk of developing breast cancer, and that newly elevated levels of testosterone may be heralding the onset of breast cancer. Remember that high testosterone was listed earlier as one of the profile items of women at higher risk of breast cancer, along with high estrogen, low progesterone, low iodine, low thyroid function, low DHEA, low vitamin D3, and high night time cortisol. The very small amount of testosterone that women normally produce in their pre-menopausal years has been shown to actually help protect against breast cancer. Again, the right amount of the hormone (physiological) is beneficial but too much of it reverses the situation.

Losing excess weight and supplementing progesterone can down-regulate testosterone. In the case of a high-risk hormonal profile of elevated free testosterone, along with increased thermal patterns on infrared imaging, I have a low threshold for ordering MRI breast structural imaging, or other structural studies. I aggressively put women in these circumstances on the *Proactive Breast Wellness* protocol, with careful and frequent monitoring of laboratory values and repeated structural studies and infrared imaging in six months.

At normal lower levels, testosterone plays an active beneficial role in bone and muscle strength, cardiovascular protection, energy levels, stamina, lean body mass, positive mood, feelings of security and confidence, and libido. At subnormal levels in women it can result in fatigue, muscle weakness, balance and coordination difficulties, indecisiveness, and lack of sex drive. After the age of 35, there is a slow but substantial loss in natural testosterone levels for most women. Some practitioners have recommended supplementing testosterone if there are signs of deficiency, confirmed by laboratory testing.

The use of testosterone in women as a hormone replacement option has been controversial. Significant adverse effects, particularly liver damage, have been noted for synthetic testosterone-like products. Bio-identical testosterone used at physiologic levels can improve the well being of some women. However, some women may convert a small portion of the testosterone into estrogen, and the long term effects on breast and other tissues are difficult to ascertain.

I Suggest You Avoid Long-Acting Inserted Hormone Pellets and Birth Control Pills

I have recently become rather concerned about the safety and ethical use of inserting pellets into women, particularly testosterone and estradiol pellets. When I am using the infrared camera, I can actually see the alterations in physiology and metabolic changes that these pellets cause. The drug companies tout how safe the product is, but they do not actually "See" what these pellets are doing to the tissue.

I know of a local practitioner who uses pellets for weight loss, menopause and mood issues in his patients. The infrared scans I have seen of women who have had pellets inserted are way too vascular and their labs at six weeks post-pellet insertion, when theoretically the woman should have come down to a treatment base line, but they sometimes have three to five times the testosterone level that a healthy man might be expected to have on his labs. As mentioned earlier the estradiol increases the vascularization of the breasts. The estradiol or testosterone pellets cannot be removed and eventually are supposed to be absorbed after four to five months. If that same woman has an early breast cancer, I feel these pellets are very dangerous because they appear to actively increase vascularity and blood flow. My issue with this is if the woman has a new breast cancer tumor developing and you provide the tumor with unlimited oxygen and nutrition, this will increase the tumor doubling time. Dr. Zava and ZRT Laboratories have shown that women who have elevated free testosterone levels fit the profile for women who have an increased risk of developing breast cancer or have breast cancer at the time of the laboratory testing. These pellets unfortunately appear to increase vascularity and markedly elevated testosterone levels.

My concern extends to two similar implants available in the U.S. called Implanon and Nexplanon, which is gradually replacing Implanon as a brand of birth control pellets. Each implant is a plastic rod about the size of a matchstick. The rods contain a form of the hormone progesterone which is a synthetic progestin called etonogestrel. These new pellets which are usually inserted into the upper arm under the skin are touted to provide long term, up to three years of worry free birth control. At three years they need to be surgically removed. I have only examined a few young women using infrared thermography who have had these birth control implants and the amount of vascularity was incredibly alarming.

My suggestion is to use another method of birth control. All varieties of birth control pills seem to also increase metabolic activity in the breasts with increased vascular patterns, which over time I do not think will bode well.

Avoid Supplementing Testosterone in Breast Cancer Patients

Most practitioners agree that testosterone supplementation should not be used by women with breast cancer, or by those with a high risk of breast cancer, such as noted on infrared imaging, or in women with known genetic cancer tendencies. The use of testosterone supplements must be very carefully individualized, and should be done only with the attention of a knowledgeable health care provider.

DHEA Metabolism in Breast Cancer

Women with active breast cancer have lower levels of DHEA, otherwise known as dehydroepiandrosterone, which is a hormone primarily produced in the adrenal glands, the organ that also makes adrenaline and cortisol. DHEA is higher during teenage years and peaks around age 25, and then slowly goes down with age. DHEA is a precursor of progesterone, testosterone, and estrogen production in the body. Unfortunately, there is no way of knowing which way it will metabolize when taken as a supplement. DHEA should be given conservatively to menopausal women. Some DHEA could convert to estrogen, and any issues with estrogen dominance need to be addressed first.

DHEA is a hormone that can be purchased without a prescription, and I feel that many people are over-using this preparation. It is available in capsules, sublingual drops, or topical creams and gels. If you are choosing to use this product, I suggest a starting oral dose of five milligrams, with perhaps an increase to 10 milligrams. The topical creams and gels need to be only a portion of the oral dose. I might suggest 0.5 to 2.0 mg topically. An oral dose is preferred as much of it is converted to DHEA sulfate, the more biologically active form in the brain. In addition to increasing DHEA, the capsule form may elevate testosterone more than the sublingual drops. This is a concern with respect to breast cancer risk. I do not use DHEA with my clients because its effects are unpredictable. If you are still considering the use of DHEA, popular now in some of the anti-aging literature, then consult with a medical provider and have regular laboratory monitoring at least every three to six months. DHEA is important in optimizing immune function, which is a critical aspect of protection from getting cancer.

Meditation – a Hormone Healing Tool and Receive Your FREE Copy of *Waves of Serenity*

For a completely safe approach, you might instead consider starting a meditation program. Stress decreases the body's production of DHEA while at the same time increasing the consumption of DHEA. Meditation is a powerful tool for stress reduction. If you reduce your stress, it helps to keep the stress hormone cortisol low, and DHEA high. Since high night time cortisol and low DHEA appear to be harbingers for breast cancer, this easy, safe, no-cost approach would certainly be a benefit.

I have included my 45-minute progressive muscle relaxation/guided beach imagery program *Waves of Serenity* FREE as a download or CD available from my website Store. It has been included in the *Proactive Breast Wellness* program and the *Protect Your Breasts* book and eBook to help you decrease stress and insomnia. Enter the password code **PBWBOOK** to get your FREE copy. *Waves of Serenity* was created to guide beginners unfamiliar with meditation techniques so they would have a relaxation tool available to them particularly if they were facing surgery or hospitalization, or were otherwise stressed. You can sample the experience of the soothing narrative of a beach walk, harp, and ocean sounds as an audio and video clip on my website. Listen to all or part of *Waves* on a daily basis to improve your health! You can also give a loved one a "Gift of Health" from the website Store with your own healing message.

I also wished to add here that you should also access and receive the FREE Data Resource Download or Data Disc CD that goes with the eBook and printed version of "*Protect Your Breasts.*" There you will find over 1,000 pages of medically indexed materials by chapter including the medical articles which are discussed in this book. Instead of putting in the footnotes in the eBook and book version, you will find them on the resource download since it was originally created for the audio digital download version. It also contains other resources that will enhance your exploration of this subject to assist you in improving your health.

Hormone Laboratory Testing

Laboratory testing can be beneficial in identifying your hormone levels to help your practitioner get an overview, and then they can make informed suggestions as to how to proceed for your treatment program. I also like the phrase "treat the patient, not the numbers," so know that these laboratory levels are just a snapshot in time and need to be placed in the context of symptoms and other factors. The laboratory values can help your practitioner identify estrogen dominance, progesterone deficiency, and a host of other conditions.

How to Follow Your Progress

Please reference and print the PCCA Hormone Symptom List and How to Do an Axillary Temperature Journal for 5-6 days and then average the temperatures. Get this worksheet from the free data resources located in the Getting Started section or at the end of the book in the Worksheet section. Make several copies and keep an original set. As a baseline before you start the PBW protocol, check off your symptoms and enter the date on the work sheet to monitor your progress. Share the symptom and temperature readings with your provider as you begin to improve. Make the changes in diet and supplements on the PBW protocol and then recheck your temperature and symptoms on another copy of your worksheet in six to eight weeks to check for improvement. Also continue to monitor your progress through laboratory testing, but the symptom and temperature worksheets are free to do.

I utilize hormone laboratory testing to assist in my decision-making process when evaluating women with the potential for breast cancer, as well as in designing their bio-identical hormone therapy. As you may recall earlier in the program, there seems to be a hormone profile that accompanies breast cancer, with high estrogen, low progesterone, high testosterone, low iodine, and low thyroid levels. In addition, low vitamin D3, low DHEA, high night time cortisol, and high homocystine levels are also markers for increased breast cancer risk. When I find this kind of profile, I am more aggressive with the *Proactive Breast Wellness* program.

Another example of using laboratory information is earlier referral for breast MRI or surgical biopsy, even in the absence of abnormal findings on conventional mammogram or breast ultrasound. I would especially refer them if the mammogram or ultrasound were borderline, or if their breast infrared scan is suspicious or abnormal. Infrared imaging of the breasts is a way to identify abnormal vascular patterns and abnormal hot spots that can be associated with increased metabolic activity of breast tumors, as well as possible precancerous changes. I discuss the use of such imaging techniques in more detail in Chapter 8 Diagnostic Breast Imaging.

If you and your clinician have decided to embark upon a therapeutic regimen in addition to diet and supplements, your clinician will probably recommend that you get a baseline measurement of your hormone levels. This can be done by serum, blood spot, saliva, or dried urine testing.

Serum testing evaluates total (bound and unbound) hormone levels. It requires a clinician's order and is available through your local laboratory. Allopathic clinicians tend to be more familiar with serum testing and naturopaths usually order saliva and blood spot testing.

Saliva or blood spot testing are able to identify free hormone levels instead of the protein-bound hormones that are typically obtained from a serum blood sample. It is free hormones that are biologically active and more likely to reflect true hormonal activity. The capillary finger stick blood sample may also be more accurate than serum venous testing from a traditional venous blood draw. Venous blood has already traveled out to the end organs and the hormones have been somewhat depleted. The capillary blood spot test is taken from a finger stick, which is theorized to have more active hormone circulating than a venous sample.

I use both serum and saliva or blood spot testing, depending upon many different factors. These can include expense, insurance, convenience, desire for accuracy, and other factors.

Saliva and blood spot testing can be requested with or without a clinician prescription. For insurance reimbursement, a clinician's order may be required. You can receive saliva test kits and blood spot kits through the mail to evaluate your hormone levels and to monitor progress.

ZRT Lab in Beaverton, Oregon offers saliva, blood spot, and dried urine test kits from their website. I have been pleased with the detailed and accurate reports that I have received from Dr. David Zava and his staff. ZRT Lab will send you a report directly to your home. You can share the report with your provider. Feel free to compare pricing with www.ZRTLab.com or 1-866-600-1636.

Also check out the section at the end of this chapter on dried urine metabolite testing. I have been using DutchTest.com

Cost of Hormone Testing and Insurance Coverage

Laboratory testing can be a financial concern. Please visit our website for a detailed section from ZRT Labs that should be able to answer your hormone testing questions.

When ordering multiple tests, panels of multiple items are usually more economical than ordering tests from the a la carte menu. Ordering individual tests may be most appropriate when you need repeat testing to evaluate your response to therapy. If you are a person without insurance coverage, have a high unmet deductible insurance plan, or you have to pay for all of your lab testing, or you simply desire more accuracy, then doing the testing with the ZRT or Dutch Lab home tests, are an excellent choice.

I have compared the ZRT and Dutch Lab tests with several hospital labs prices and, for the most part, they are comparable. With some tests, the home tests are less expensive. It is reasonable to compare prices with your local lab. Do remember that a venous blood drawn specimen will not give you information about what free hormones are circulating in your body available for use. The venous draw will give you the depleted amount of hormone, as it returns back from the organ to the heart.

If your insurance pays for most of your lab testing if it is done by serum through your local lab, but not for saliva or blood spot testing, then I suggest proceeding initially with the serum testing if cost is your primary concern, with an exception for progesterone testing when you are using topical progesterone preparations or any topical hormone use. Topically applied hormones are not evaluated as accurately by serum testing. You can later be selective in using some of the saliva or blood spot testing to monitor your progress.

Please note: Most conventional serum labs do not use tests for androgens (testosterone and DHEA) in women that are sensitive enough for the small amounts women produce. Using serum testing for androgens will be of little benefit in most cases, whether you are supplementing these hormones or not.

Another cost saving suggestion: ZRT created a Medicare Test Kit that can do blood spot tests and complimentary bill your Medicare insurance. This special kit only does blood spot testing and not saliva testing. You can contact them or check this out on their website for more information. www.ZRTLab.com or 1-866-600-1636.

What Tests Should You Take to Find Out about Your Hormone Balance?

How you are taking your hormones makes a difference on which test to choose.

I would like to share some recommendations with you as to what I usually order for my clients so you can send in your own test kit. You may also wish to speak with your primary care practitioner so you can add these tests to the labs that they may be ordering for you on your next visit to their office.

If you are using a saliva or blood spot test kit, I suggest you order the combo kit with which you can request both types of tests in one kit. If you are doing hormone replacement using sublingual supplementation, then I suggest doing blood spot or serum levels instead of saliva testing. Topical progesterone therapy at physiological doses increases salivary, capillary blood, and tissue progesterone to high luteal levels, but does not significantly increase serum progesterone levels. Serum should not be used to evaluate the effectiveness of topically delivered progesterone.

I would first recommend ordering a Female Hormone Profile Three kit that measures estradiol, progesterone, testosterone, DHEA sulfate, and four cortisol levels throughout the day. If you or your clinicians have concerns about adrenal fatigue, then I would suggest using the ZRT Female Hormone Profile Three kit.

A morning reading of cortisol levels by itself is not at all beneficial and can be misleading. Even the twice a day cortisol reading can give a false interpretation. If you take four cortisol readings as a saliva test, as in Female Hormone Profile Three, you may see a high morning and nighttime cortisol reading but low levels during the day. If you have been under a lot of stress and feel you may have adrenal fatigue, doing four cortisol tests in a day will give you better information as to the state of your adrenals.

If you do not have concerns about adrenal fatigue or you have financial constraints, then I would suggest you order Female Profile Two, which has a morning and nighttime cortisol level as a baseline.

ZRT then calculates an estrogen / progesterone ratio, which helps identify estrogen dominance in all profiles. You will receive this information on your report that comes to your home.

Vitamin D3 Testing is Essential

I strongly urge you to check your vitamin D3 level either by blood spot or by serum, ordered as a 25-OH vitamin D3 measurement. This should be repeated annually if you are using dosages of more than 2,000 international units per day since vitamin D3 is fat soluble. In Eugene, Oregon, I was told by the lab director that 75% of the vitamin D3 levels that are tested in his six labs are subnormal or below 32. That means that three quarters of the entire population of Eugene, Oregon is below normal! At this latitude, women simply will never make enough vitamin D3 by being out in the sun during the summer. If you lived in Arizona or Florida and sat poolside for five hours a day, you might produce enough vitamin D3. This is why it is so important to get your lab tests done!

Depending upon the lab, the range is usually 32 to 80 or 32 to 100. Your target is to get your levels over 55 and possibly to 70 to 75. As noted earlier, this will probably require that you take 5,000 to 6,000 IU per day and it may be a number of months before your levels are high enough. In the Pacific Northwest, the recommended dosage has been increased to 8,000 IUs a day if your labs are in the 65 to 75 range just to maintain your levels due to rain and cloudy weather for months. Some research suggests that 82% of all cancers could be eliminated if vitamin D3 levels were optimal, which is in the 65 to 80 range.

Retest Your Vitamin D3 in Three to Four Months to Check Your Progress

Important: Review Chapter 2 on supplements and the PBW protocol supplement list to determine how much vitamin D3 you should be taking based on your lab value. You may actually need to be on a clinical strength of 25,000 IU once to three times a week for four months or if you have upcoming surgery or a biopsy in the near future. Having your vitamin D3 in the optimal range prior to surgery or biopsy will improve your survival rate by 65%. To learn a lot more, go to The Vitamin D Council website.

Thyroid Dysfunction

If you have symptoms of thyroid dysfunction, I recommend checking thyroid function tests by serum at the hospital or by blood spot testing. These tests include total T4, free T3, free T4, TSH, TPO or thyroid peroxidase, and a thyroglobulin antibody evaluation. I am a big proponent of testing at least the TPO if not the thyroglobulin antibody antigens initially. The reason is twofold. Autoimmune disorders are the number one cause of all thyroid disorders, and if there is one occurring, it skews the other test results. So at least the TPO should be done on initial testing.

In my experience with the infrared camera, I can identify sub-clinical hypothyroidism on the infrared scan due to the fact that one thyroid pole is usually working harder than the other side and there is a thermal shift. The infrared camera can also identify a "Thermal bullet" or hyperthermic scan if there is a thyroid nodule or thyroid cancer. When I observe this, I send the woman off for a full thyroid laboratory evaluation and possibly a thyroid ultrasound.

Many of these women only had a TSH done by their physician and told it was normal yet they have an extensive list of hypothyroid symptoms. Please refer to the PCCA Hormone Symptom List in the worksheet section at the end of this book to further evaluate your symptoms. Pursuing a more thorough testing may lead to a diagnosis of hypothyroidism beyond doing just a TSH. If only a TSH level is done, that will probably not identify an autoimmune thyroid disorder. This is why it is important to do a more robust thyroid laboratory panel.

ZRT Labs have combined the advanced technology of measuring iodine in dried urine (DU) with that of thyroid hormone measurements in finger prick dried blood spots (DBS) to create what we call the Comprehensive Iodine Thyroid Test. The iodine-thyroid profile is designed to evaluate not only the availability of iodine, but also its capacity to be utilized for thyroid hormone synthesis. The thyroid glands capacity to utilize iodine for thyroid hormone synthesis is determined by measuring thyroglobulin, TSH, total T4, free T4, free T3, and TPO antibodies in finger-prick whole blood dried on filter paper.

I do not believe the 24-hour urine challenge test for iodine is valid. It takes 48 hours to clear an iodine dose from the body, so you cannot tell after 24 hours if you have excreted enough. Being guided by a 24-hour urine challenge test will most likely result in an overdosing of iodine.

Other Annual Tests Used To Monitor Your Health

Here are some suggestions for tests that should be considered on an annual basis and they are frequently included in your annual exam by your physician. If you have not been to a doctor in awhile, you can also test this yourself to see how you are doing.

Your clinician may order an advanced lipid panel to evaluate your Cholesterol, HDL, Triglycerines, and LDL. These are all tests that evaluate your cardiac health and give you some idea about relative risk for future coronary events. This is important so you can make dietary changes now. You need to do a 12 hour fast prior to testing for more accuracy.

Do a Complete Metabolic Panel (also done after a 12-hour fast). These tests will help you and your physicians evaluate kidney and liver function plus check for diabetes because it includes a glucose level. A hemoglobin A1C level may be ordered if there are concerns about diabetes mellitus.

Add a C-reactive protein (CRP) which helps to evaluate inflammation in the body. This may be cardiac in origin or you may have some other inflammatory issue going on or some auto immune problem that may need further attention.

Include a CBC (complete blood count) which is looking for anemia plus white blood cells to see if there is an infection or a shift. Add a serum ferritin test. Iron is essential for human life and one of its roles is to provide hemoglobin which binds with oxygen and carries the oxygen to the cells. One quarter of people may have elevated ferritin levels or iron overload. This may cause oxidative damage to your liver (cancer), heart (arrhythmias), Alzheimer's and pancreas (diabetes). If you check your ferritin level annually and it is elevated, it is easy to fix by donating blood several times a year.

Include a Vitamin B12 for pernicious anemia. This is of interest if you are experiencing fatigue or have vague numbness and tingling of your lower extremities. This is particularly important if you are a vegan or vegetarian and avoiding organ meats. About 55% of adults over 50 years of age have pernicious anemia. It is worth checking and then you can take some Vitamin B12 drops if you are low on the lab report.

Many of these lab tests can also be done through ZRT test kits. Again, compare costs with your local lab where you can do a blood draw, or the ZRT and Dutch Test sites, to find the most cost effective way to evaluate your health.

Consider Doing Dried Urine Hormone Metabolite Testing

This is an area that I am now beginning to explore and find fascinating. Most providers order the lab testing as just discussed to get an idea about your sex hormone levels, thyroid, adrenals and other aspects of your health. I would have you do all these basic testing as reference. But what if all your values seem "Normal" but this still does not explain why you do not feel well? Perhaps the answer lies in your own metabolic pathways and how you metabolize or break things down.

Your body functions in a very individual manner in some areas. Check out DUTCH Labs (Dried Urine Test for Comprehensive Hormones) at DutchTest.com by Precision Analytical, Inc. to do advanced hormone testing.

Here is some information from Mark Newman, MS and CEO of DUTCH.

> *"Millions of women suffer from hormonal imbalances. Whether it is menopause, weight gain, fatigue, low libido,*

premenstrual symptoms (PMS), mood swings, or depression, these symptoms can lead to more serious problems if misdiagnosed. Identifying the root cause of chronic health issues is certainly correctable, but only if properly identified. The DUTCH test was created to provide insight into many of these concerns, working to deliver the most complete assessment of sex and adrenal hormones, along with their metabolites, in one easy to administer test. No blood to draw, spitting in tubes or filling up jugs of urine. Our dried urine collection process is great for baseline measurements of women with hormonal imbalances and for Hormone Replacement Therapy (HRT) monitoring. After utilizing the DUTCH test, you will be able to work with your medical provider to continue to track and evaluate hormone levels, ensuring they are at their optimum balance."

I encourage you to work closely with your primary care physician or naturopath to follow your progress as you get your testing done and then decide upon a plan of action. Obtaining some baseline lab testing will be very beneficial so you may monitor your progress as you begin to start making changes to your diet, supplements and possibly bio-identical hormone replacement regimens.

CHAPTER 6

Environmental Toxins and Dangers of 5G

More and more research is finding that things in our environment that were previously thought to be safe are actually toxic, some of which have been shown to increase cancer incidence. It is also becoming increasingly clear that it is not just the dose of a particular toxin that is important, but also the timing, duration, combination, and types of exposure. Many of these toxic items are related to technological advances and chemicals developed within the last century, and probably account for much of the increase in breast cancer over the past 40 years. Some of the toxins have become so embedded in our societal structure that, at first glance, it might seem that it is impossible to avoid them. However, with knowledge of where the toxins may lie, you can be empowered to decrease your risk. In this chapter, I will discuss some of these toxic sources, and concentrate on the ones that are suspected to contribute to increased breast cancer risk.

Your Genetic Risk is Less Than Seven to Nine Percent: That Means You Can Do Something By Making Changes To Decrease Your Breast Cancer Risk

Breast cancer is caused by a complex array of multiple factors. A genetic predisposition to breast cancer probably plays a role in less than seven to nine percent of cases. The remainder is probably the result of environmental influences that alter gene expression, damage genes, or alter the production or function of estrogen or other hormones. It may take more than one factor to promote cancer, and not everyone who is exposed to toxins will get cancer.

Estrogens: The Ones You Produce vs Estrogen-Like Compounds

Over time, estrogen, especially when unopposed by enough progesterone, has been found to promote breast cancer. This includes natural estrogens, synthetic estrogens, and xenoestrogens / estrogen mimickers.

With natural estrogens, increased cancer risk is seen in women with onset of menstruation before age 12, women who have delayed their pregnancies until later in life or do not get pregnant, and in women with late menopause after age 50. Synthetic estrogens play a role in terms of hormonal contraceptives and estrogen replacement therapy. Progestins, which are synthetic progesterone-like compounds, are within this group. In the environment, it is the xenoestrogens / estrogen-like chemicals that seem to play a larger role in the increasing incidence of breast cancer.

As mentioned in earlier chapters, xenoestrogens are estrogen mimickers that act like estrogen. More and more of these hormone disruptors are being identified with research, as scientists observe their effects on the growth of breast cancer tumor cells and in laboratory animals. These chemicals are pervasive in our environment, found in plastics, pesticides, herbicides, fungicides, petrochemical fuels, fire retardants on clothes and furniture, solvents, auto fumes, detergents, and prescription drugs. Definite links to cancer have been found for the xenoestrogens bisphenol-A, or BPA, used in polycarbonate #7 plastic, and polyvinyl chloride, or #3 PVC plastic.

Pesticides have definite links to breast cancer. The chemicals used to soften plastics such as phthalates and adipates are known to be hormone disruptors, and are suspected to increase cancer risk.

Parabens, a class of chemicals ubiquitous in cosmetics, pharmaceutical, food, and personal care products, have been found to be estrogenic. These are found in 99% of the leave on products and 77% of the rinse off cosmetics or body care products. Ingredients in sunscreens have been implicated. And the list goes on. Parabens were found intact in breast tumor tissue in a 2004 study from England. Check out my website in the Take Action section where you can search for safer body care products on a cosmetic link.

Food additives such as bovine growth hormone (BGH) and Zeranol, a beef cattle growth stimulant, have estrogenic properties. Bovine growth hormone is also added to dairy cattle feed and is found in the milk of non-organically raised herds. These growth hormones are also given to conventionally raised chicken, turkey and pigs. Another major reason to start eating organically raised meats.

Even natural plant products with estrogenic properties, called phytoestrogens or plant estrogens, must be considered in this estrogenic soup, as discussed earlier regarding avoiding the use of non-fermented soy, flax and hemp seed products, hops, black cohosh, red clover, and dong quai.

Other Sources of Environmental Carcinogens to Avoid

Not all known cancer-promoting chemicals are known to be xenoestrogens. Some may do their damage in other ways.

There are many known carcinogens in petrochemicals, auto exhaust, organic solvents, cigarette smoke, and air pollution. Barbecuing or grilling meats and fish releases aromatic amines that might be carcinogenic.

Even though known carcinogens called PCB's have not been permitted in new manufacturing since 1976, many of the products made with PCB's are still in use, and others are in landfills where they may be contaminating ground water. Dioxin, a potent toxin produced by the incineration of PVC plastic, is very durable in the environment and stored in body fat, and can be found in the bodies of every human.

Radiation exposure has long been associated with increased incidence of cancer, ever since the experiences of atomic bomb survivors were studied. Scientists agree that there is no safe dose of radiation, and that the more one is exposed, the greater the risk. There is also evidence that the earlier in life the exposure occurs, the more risk may be encountered over the remaining lifetime. Ionizing radiation, the kind that can disrupt genes, is of greatest risk. In our daily lives, modifiable radiation exposure is primarily that from medical diagnostic testing, such as X-rays including dental X-rays, CT scans, and nuclear scans. Less common are dosages from radiation therapy, as well as spillovers from nuclear power plants and research. In medical usage, it is a balancing act to decide how much the information to be obtained can be weighed against the risk of the radiation exposure. The increased use of CT scans has become of increasing concern. This is especially true the younger a person is.

Conventional mammograms offer their own radiation exposure, although the typical dosage of radiation has decreased over the years from two rads in 1976 to 0.2 rads or less per procedure today. Digital mammograms use about three quarters of the radiation used for conventional film mammography. In recent years, medical physicists have switched from evaluating testing based on rads to measurements in sieverts and milli-sieverts It appears that the lowering of radiation exposure with mammograms has resulted in less sensitivity and therefore higher levels of non-detection. It is currently quoted that a routine mammogram gives the same amount of radiation exposure as three months of background radiation from the sun in daily life. Studies are still being done to assess the risk of repeated mammograms over time, and the risk needs to be weighed on an individual basis depending upon age, type of breasts, and risk factors. MRI scans, ultrasound diagnostic procedures, or infrared thermography do not cause ionizing radiation exposure.

Many more details will be provided in Chapter 8 on diagnostic imaging since the evidence-based research, especially on mammograms, has changed dramatically in recent months. The Nordic Cochrane Institute published a study spanning ten years and including over a half a million women stated that, "Mammograms were ineffective and may cause more harm than good." That should prove interesting reading for you! Many other articles are on the www.InfraredBreastHealth.com website in the Research section.

Are You or Your Family Being Hurt By Your Cell Phones and Wireless Devices?

The links between cancer and other types of non-ionizing radiation, called EMF's or electromagnetic fields, are much weaker and hard to define. EMF's are everywhere that there are electrical circuits, radio waves, or microwaves. One possible association is that EMF's may decrease melatonin levels, a pituitary hormone excreted during darkness. Lower levels of melatonin may be associated with higher levels of cancer. This is still an area of active research, but the links of non-ionizing radiation to cancer were previously believed to be much less than ionizing radiation. However, an article came out in September, 2013, discussing concerns about EMFs and cell phones causing breast cancer when the cell phone was carried in a woman's bra. Women need to know about these findings and be more conscious of their cell phone usage. The article and the breast cancer images in the shape of a cell phone can be viewed on my website in the Blog section. Use the speaker on your phone and do not carry the cell phone next to your body in a pocket and shut it off when not in use.

In this EMF article, the author points out that,

> *"One of the first clinical reports of a possible carcinogenic effect of exposure to EMR from cellular phones suggested that cell phone users were at increased risk of developing brain cancers but now they are looking at breast cancer risk as well. Breast cancer occurring in women under the age of 40 is uncommon in the absence of family history or genetic predisposition, and prompts the exploration of other possible exposures or environmental risks. All patients in this study regularly carried their Smart phones directly against their breasts in their brassieres for up to 10 hours a day, for several years, and developed tumors in areas of their breasts immediately underlying the phones. All patients had no family history of breast cancer, tested negative for BRCA1 and BRCA2, and had no other known breast cancer risks."*

We also know that carrying a cell phone against our ovaries or over our heart is not prudent. Sperm counts are dropping in young men and researchers think there is a correlation with men carrying their cell phones in their front pocket of their pants. Men and boys should not carry their phone in a shirt or jacket pocket over their heart. Talk to the men and boys in your life.

Use the speaker on your phone as often as you can so the phone is not held up against your head and you are not holding it. Australia has made it a law that children under 13 should not be using cell phones because they have found a higher rate of brain and parotid cancers in children.

If you still have a land line at home, use a corded version and get rid of the bases, which are sending out waves to your portable hand set.

If you use a computer, get a modem, limit wireless as much as possible, and shut off the wireless beam when at home and the computer is off. Do not hold the computer on your lap when watching videos or your children are using wireless games. Think where that electromagnetic energy is going.

Another thing to do is move your electrical alarm clock or any other corded devices at least three feet from your head. I would also suggest you leave your cell phone in the bathroom so that is not up against your head either. If you can rearrange your bedroom furniture so you do not have your head up against an electrical wall outlet that would be beneficial. This is particularly important if you have a child with ADD or ADHD. There is a link between these conditions and EMF.

Practical Ways to Reduce Environmental Exposure

All this environmental exposure to cancer-causing substances can seem overwhelming sometimes. However, there are practical ways that you can reduce these exposures. I will review some of these now.

Since estrogenic exposures are a major concern, the appropriate use of bio-identical progesterone to counteract estrogen's cancer causing effects is a very important step in reducing your cancer risk. The other step is to avoid exposure to these environmental toxins as much as possible.

As discussed in the dietary chapter, avoid the use of plastics with food and water. This is especially true for items that are heated. To sum up the good and bad plastics by the numbers, avoid numbers three, six, and seven. The safer plastics to use are numbers one, two, four and five. My best advice is to store things in glass and stainless steel when you can, instead of plastics.

Remember that your drinking and cooking water is safest if it has passed through a solid carbon block or reverse osmosis filter, as mentioned in a previous chapter. I use a Multi Pure solid carbon filter, which can be taken with you if you move.

Pesticides, herbicides, and fungicides are best avoided. I have previously mentioned using only organic foods and beverages, but it is also important to decrease your other environmental exposures. Reduce or eliminate your personal yard and garden use of pesticides and herbicides and lobby your neighbors to avoid pesticides as well. If there is aerial spraying of herbicides or pesticides in your area, request that the sprayers notify you and your other neighbors before it is to occur so that you and your family can vacate the area. You can contact the people at Beyond Toxics, a group in Eugene, Oregon, that has been active in trying to prevent toxic trespass here in the Pacific Northwest. They refer to this problem as "Toxic trespass" and more communities are trying to protect their citizens.

Minimize your exposure to solvents, gasoline, auto exhaust, and, of course, cigarette smoke. An example is turning off your auto intake fan when sitting in traffic. Avoid breathing the fumes of paints and solvents and dispose of waste solvents safely. You may need to purchase a small particle double canister gas mask if you are expecting to work on a home improvement project. Your local fire department can advise you what type to get and where to purchase the equipment. A paper dust mask is inadequate.

Danger from Your Cosmetics

Cosmetics and other personal care products such as shampoos can be a source of parabens and other toxins. Avoid these products when possible, reading the label carefully. Another option is an online information tool where you can look up your cosmetics and hand creams. Type in the name of the product and you will be given a rating between zero and ten as to whether or not it may have harmful ingredients. A link to this tool is on my website in the Take Action section near the bottom of the list of organizations trying to protect your health. You can also do a reverse search to find safer products with this cosmetic research tool.

Are Your Laundry Products Making You Sick?

Conventional dryer sheets and liquid fabric softeners can contain toxins that are designed to stay in the clothing for a period of time, and can leach out onto the skin. Some of the toxins have included benzyl acetate (linked to pancreatic cancer), benzyl alcohol (which can be a respiratory irritant), limonene (a known carcinogen), and chloroform (a neurotoxin and carcinogen). There are some vegetable-based greener products available including those made by Seventh Generation and Ecover. A quarter cup of baking soda can also soften fabrics and decrease static cling. A quarter cup of vinegar added to a wash load can soften fabrics, but does not help static cling. If static cling is your primary concern, the Canadian product Maddock's Static Eliminator can be very convenient. It consists of two chemical-free reusable fabric pads that when used in a dryer eliminate static. These can be purchased on line.

How to Limit Radiation Exposure

With respect to radiation exposures, it is natural to question the wisdom of annual mammograms starting at age 40. This is an issue that needs to be individualized and I encourage you to discuss this with your knowledgeable clinician. Recommendations from the American Cancer Society and the U.S. Preventive Services Task Force are discussed more in detail in Chapter 8 under imaging.

Other non-elective X-ray, fluoroscopy, and CT scan procedures should be considered carefully with your clinician with respect to risks versus benefits. The younger the person being evaluated, the more important is the discussion.

Avoid frequent annual dental X-rays as well as always insisting on a neck and abdominal shield. The thyroid is very sensitive to radiation exposure and the thyroid plays a major role in protecting you from breast cancer. Sixty-five percent of menopausal women are hypothyroid! According to the Mount Sinai Hospital Autopsy Department, 100% of ninety year olds had thyroid cancer, so it is important to protect and support your thyroid function.

Avoid GMOs by Eating Organically When Possible

GMOs or genetically modified organisms are rampant in our foods. Educate yourself about the dangers of GMOs and how they have adversely altered our food supply and have been destroying our gut flora, which keep our immune system healthy. Please go to my website and view the pages on the Dangers of GMOs and the Take Action section and learn about other agencies or nonprofits that are trying to protect your health and the health of your family. Watch the video in the Take Action section entitled *Genetic Roulette*. It will change the way you think about all your food and what you might be feeding your family!

4G and 5G Imminent Threat to Your Health

I have become passionate about Anti 5G after watching the recent on line 5G Summit! I beg you to go to the following websites and educate yourself and start protecting your family. A good starting place is www.SolutionsForHumanity.net, www.GreenMedInfo.com, www.TakeBackYourPower.net, and www.HealthTalksOnLine.com. On the SolutionsForHumanity.Net site there is a "Streamlined Actions" section that within three minutes you can inform ALL YOUR Local, State and Federal Representative that you "Oppose 5G". There is also a Networking link where you can put in your state and find a local group. If there isn't a local group, start one. Find out what other groups are doing to be successful in your own local Anti-5G movement.

On the 5G Summit series, there was a link to an Attorney Raymond Broomhall site to get legal templates and Anti 5G support letters that you can share in your community. Attorney Broomhall is a Barrister in Australia and has been successful in preventing thousands of small cell 5G towers going up and was also able to have cell towers and installations removed. Here is his site: emrlegaleducation.com There is hope that a small group of citizens in your town can have beneficial effects in stopping 5G and electro-magnetic radiation, which will aversely effect your health.

Not saying "No" to your local city government means "Yes" to your city council representatives. When 5G towers / wireless is put into your neighborhoods plus in and near schools, daycare centers, hospitals and elder care facilities without consent...this is a horrible threat to your health and the health of your families! My book is about preventing breast cancer but you have to look at 5G and EMFs with a wider, more sinister lens and start reading. Then you too may start talking with friends and family about taking action to stop 5G and Electro Magnetic Frequencies also known as EMFs and start taking action in limiting your exposure in your own home. The websites above have loads of information on how to make your home safer. Start today!

There have been thousands of medical and scientific articles done showing the harm caused by electromagnetic radiation, which has been based on what 3G, and 4G had been radiating, 5G will be even worse. The wireless industry keeps touting articles done by the US military in the mid 1990s, that EMFs were "Safe". I suspect you would not want to go to a doctor who is treating you for some medical condition and they are doing so based on the information they received on that topic 25 to 30 years ago! The military is interested in 5G for spy communications, satellite surveillance, tracking people and their cell phones and with nano-chips plus the weaponization of EMFs for crowd control or use on the battlefield.

There are current discussions in using the nano-chips with a COVID vaccine—by the way, do not take the vaccine, there have not been or will be any safety clinical trials done on the COVID vaccine! None of the other 72 vaccines available now in the US on the FDA site, have had longer-term safety studies done either! Vaccines are considered a "Biological" and the FDA does not require large double blind studies or animal trials on vaccines like they require on medications—more than terrifying! They may do a follow up in three days to see if the new vaccine caused any redness at the injection site...but they do not follow large numbers of people for years to see what happened to them or what complications occurred. Most medications go through a five-year clinical trial before they are sold to people, vaccines do not. You can also check out *The Truth About Vaccines* by Ty Bollinger, the videos and website information, is really an eye opener! If you have small children in your life I strongly encourage you buy this book: *The Vaccine-Friendly Plan: Dr. Paul's Safe and Effective Approach to Immunity and Health from Pregnancy through Your Child's Teen Years*. Or check out the site for "The Children's Health Defense" which is a site run by Robert F. Kennedy or watch www.vaxxedthemovie.com

Back to 5G, no one can or has produced any current articles or scientific studies that EMF electromagnetic radiation/2G/3G/4g or 5G are safe! You would think that these companies before flooding our towns and schools with these devices would follow a "Precautionary principal" of doing the research first before harming citizens and children with the technology which is unproven for safety. You, my dear reader will be just another guinea pig for the public relations campaign for wireless and 5G technology. They claim it will be "So much faster, so you can stream videos on your Smart phone in the park"...for goodness sake, get a bird book or exercise. What you need is fiber optics and a wired modem and watch your video at home and protect your health! This is a wakeup call!

There is irrefutable evidence that ALL CANCERS have increased with electromagnetic radiation. We have been focused on breasts in this book, but there are a lot of other places in my body I would not like to find a cancer in. I suspect this would be alarming to you as well. EMFs also have been proven to cause neurological problems, ADD, ADHD, Autism, Parkinson's, Dementia, and Alzheimer's. It causes sterility in lab test animals, decreases sperm counts in humans and decreases viable human egg production and causes infertility and libido problems. There are increases in learning disabilities, nausea, headaches, tremors, a sense of prickling or burning sensations on the skin, sleep problems, increased depression and suicide rate increases in high EMF settings.

In Summary

Some of these suggestions for reducing risks of environmental toxins are easy, some are troublesome, and some are more expensive than others. The first step is to develop an awareness of the problems, then to gradually introduce safer practices in your day-to-day life, both for yourself and your family members. Although not always measurable, any reduction in exposure is a step toward improved breast health and your general health.

CHAPTER 7
Breast Care

There are some factors of breast care and care of surrounding tissues that may influence breast cancer risk. These include breast lymphatic drainage, the importance of physical activity and weight management, bra choices, fibrocystic breast treatments, and choice of underarm deodorants. Some of these changes are easy to make and will improve your breast self care.

The Importance of Your Lymphatic System

There may be a tie-in between the lymphatic system and breast cancer. Lymph is a fluid that travels from peripheral tissues through its own set of vessels, passing through lymph nodes and spleen, then back to the blood stream. It is an important part of the immune system to remove cellular debris, white blood cells, cancer cells, and pathogens. The lymphatic system is a closed system, much of it lying just below the surface of the skin.

For many women, these lymph vessels become congested, and the flow of lymph decreases. Many clinicians suspect that this congestion may increase breast cancer risk. One of the factors contributing to congestion is that women in this era have a more sedentary life style. Our ancestors just two generations ago had more physical activity in their lives, at work and at home. Women lived on farms, did manual labor, and had fewer labor saving devices. Upper body lifting, reaching, pulling, carrying encouraged the movement of lymph through the vessels. Now our lifestyles involve lots of sitting at desks and computers. Few of us are using our bodies in a physical way anymore.

One of the other issues that impact lymph congestion is our choice of fashion styles. Bras were first introduced in the early 1900's. Later fashion styles changed again to include under-wire bras that came on the fashion scene only about 20 years ago. Now it is difficult to find bras without under-wires. The issue with this is that the firm under-wire presses against the chest wall, limiting the natural flow of the lymph vessels. Women two generations ago may not have been wearing bras at all, using cotton chemises, camisoles or slips instead and their clothing was not as tight. One of the other issues with the under-wire bras is that they tend to push against the breast tissue, creating areas of chronic contusion or bruising that may even become tender.

With the obesity epidemic that accompanies our more sedentary life style and poor eating choices, many women have larger breasts that they may feel require more support. The weight of the breasts themselves can become a compression agent.

Bras and Tight Clothing

I recently discovered some fascinating articles on the website http://www.greenmedinfo.com/blog/breast-cancer-cover-continues. "The articles reported that, "bra-free" women have about the same incidence of breast cancer as a man, while the tighter and longer a bra is worn, the higher the incidence rises, to over 100 times higher for a 24/7 bra user compared to a woman who is bra-free.

The article continues, "You probably didn't hear about a recent study from Brazil, published in May, 2016 in the Journal Advances in Oncology Research and Treatments; Entitled,

'Wearing a Tight Bra for Many Hours a Day is Associated with Increased Risk of Breast Cancer'. The study echoes another recent study, done in 2015 in Kenya, which also confirmed the bra-cancer link. "This study demonstrated the existence of a relationship between the use of a tight bra when associated with an increased number of hours wearing it and the risk of breast cancer among pre and post-menopausal women."… "Studies from Venezuela, Scotland and numerous studies out of China also agree."

The Green Med Info link goes on to say,

> *"Fortunately, more women are questioning the need for a bra, and that leads to questioning the need to accept the discomforts and diseases bras cause. Headaches, backaches, nerve damage to the hands, deep shoulder grooves, droopy breasts, breast pain, cysts and lumps, and breast cancer are some of the problems bras cause."*
>
> *"Like the corset, bras are harmful garments that constrict and shape the body through pressure, which impairs circulation, especially the circulation of the immune system's lymphatic pathways. This results in fluid accumulation in the breasts, causing cysts, pain, and tissue toxification."*

My personal comfort and healthy breast suggestion is to reduce restrictive clothing whenever possible. When you come home or plan to work in your garden, consider taking off your bra and wear a soft shelf camisole or a loose top. In cooler months, I may go to work without a bra and wear a vest or heavy sweater over my blouse and no one is the wiser. I am much more comfortable and our grandmothers probably had the same fashion sense.

The other major issue with women being overweight is the estrogen dominance factor. Estrogens are metabolized and stored in fat tissue and as we become middle aged we begin to hold body fat around our midriffs, thighs, and breasts. This increases breast cancer risk, particularly when our progesterone drops in the perimenopausal and menopausal periods. This creates an estrogen dominant situation. In addition, larger breasts are harder to self examine and image, potentially delaying diagnosis of tumors compared to tumors in smaller breasts.

Lymphatic drainage massage

Lymphatic drainage massage is another easy way to improve lymphatic flow. All women should learn how to do lymph drainage massage. It is a systematic gentle stroking massage that moves the lymph fluids in the proper direction and pattern to allow emptying of congested areas. I strongly recommend that you find a lymphatic drainage massage therapist and go for at least one consultation visit to learn how to massage your own breasts. These therapists are usually licensed massage therapists who have taken additional training in lymphatic massage. You can check the internet, or call a couple of the therapists to find who might be doing this kind of therapy in your area. Another way to locate a lymphatic drainage therapist is to contact your local cancer center and ask who sees their breast cancer patients.

I have had personal experience with a lymphatic drainage therapist. I had a slightly tender thickened area that after the one-hour visit had disappeared and was no longer tender. My breast tissue felt as though I had breast fed for an hour and a half, I had lost a half-cup size, and my breasts felt softer for the next three to four days. Your breasts should feel like good bread dough or like your buttock, soft and supple.

The intention of visiting a lymph drainage therapist is to learn how to do the massage yourself to drain the main lymph channels and how to do the massage in the shower two or three times a week. It is also possible to have your partner trained to assist in the massage. Please go to the website to the "Protect Your Breasts" area to watch a free five-minute YouTube video by Daya Fisch, MS, CMT, from Carmel, California. She trains lymphatic drainage therapists and she has created a detailed YouTube demonstration that she allowed me to share. You may also purchase her 60-minute lymph drainage massage DVD from my website Store.

Dry brushing is another way of moving lymph fluid. This is a technique in which a natural bristled brush is used to lightly stroke the body to help move lymph fluid just under the skin to the larger lymph nodes. This is done from the feet up to the groin, from the waistline down to the groin, from the hands to the armpits, and from the upper abdomen and chest towards the armpits. The diagrams on the website for lymphatic drainage will also be helpful for dry brushing. There are other references on the data disc/resource download for you to review.

Dense and Fibrocystic Breasts

Dense and fibrocystic breasts are now common, found in a third or more of the female population in the US. This further increases the difficulty in identifying breast masses because of the overlying general nodularity of the breast tissue, both on physical examinations, as well as with mammograms. Natural density decreases as women age, and after childbearing. Fibrocystic changes do not represent a disease, but rather a normal change in breast anatomy. Sometimes the nodularity can be accompanied by tenderness or pain. I have found that a lot of the nodularity and tenderness can be eliminated in six months if the women stop caffeine, coffee and chocolate.

Many providers also suggest using vitamin E at 200 to 400 IU's daily, in addition to evening primrose oil at 3000 mg daily for fibrocystic breasts. I recommend the natural mixed gamma and alpha tocopherol vitamin E. Fibrocystic changes may also improve with increased dietary iodine, diluted iodine solution applied directly to the breasts, topical progesterone, hormone balancing, fish oil supplements, and the use of an alkaline-based diet.

To give you some more information on how to use topical iodine and breast care, I have included a sheet to print out in the Getting Started section. These instructions and purchasing sources to save you money are also in the data disc/resource download and on the website Supplement Virtual Dispensary.

The use of topical Lugol's 2% iodine solution has been very beneficial for many women in my practice who have fibrocystic or tender breasts. There is an in-depth section on iodine in Chapter 2 under Supplements in the iodine section to further educate you on daily dosages of iodine either used topically or orally and the nuances of how much to use if you are on thyroid replacement medication or not. I recommend reviewing that section as well.

In this section on breast care, I will review how to use iodine topically. I like using Lugol's 2% solution, also called half-strength Lugol's, where one drop equals three mg of iodine. (Note: We are discussing one drop, not a dropperful). I suggest you find a cute tiny container that would look lovely in your bathroom and put about a teaspoon of organic coconut oil in the container and stir in one drop or three mg of iodine. Use this breast massage oil and massage into tender or lumpy areas on your breast. If you wish to add a bit of pure organic essential oil like lavender or rose oil to the blend, you may increase your pampering experience. Some women prefer to put one drop of iodine directly on the breast and then apply some coconut oil or some progesterone cream on top of the iodine and massage it in. Using the iodine directly on the skin for some women has had a drying effect so using a moisturizer on top seems to work best. Also, remember that iodine can stain so be careful of any potential spills and consider wearing old night wear or a tee shirt and not put on a white silk blouse after application. Your breasts should start to be less tender and softer within a few weeks. If, however, you may also be borderline hypothyroid, which is a common cause of fibrocystic breasts, I would review Chapter 2 because you may need to use more than just the three mg dose of iodine topically.

Remember you can get 20% off all these supplements from my website in the Supplement Virtual Dispensary, which will save you money!

Avoid Antiperspirants

Another area of risk reduction is to make the best choices in antiperspirants. Most antiperspirants contain aluminum salts to decrease perspiration from sweat gland production. Although no definite proof has been found that breast cancer is caused by aluminum antiperspirants, there are some associations that have bothered me. Eighty percent of breast cancers are found in the upper outer quadrant of the breast, close to the areas where antiperspirants are applied. In a surgical study published in 2007 in the Journal of Inorganic Biochemistry, aluminum content was measured in surgically removed breast tissue. They found that the aluminum content of the breast tissue and breast tissue fat was significantly higher in the outer regions of the breast in close proximity to the area of highest antiperspirant use. These researchers also indicated that aluminum is a metallo-estrogen, capable of binding to cellular estrogen receptors and then mimicking the actions of physiological estrogen. They also indicated that aluminum is known to damage DNA and has been shown to be carcinogenic. Some people also theorize that the reduced excretion of sweat glands may impair some toxins from being eliminated. Although there has not been a clinical study to my knowledge to prove that aluminum antiperspirants cause breast cancer, I suggest that for now it is wisest to avoid using them as much as possible until more is known.

Find Better Personal Care Products

An alternative to antiperspirants is to use deodorant products without antiperspirants. Tom's of Maine has an herbal product. Even simple things such as witch hazel applied with a cotton ball, diluted lemon juice, baking soda, or the use of plain soap and water can decrease odor. A friend of mine also suggested the Thai-Deodorant-Stone-Crystal which is also supposed to not contain any aluminum.

I have provided you a fabulous link on my website, in the Take Action section, to evaluate all your personal care products, rating them on a zero-to-ten scale for toxic elements. Type in the name of your current product to see how it is rated and then you can do a reverse search of different products and body care items to find products that have fewer toxic ingredients. This can help you choose safer products for you and your family.

Exercise and Breast Health

This next section is about a woman's weight and how you can improve your breast care and general health by making some changes and adding an exercise program. A woman can potentially reduce her risk of breast cancer or its reoccurrence simply by embracing an exercise program that could be as simple as walking 30 minutes to an hour three to four times a week. Bouncing on a rebounder also helps with lymph drainage. Any exercise that suits you would be beneficial and could reduce risk by at least 65% and it will also improve your cardio vascular status, sleep, and mood!

Obesity, Bovine Growth Hormones, and GMOs

A recent 2015 study suggests that 65% of American women are obese and the average dress size is now 14 with an ever-increasing plus size category in all the stores. You can also see this in our children. Sixty-five percent of eighth grade children are now clinically obese and young girls are developing breasts at eight or nine years of age when we used to see breast development at 12 or 13. There were hardly any obese children in the 1950's and 1960's. If you are a middle-aged woman, just think back to your third grade class photo. Those were the times our mothers made everything from scratch and it was the pre-GMO, pre-bovine growth hormone or high fructose corn syrup era. Children were sent out after school in their play clothes to run around, ride bikes, play ball, etc. My mother's idea of a snack was some fresh fruit with a glass of water with some lemon or organic milk. Organic milk was the only milk available back then. Cheese sandwiches were made from real organic cheddar, not "cheese food" slices packaged in saran wrap sleeves.

Most women are never happy with their weight and it is becoming more challenging with food additives, hidden sugars, bovine growth hormone, and GMO foods that are making pesticide manufacturing plants in your own intestines hence hindering proper absorption of nutrients, plus environmental toxins that have estrogenic impact on our waist lines.

The *Proactive Breast Wellness* and *Protect Your Breasts* program will help you lose weight, maintain better hormone balancing, evaluate your thyroid function and dietary choices. Once you start making these changes in your home, it will improve the health of your whole family!

CHAPTER 8

Diagnostic Breast Imaging

I will start with the imaging options that can be used to evaluate your breasts. At the end of 2015 and in 2016 there have been several additions to the body of research regarding breast cancer imaging and what used to be considered standard of care vs. evidence-based medicine.

First, I will give you an overview of the history of imaging options. In the next chapter, I will include cryoablation or freezing breast cancers in place using a bit of local anesthesia in a 20 to 30 minute office visit: the physician only needs an office ultrasound device. The woman can then go off to lunch and maybe take two Tylenol and her cancer has been killed! This literally will change the face of breast cancer care. Chapter 9 is about the future of breast cancer care and prevention IS the cure!

The subject of breast imaging is fraught with controversy and is dependent upon which organization, which study quoted, and even which country uses which standard. Currently there does not appear to be any correct answer for what to do and both women and clinicians are trying to make choices as to the direction they will choose as it pertains to a woman's breast care.

Since the experts can't decide what we are supposed to be doing in regards to imaging, perhaps it is time to consider that "Prevention IS the Cure" and start educating ourselves about reducing risk factors like environmental impacts in our homes, making lifestyle and dietary changes, and making positive changes for ourselves. These are all the things my book *Protect Your Breasts* and my *Proactive Breast Wellness* protocol provides to women.

Mammograms: A Historical Perspective from the 1960s until 2015

Let us take a look back in time to assist us in understanding how some of the standards of care came to be in the arena of breast imaging and breast cancer evaluation and treatment. Many of us, both as women and also health care practitioners, marched along following the standard of care recommendations. These recommendations were handed down to us through our professional organizations and literature that then translated into what a physician or medical practitioner told their women clients. These same recommendations were also broadcast through the media and published in women's journals so that we all would be aware of what we were supposed to be doing to take care of our breasts.

We were told to be responsible for our health, to go for our check-ups, and, twenty years ago, we were told to go for our annual mammogram screening. Many of us did what we were told to do to protect our health, or so we thought. Few of us considered where these recommendations were coming from or who made them or who did the research. We trusted our doctors and looked to our professional organizations to help guide our decisions.

A lot of us did not notice that over the years more and more of the research on which these standards of care were based were funded or conducted by groups or industries that stood to financially benefit from the cancer industry itself. These groups make money when people are ill and their profit margins go up if there are more people to treat. The pharmaceutical industry funds the major portion of the research studies done at research facilities or medical schools. They hire experts in the field to be spokespersons doing research on their drug or imaging and test equipment. Yet the third cause of death in the United States is properly prescribed pharmaceuticals, which is a bit sobering.

The American Cancer Society and The Susan J. Komen Foundation take in millions of dollars looking for or "Racing for The Cure" and there is hardly any significant effort spent on breast cancer prevention beyond lip service slogans like "Don't smoke, exercise, and eat healthy," whatever that means to them. The cure does not appear to be any closer than when they first started raising money decades ago. I have not seen these cancer foundations going after the environmental polluters, GMOs, herbicides, pesticides, plastics, or industries that are involved with fracking or polluting our water supplies, sources that are making our population sick in the first place.

We Rely on Screening to Save Us

Dr. Christianne Northrup, MD, a visionary in women's health and education, in a recent 2015 on-line article at www.drnorthrup.com/new-mammography-guidelines makes this statement:

> *"Cornelia Baines, MD, professor emerita at the University of Toronto and former director of the Canadian National Breast Screening Study, put it succinctly when she said, 'I remain convinced that the current enthusiasm for screening is based more on fear, false hope and greed than on evidence."*

Dr. Northrup and I agree with Dr. Barnes completely.

Dr. Northrup goes on to say:

"Still, for the moment, major medical organizations such as the American Cancer Society and the American College of Obstetricians and Gynecologists continue to support the regular use of mammography for women starting in their forties. The American College of Radiology was so opposed to the change that it even went so far as to ask the task force to reverse its recommendation. Some medical groups, however, including the National Cancer Institute, announced they would reevaluate their guidelines. This dichotomy isn't difficult to understand. Both inside and outside medicine, we as a culture have come to rely on screening to save us. And even though the evidence doesn't support it, individual women and their doctors often feel safer if they perceive that they've covered all the bases."

These actions may in themselves be motivated due to fear of malpractice suits against the medical professionals so testing continues to show "Due diligence."

Mammograms and the "Standard of Care"

How did they come up with these standards and whether mammograms really did what they told us the screening would do? This has become a hot topic especially since "Evidence Based Medicine Studies" have been evaluating this premise.

I will now cover the historical perspective on mammography, the standard of care and how that evolved since most women today have become familiar with or have gone for mammograms since they originated in the 1960s as a breast cancer screening tool. Mammograms were promoted as able to find cancer early when it was the most treatable. Mammograms were supposed to save our lives. They became a rite of passage into womanhood.

Later in this chapter, I will present other research on what we now call evidence-based medicine, studies that looked at whether mammograms really did what they told us the screening would do. These are large population studies that look at outcomes over time.

Here is an historical tour of mammography and what we have been told to do to take care of our breasts. You can see how the studies and recommendations are contradictory, which has lead to a lot of frustration and fear.

Mammogram Recommendations Before 2009

Before 2009, we were told that a physical examination of our breasts, coupled with an annual clinical breast exam by an experienced examiner, would detect approximately 61% of detectable breast cancers. In the United States before 2009, annual mammography had been recommended for women over the age of 40. In November 2009, the U.S. Prevention Services Task Force recommendations on breast cancer screening came out and they recommended the following, and I quote:

> *"Screening mammography every two years for women aged 50 to 74 years. The decision to start regular, screening mammography every two years before the age of 50 years should be an individual one and take patient context into account, including the patient's values regarding specific benefits and harms."*

> *"The 2009 US Prevention Task Force concluded that the current evidence then was insufficient to assess the additional benefits and harms of screening mammography in women 75 years or older."*

> *"The 2009 Task Force recommended against teaching breast self-examination and concluded that the current evidence*

was insufficient to assess the additional benefits and harms of clinical breast examination by a practitioner beyond mammography screening in women 40 years or older."

"The 2009 US Preventative Services Task Force conclusion was that the current evidence was insufficient to assess the additional benefits and harms of either digital mammography or magnetic resonance imaging (MRI) instead of film mammography as screening modalities for breast cancer."

Recommendations for Mammography from 2012 and Beyond

To add to the confusion about what a woman should do, I would like to quote the American Cancer Society Guidelines for the Early Detection of Cancer from their last revised medical review, March 5, 2012.

"The American Cancer Society suggests: Yearly mammograms are recommended starting at age 40 and continuing for as long as a woman is in good health."

Another recommendation is to do a "Clinical breast exam by a practitioner about every three years for women in their 20s and 30s and every year for women 40 and over. Women should know how their breasts normally look and feel and report any breast change promptly to their health care provider. Breast self-exam is an option for women starting in their 20s."

No Country in the World Besides the US Recommends Mammograms for Asymptomatic Premenopausal Women

The 2009 US Prevention Services Task Force and many cancer organizations have supported the common belief that early detection means a greater chance of cure. However, there is much controversy over the use of routine mammography, especially in asymptomatic premenopausal women. In fact, no country other than the United States recommends routine mammogram screening for premenopausal women.

Screening Mammograms Miss 25% of All Cancers and With Dense Breasts, 40% of Cancers are Undetected by Mammograms!

So that suggests that we should be asking how many mammograms are not accurate or are inconclusive. Was your own imaging one of those case statistics? How chilling!

Lobular Cancers Are Undetected Over 70% of the Time by Mammography

Lobular cancers are another worrisome cancer for radiologists and surgeons. These are soft fleshy tumors and they do not create microcalcifications so the mammogram cannot identify them 70% of the time. They sometimes become quite large when they are finally palpable and the lobular cancers are known to be a more aggressive form of breast cancer. This form is easily seen on infrared thermography because they usually have established blood flow leading to them to feed the tumor and have a hyperthermic feature over the tumor itself. More on breast infrared thermography will be discussed later in the chapter.

What is a Birads or Bi-RADS Score All About?

A BI-RADS scores range from 0 to 6. BI-RADS 0 score identifies a mammogram study that is still incomplete. The X-ray may have been cloudy, making it difficult to read the images. This can happen, for example, if you moved at the precise moment the picture was taken.

In any case, further information is needed to make a final assessment and assign the true BI-RADS score. If you've received a BI-RAD score of 0, you need to make sure that additional imaging is done, such as some extra mammography views or an ultrasound.

BI-RADS 1: This score is good news! It means that your mammogram is negative (that is, no evident signs of cancer were found) and that you should continue to have routine screenings.

BI-RADS 2: This score also means that your mammogram is normal, with no apparent cancer, but that other findings (such as cysts) are described in the report. You'll be instructed to continue your routine screening.

BI-RADS 3: Now we are entering a gray zone. A BI-RADS score of 3 means that your mammogram is probably normal but that there's an approximately 2 percent chance of cancer. You'll be asked to follow-up with a repeat mammogram in six months. And if you have a family or personal history of breast cancer, the radiologist may opt to do more tests now rather than wait.

BI-RADS 4: This score means that the findings on your mammogram are suspicious and that there is an approximately 20 percent to 35 percent chance that a breast cancer is present. To make a diagnosis, the doctors will need to perform a biopsy to get a small tissue sample. More than 90 percent of women with a BI-RADS score of 4 can have a core biopsy performed without the need for general anesthesia or an incision in the breast. At many breast centers, if a biopsy is warranted they are commonly performed the same day the mammogram is read. Nationally, the rate of open excisional biopsies is much higher than necessary. More than 90 percent of biopsies done are usually core biopsies.

BI-RADS 5: This score means that your mammogram results are highly suspicious, with a 95 percent chance of breast cancer. You will need to have a biopsy for diagnosis. Talk to your doctors about what course of action to take.

BI-RADS 6: This means that you have already been diagnosed with breast cancer and the pathologist has confirmed the diagnosis.

Have Dense Breasts? Mammogram Reports Now Need to Tell You Your Status

In 2014, radiology centers were required to include language in mammogram reports that told the woman if she had dense breast tissue or not. The language might say, "Due to the dense tissue in your breasts, mammograms may not be able to visualize a cancer or the density decreases visibility of certain cancers. You should consider speaking with your doctor and possibly do other imaging studies or have a biopsy if needed." At least women are now told that their tissue could not be properly visualized instead of being given a false sense of security with a "good health letter" that reports that your annual mammogram had a "normal or negative" result. What is also distressing is that lobular cancers, which were mentioned previously, are undetected over 70% of the time with mammography regardless of your breast density.

There Are No Evidence-Based Medicine Studies That Show That Mammograms Decrease Breast Cancer Death and the Radiation May Be Causing Cancers

Now we should be looking into Mammogram Effectiveness: Fiction vs. Evidence-Based Medicine. This research is shaking the radiology and breast cancer world after The Nordic Cochrane Collaboration Study of over a half million women showed that mammograms are ineffective!

Previous to 2009, self breast examination, or SBE, clinical breast examination by a medical provider, and routine mammogram screening had been commonly recommended as primary ways of detecting breast cancer. This information was presented with the common understanding that early detection results in fewer breast cancer deaths. Dr. Peter Gøtzsche, director of the independent Nordic Cochrane Collaboration, states "However, this understanding is a myth. There is no evidence that long-term breast cancer survival is enhanced by these mammogram techniques." There is also increasing concern and evidence that repeated ionizing radiation from routine mammograms, especially in younger women, may actually increase cancer risk.

A 2008 study in the American Medical Association's Archives of Internal Medicine reported a 22% higher rate of invasive breast cancer in a group of Norwegian women with mammograms done every two years compared to those with mammograms every six years, which is the Norwegian standard of care.

In 2009 in the United States, based on the US Preventive Task Force it was recommended that mammography be done every two years for women between 50 to 74 years of age. European and Scandinavian countries currently recommend routine screening mammograms only every six years. England's current recommendation is every three years after 50 years of age. Screening mammograms are not recommended at all before the age of 50 in England.

In the 2008 Norwegian study in the American Medical Association's Archives of Internal Medicine, "The study presented information that suggested the possibility that mammograms were actually causing breast cancers that would otherwise not have occurred. Also, mammography indicated some areas that were worrisome when first viewed but that had spontaneously regressed on their own six years later." This information raises serious questions about the role of routine mammography.

Between 15% and 25% of Breast Cancer Cases Are Over-Diagnosed

Based on the previously referenced study of women in Norway, researchers estimate that between 15% and 25% of breast cancer cases are over-diagnosed. This means that these women had false positive mammograms and then they had unnecessary surgery and treatment. Their report summary states, "Mammography might not be appropriate for use in breast cancer screening because it cannot distinguish between progressive and non-progressive cancer."

Many European countries are currently reassessing their mammography recommendations after this Norwegian study and the Nordic Cochrane Institute's study of half a million women on the ineffectiveness of mammograms.

Research from the Harvard School of Public Health, Harvard Medical School, was published in the Annals of Internal Medicine April 3, 2012, entitled *Overdiagnosis of Invasive Breast Cancer Due to Mammography Screening: Results from the Norwegian Screening Program*. I quote the article:

"Research suggests that routine mammography screening, long viewed as an essential tool in detecting early breast cancers, may in fact lead to a significant amount of over diagnosis of disease that would otherwise have proved harmless".

The Nordic Cochrane Collaboration Study of Over a Half Million Women Show Mammograms Are Ineffective, Breast Cancers Misdiagnosed and Women are Harmed

The Harvard publication in 2012 was prompted by a large study done by Dr. Peter Gøtzsche, director of the independent Nordic Cochrane Collaboration, who published a book and studies that shook the radiology world.

Dr. Gøtzsche and his team spent more than 10 years investigating and analyzing data from the trials of breast screening that were run, mostly in Sweden, Norway and Denmark, before countries such as the UK introduced their national programs. Their massive research study included more than a half million women over a ten-year period. Gøtzsche has maintained for more than a decade that the results of mammogram testing do not support mass screening as a preventive measure.

Dr. Peter Gøtzsche, states, "Screening does not cut breast cancer deaths by 30%, it saves probably one or two lives for every 2,000 women who go for a mammogram, but it harms 10 others."

If this was a pharmaceutical study and you gave a drug to 2,000 people and it only helped one to two people, the drug would never have gone to market!

One in Three Cancers Detected by Screening Mammograms Were Misdiagnosed and Six Times in Ten, the Woman Will Lose a Breast. Half of All Breast Cancers Are Found Between Screenings

Dr. Gøtzsche found that cancerous cells that will go away on their own or never progress to disease in the woman's lifetime are excised with surgery and sometimes, six times in ten, she will lose a breast. Gøtzsche's group also found that one in three cancers detected by screening mammograms was misdiagnosed. These women had things done to them due to fear of possibly questionable imaging or equivocal biopsy reports. Please review this background information about biopsy accuracy in the next couple pages under the HIER Pathology Summary by Fred Husher.

I had received a report from the Mt Sinai Autopsy Department that stated that 82% of all 80 year old women had breast cancer cells at the time of autopsy, but it was not the cause of their deaths.

Treatments with radiotherapy and drugs, as well as the surgery itself, all have heavy mental, physical and financial costs. The Cochran Institute showed that, "Half of all breast cancers are found between screenings so one would wonder why routine screening mammograms are still promoted?

Dr. Gøtzsche goes on to state:

> *"Breast cancer screening with mammograms can no longer be justified because of the harm to many women from needless diagnosis and damaging treatment outweighs the small number of lives saved."*

Gøtzsche is then quoted saying:

> *"I recommend women do nothing apart from attending a doctor if they notice anything themselves. Breast cancer deaths have gone down, but I feel it is due to better treatment and women who have increased awareness, who then go to the doctor as soon as they find a lump. These factors are probably more responsible for the decrease in deaths – not screening with mammography."*

Gone for Routine Mammograms since Age 40? There is a 100% Chance They Will Find Something Questionable and Want to Do a Biopsy or Surgery

Since women in their forties tend to have denser and more fibrous breasts, a false positive reading on mammograms is more likely and will then require biopsy. Andrew Wolf, MD, an associate professor at the University of Virginia School Of Medicine, supports these findings. In an August, 2003 review article on breast cancer screening in *The Consultant*, Dr. Wolf states:

> *"If a woman begins getting regular mammograms at age 40, there is virtually a 100 percent chance that some kind of abnormality will show up that will warrant at least a follow-up mammogram, an ultrasound scan, or a call from the physician recommending a six-month follow-up examination. It is also likely that over the course of a lifetime, she will undergo an unnecessary breast biopsy."*

Annual Mammograms No More Effective Than Breast Exams for Reducing Mortality

Mammography doesn't appear to reduce mortality from breast cancer any better than a simple breast exam (which also doesn't decrease mortality according to the American Cancer Association and some of these foundations have suggested dispensing from examining your own breasts altogether). What is a woman to do with all this conflicting information?

According to a 2000 study published in the Journal of the National Cancer Institute, that included nearly forty thousand women between the ages of fifty and fifty-nine, researchers found that annual mammograms were no more effective than standard breast exams in reducing breast cancer mortality.

Cancers Detected at Age 70 and Above Are Unlikely to Kill a Woman

In another study published in the Journal of the American Medical Association, Dr. Miller found that women age seventy and older benefited very little from having a mammogram. Dr. Kerlikowske, the author of this study, states that, "The cancers detected at this age never would have killed them."

As noted earlier in this book, breast cancers are actually slow growing and take 10 to 12 years to be identified by mammograms. The mass has to be greater than 3 mm for mammogram detection and about 6 mm for targeted ultrasound detection. These older women have a greater chance of perishing from heart disease than from breast cancer.

I heard a local radiologist here in Eugene who was presenting to a local Nurse Practitioner Conference in 2016 actually say that his recommendation to his 72 year old mother was to go for her annual mammogram. He felt that women should continue to go routinely until 10 years before their anticipated death. I felt that is was a rather bizarre comment and supported my view about the cancer industry and unnecessary testing that mostly brought in funds to the medical complex.

Mammography Is a Recipe for Net Harm – More Risk than Benefit

The medical community prides itself on evidence to drive important decision-making. But when the evidence is contrary to entrenched medical practice, it has a hard time coming to terms with the information. Such is the case with mammography recommendations. All of the data now available point to significant net harm and far more risk than benefit, from routine mammography. If this were a drug, the US Food and Drug Administration (FDA) would never approve it. In 2014, the Swiss Medical Board, after reviewing all of the data, recommended abolishing screening mammography in Switzerland. Since Switzerland has socialized medicine, they apparently felt that if mammograms were ineffective, then why should the state pay for it? This is a rather practical approach! This was published in the New England Journal of Medicine 2014.

It is interesting that in May of 2015, the US Preventive Services Task Force (USPSTF) issued new draft recommendations regarding who should undergo screening and how often. These recommendations came out after the 2nd Nordic Cochran Institute publication. In recent past years there was no support for routine screening in women younger than 50 or older than 74 years. But there was abundant data in this last 2015 report that the USPSTF was not at all supportive of continuing this annual screening practice. In fact, for the first time ever, the US Preventive Services Task Force in 2015 said that mammograms were now considered a Category C. These categories were created to educate the provider and the public as to the level of risk a drug or procedure carried.

In this case, a Category C means that the mammograms may do as much harm as good and the May, 2015 USPSTF recommendations did not specify how often women should even have a screening mammogram anymore. The report said that it is now "A personal decision for the woman and that she should discuss her personal circumstances with her physician but the USPSTF was not making a recommendation that she go for a screening mammogram any more".

> *"A systematic assessment based on all of the evidence available from 1960 to 2014 showed that for 10,000 women in their 50s, who are screened annually over the course of a decade, there are only five individuals whose breast cancer deaths are prevented". This was published in JAMA 2014 by Elmore and Kramer. In another study by Elmore in JAMA 2015 regarding diagnostic concordance among pathologists interpreting breast biopsy specimens found that "There are over 6100 women who have false-positive tests that lead to additional imaging and unnecessary biopsy procedures. This greater than 60% false-positive rate is an indicator of a remarkably poor test with respect to accuracy, no less the large toll of emotional turmoil and financial cost that it engenders."*

Your Biopsy Pathology Report May Also Be Inaccurate.

What about all of the biopsies that are performed? A recent study also underscored yet another level of imprecision: the problem of interpreting biopsies by pathologists. It has been noted that there is agreement among three pathology experts regarding the presence of cancer only 75 percent of the time. So now we have to take into account the skill and the opinion of the pathologist who is looking at your slides and he or she may not agree with their own colleagues. So what happens if your biopsy tissue falls into that 25 percent category? Added to the net harm of mammography which appears to be over-diagnosis, which occurs in 20 to 30 percent of women who have an abnormal mammogram result but in whom cancer would not be apparent by biopsy in that worrisome 25% category of biopsies done.

The summary below outlines a major problem within the pathology world. This information was sent to me by Fred Husher, a friend of mine for 25 years. He has 10 USA patents to his name and a desire to make a difference in the world. I regard Fred Husher as a "Renaissance man" who is also gifted with a photographic memory. I have enjoyed watching him grab a 500 page book when he is trying to look something up and he simply opens it to the page that he had read it on, which may have been years ago. He does not need the index.

Fred started out as an electrical engineer and became an inventor and has a wide range of interests and capabilities including creating a robot that does hip surgery, devices that track pollution downstream for the Woods Hole Oceanography Department so they would know who was polluting and with what pollutants. Fred was involved with microwave technology when cell phone telecommunications were just a glint in the eye of engineers and physicists. He restructured and ran the Research and Development Division of Beckman–Coulter to redesign all their Coulter Counters that do blood analysis in hospitals across the country and the world. He has become an expert in biochemistry, optics, hemodynamics, and tissue pathophysiology.

Fred Husher's interest in pathology biopsy inadequacies started in about 2000 when his dear sister had a rare melanoma of the eye that was misdiagnosed by the pathology department at the Massachusetts General Hospital in Boston.

As a scientist, he was plagued with why this had happened. He has discovered what is wrong with current tissue pathology processing but he has also created a solution to the problems that will save millions of lives. I have included his contact information. He anticipates presenting this research to pathologists at the time of my book publication. I am including this information so you may be better informed and to pass this on to other medical providers, surgeons, radiologists and pathologists so hopefully, if you have a biopsy planned you may get a more accurate result.

HIER Pathology Summary by Fred Husher

Scientists and pathologists are encouraged to contact Fred Husher www.linkedin.com/in/fred-husher-a947456

As of June 2017, Husher sent this update:

> *"I am to speak at a Pathology conference later this month June 2017 in San Diego. July will be in Chicago where I meet with the head of the FDA, and early August 2017 I will be in Milan at the European World Pathology Conference".*

> *"We all but have the FDA approval for the slide and WHO is knocking at the door. ISO is aware of the technology and will look at it once we are in production. Mainland China will be adopting the slide in Fall 2017. So you can see this is going off at a rate I could never have believed possible. I have also extended the technology for H&E and PAP smear staining. So we have about 80% of the staining technologies covered".*

> *"The overwhelming reception has been great and in most cases we are the star of each conference we go to. Six patents have been filed so far and another six are in the pipeline. So it is now generally accepted we are the judge and jury on slide coatings and in the diagnostic processing of the*

slides. My solution has changed IHC from subjective or objective wherein we can generate a ruler for the digital image that given the antigen density as a number against the stain color. This is a huge paradigm change and it is truly scaring the pathology community".

The following is an explanation for why your own pathology report may be inaccurate.

"We have just completed our studies of the HIER process and have been able to prove that the accepted methods actually destroy much of the exposed proteins before the staining can take place. The industry believed HIER temp is nominally 95°C. Our testing has proven that at or above 95°C proteins denature and break apart nearly completely. At between 91 and 93°C, the formaldehyde fixation is removed and the proteins remain undamaged. Thus, staining will often show as a false negative unless the section is densely loaded with the protein carried antigen sites. Hence, by the time the staining shows something, you are already in serious trouble."

"We have known for some time that the HIER process is being run at too high a temperature, but had not worked out a controlled study to prove it previously. Depending upon the HIER process used: rice cooker bath, under slide heater (Leica Bondmax and Ventana auto stainers), pressure cooker, or in some cases microwave oven. The HIER process is to disengage the formaldehyde fixation done to the tissue block to prepare it for sectioning. The heat and acid/base buffer causes the Schiff base bonding of the formaldehyde to free amines within the tissue to decouple. With the formaldehyde removed the proteins and their antigen sites become exposed so that the staining can take place. Some labs use pressure cookers that operate at 125°C in order to accelerate the processing time. What they claim is that the

physical morphology is still present, and to a large degree I concur. However, most pathologists look for the stain presence before they pay attention to the cell structure and that cannot occur if the antigen sites are damaged."

"Our testing capability now allows us to have very tight control over the heating of the slide, better than used by Leica and Ventana. At 90 to 91°C we see very little degradation to the HIER processed slide vs. the control. As the HIER temperature is increased the percentage of damage increases until at 95°C much of the proteins are damaged."

"We know that our test conditions are an extreme condition as there is only a monolayer of protein in our deposit whereas in/on tissue the proteins are layered. Think of the layering much as an expendable heat shield for a space capsule. However, the damage behavior effects remain. If the cancer presence is early there may well not be an overly thick mass of the proteins, which means the HIER process is very likely to kill what little is present."

Fred Husher goes on to say:

"I need to explain that our need for a much better biocapture adhesive drove us to develop our technology so we could support our control slide development efforts. Using the control technologies allows us to critically evaluate staining activities and slide processing with objective measurements."

"Clearly what we have developed challenges the foundation of the pathology world. We have proved they have been wrong and wrong for a long time. Worse yet the stainer companies have 100's of millions of dollars at risk with their products and our technologies challenge the viability of their installed base of instruments already in medical facilities."

"In conclusion the pathologists do not know what they do

not see and they have no way to determine what the degradation effects are of the HIER process."

"So most pathologists simply accept the protocols issued by the stainer companies as being the optimal truth. In effect the blind leading the blind. Because so much is dependent upon the binding chemistry it makes it very hard for the medical community to work from a constant baseline. That is not the case for us as we make our own and have complete control over the end result."

"Our binding chemistry is entirely new and has the capability to bind to many different end groups in/on tissue. Only the Erie Plus coating is anywhere near where we are and even at that they are pretty poor, especially in regards to binding density uniformity. Again, the medical community is completely ignorant of how bad the coated slides are. In all the time we have been working on this we have yet to see any critical analysis done by anyone in regards to slide coating performance."

How chilling to realize that breast biopsies may not even be accurate using the current processing standards!

We may all thank Fred Husher if the rest of the pathology world can catch up with understanding these new developments. Please share this with as many medical types that will listen and so they may explore the possibility that their sacred way of doing things may not be effective. Fred also discovered that most pathologists who are asked to do a second opinion of some tissue will not trust the way the other pathologist did the tissue prep and staining, so they will want to prepare the tissue "Their way." Maybe that also gives a glimpse into why if 3 pathologists all look at some tissue they will only agree about 75% of the time that there is cancer present. I discussed this earlier. This information is not at all reassuring.

Husher's research may be the other reason that there may be more inaccurate diagnoses from needle or core biopsies vs. a surgical biopsy, where there is a thicker tissue sample to evaluate. It is also common knowledge to physicians that women who have had multiple needle / core biopsies seem to later develop breast cancers usually in that region. Husher's research now gives a reason related to the amount of tissue available to sample and the very real possibility that the sample was heated over 95 degrees. The target temperature should have been 90 to 91 degrees C. If you have a biopsy planned, I would share this information with your surgeon and radiologist and insist that the pathologist who is going to process your sample do so in the 90 to 91 degree C range. That may upset a few people, but it is your breast and your biopsy and you want the most accurate results possible.

Other Things You Should Know About Your Biopsy Report

Maybe this information regarding biopsy irregularities explains why many of the infrared scans are abnormal but not according to the biopsy / pathology report. What I have been seeing is an infrared thermography which shows a very abnormal TH4 or TH5 in some women, with blood flow going to the mass, but when the mass is needle or core biopsied, with less tissue available to send to pathology, the women are told that their needle biopsy is negative. Physiologically, there is suspected pathology as seen through the lens of the infrared camera but with the mistaken biopsy, the woman and physicians think they are in the clear. This is why I frequently suggest that my clients have an excisional biopsy performed instead of a needle biopsy so there is more tissue to evaluate. If the protein is over-heated and the staining does not work well causing you to not be able to rely on your pathology report, at least they have removed the cancer with a margin of tissue surrounding the mass. Otherwise they may be taking a sample of cancer cells, withdrawing the needle through the healthy breast tissue seeding the cancer cells, and then telling you the pathology report is negative, when it is not. How frightening!

The other problem with doing a needle or core biopsy has to do with the steadiness of the radiologist's hand and proper imaging of the mass usually by ultrasound. What they are attempting to do is to get the tip of the needle into the center of the mass and not go through the mass and end up actually sampling the tissue under or beside the mass. This becomes more challenging if the mass is in the 3 to 4 mm range which is about the size of a small lentil. These are more reasons for considering an excisional biopsy if you are following a conventional approach to evaluating your condition.

Infrared thermography is identifying problems three to eight years prior to detection by mammograms. I will cover more information regarding thermography a bit later in this chapter and there is a sizable research section on the www.InfraredBreastHealth.com website. Images are also available in the "Protect Your Breasts" section on the www.ProtectYourBreasts.com website.

What Does It Cost for All the False-Positive Studies and Over-Diagnoses?

I will now return to the topic of over-diagnosis of cancer based mostly on mammograms and the cost burden to your pocket and ultimately to the health care delivery system, which we all support.

Women often undergo surgery and receive chemotherapy or radiation treatment (or a combination of all of these treatments), even though there is little to no impact on prognosis. Such individuals typically believe that their lives have been saved even though the data points against that assertion. A Harvard study, published in 2015 in Health Affairs by Ong and Mandl demonstrates that the cost of false-positive mammogram results and over-diagnosis is approximately $4 billion dollars per year. This is on top of the current US cost for annual mammography of nearly $10 billion.

As you can see this is a very lucrative business for the cancer industry and a major reason why they have not been actively exploring other modes of breast cancer screening or other early detection tools like medical infrared thermography or treatment options like breast cryoablation.

In the Sinatra Health Report, April, 2004, Vol. 10, No. 4, Stephen Sinatra, MD, who is a cardiologist and interested in research, made the following comments:

> *"Mammography fails to detect cancer in 10 to 30 percent of the women who have a mammogram done. This means that one tenth to almost one third of mammography reports give you a false-negative and they tell you that there is nothing to be concerned about when there actually is. The false -positive rate is significant as well, up to 10% of women undergoing mammography will hear that they have breast cancer when in fact they don't."*

Dr. Sinatra also promotes breast thermography, especially in the under-50 age group for whom mammography is less effective in part due to the younger women having dense breasts that limits visibility of the mammograms.

It is time for us to re-evaluate how we screen for breast cancer. Until now, the use of mass screening suggests that we are unable to differentiate the risk in any given individual. So instead of a smart approach that uses family history and genetics, we have dumbed it down and treated all women the same. As a result, we have come to rely on a test that is notoriously inaccurate but has become a fixed part of American medical practice since it was introduced almost 50 years ago. With the tens of millions of low-risk women unnecessarily undergoing screening each year, any mammogram testing would be vulnerable to a high rate of false positives. Some of the recent research is suggesting that the frequent radiation, which is cumulative, may be causing us harm. If this group of low risk women without a palpable breast concern also happen to be younger women with dense breasts, which makes it difficult to see anything anyway on mammograms, I question why do we pursue this? This applies to higher-resolution scans, too, such as magnetic resonance, digital mammography, and ultrasound. Indeed, there is a better path forward.

I can't begin to make a blanket recommendation regarding the use of mammograms for routine screening. The data is coming in, and more definitive answers will be available in future years. I can only suggest that women look at the recommendations for routine mammography critically, and discuss them carefully with their knowledgeable clinicians. Personally, I suspect that non-ionizing diagnostic imaging will be the preferred screening method in the future, which will include a new version of MRI, 3D ultrasound, and infrared thermography.

I feel that medical practitioners should balance risks against benefits and communicate that with their patients. Of the thousands of women that I have seen, all of them said that their number one fear was to develop breast cancer. Because of being fear driven, it is easy to see why women keep testing and testing just to "Be sure".

The other major influencing factor is the clinician's own fear of any potential malpractice suit that might develop if they did not suggest further imaging or biopsy. These physicians may then be practicing "Defensive medicine" and potentially they are doing additional testing, imagery or biopsies to show their due diligence. It is a very fine line for both the clinician and the woman seeking answers. As I have tried to unravel "Fact vs. evidence based medicine", there are a lot of gray areas and inconsistencies which make it more challenging for a woman to decide what is best for her in order to protect her breasts.

Dr. Christianne Northrup's Suggestions to Improve Breast Health

Here is some helpful advice offered by Dr. Christianne Northrup, MD, that she shares with her patients when they are trying to make a decision about mammograms and other things you can consider for improving your health.

> *"One helpful way to assess your risk for breast cancer, which in turn can help you decide how often you want to have mammograms, is to use the National Cancer Institute's Breast Cancer Risk Assessment Tool, available online at www.cancer.gov/bcrisktool. After you answer seven simple questions, it calculates both your risk of getting invasive breast cancer in the next five years as well as your lifetime risk, and it compares each to the risk for the average U.S. woman of the same age and race or ethnicity."*

Here is some more timely advice from Dr. Northrup's program to promote healthy breast tissue in *Women's Bodies, Women's Wisdom*. Her book, along with many others, is available on my website under Resources so you may easily review and order them.

> *"Doing breast self-exams and getting mammograms (or sonograms which are also called ultrasounds) regularly, is*

not the same as prevention. In other words, it is not the same as brushing and flossing the teeth, which actually prevent cavities and periodontal disease. As one of my colleagues said of breast cancer, "We identify the risks, but we don't know what to do until they manifest as disease." Our culture uses mammograms as a fix but doesn't encourage women to change their diets, exercise, stop smoking, and learn how to be in relationships that nurture them. These are preventive changes that favor healthy breasts. But as one researcher has said, it's difficult to put together a constituency for prevention. It is treatment that gets our attention. If your sister or mother dies of breast cancer, you usually give money to programs that do research to produce better treatments; you don't start a whole-food restaurant in your neighborhood or advocate teaching eighth-grade girls how to appreciate their breasts and make sure they have optimal levels of vitamin D. Our culture is crisis-oriented, acting only once the horse is out of the barn."

"There is a third option, however. You can use thermography, or also called thermo-mammography, another disease screening as an external guidance system. And if any abnormality appears, you then have the opportunity to ask the abnormal cells what they need that they're not getting. The earlier in the disease process you make adjustments to your diet, beliefs, and lifestyle; the easier it is to transform your cells."

It is reassuring that Dr. Northrup, who is a leader in women's health, is encouraging you to make the same changes that the *Proactive Breast Wellness* program offers. Remember that trying to reduce your risk of breast cancer or its reoccurrence through lifestyle, diet, limiting environmental toxins, and maintaining a healthy mental and spiritual balance, may significantly improve and protect your health. Prevention IS the Cure! This is the goal here.

Other Modes of Breast Screening and Evaluation

Ultrasound Breast Screening

Ultrasound breast screening also called sonograms, uses sound waves to reveal breast lesions. It is frequently used to help further define whether a mass is a fluid-filled cyst or a solid tumor. Ultrasound is beneficial for women with dense fibrocystic breasts, which accounts for approximately a third of the population of women in the United States. Mammograms have limited usefulness in these patients due to poor visibility.

Ultrasound can also help women avoid unnecessary breast biopsies when a simple cyst is confirmed. It is not generally used as a primary screening tool for breast cancer according to some studies in the past but now the literature is suggesting a woman have a mammogram and an ultrasound for more clarity and information. Ultrasounds overall have about 65% sensitivity, which is better than the mammograms alone but mammograms and ultrasound together may have an 85% sensitivity.

The downside of standard breast ultrasound from my perspective is the location of the area of concern to be imaged. You have to rely on the skill of the ultrasound technologist doing the exam. I usually try to get my patients to go to a breast center where the tech does breast ultrasounds all day, not a few times a week, which may be the case in a community hospital.

If I find an area of clinical concern with a hyperthermic infrared scan and possibly a mass I can feel, I will send the woman for a bilateral ultrasound with radial views. This should take a technician at least an hour to do both breasts and her axilla. Unfortunately, I examine the woman sitting and I send an order with a map saying five mm firm mass four cm from the nipple at 2:00. The ultrasound tech examines the woman lying down and that area I was concerned about when sitting at 2:00 may now be at 4:30 when lying down. If the tech only examines the 2:00 region, she will probably not identify the area of concern.

In addition, the local radiology center that I send most of my patients to seems to be trying to streamline their process. I have been told that the tech may spend an hour imaging the woman's breasts and axilla, but the radiologist is only given four images for each breast, one image from each quadrant to review and make a report from. This facility recently has been removing all the landmarks that I have sent them where they used to type into the indication for exam section the example of "five mm firm mass four cm from the nipple at 2:00" to hopefully tell the radiologist where to look for the area of potential concern. They currently leave the whole line blank or insert, "reason for exam per patient, screening ultrasound or family history."

This has become increasingly frustrating to me as I strive to provide my clients the work-up that they deserve. I look forward with great anticipation to the next technology that will become available across the country hopefully in early 2018. There will not be any technician errors. The 3-D ultrasound provides amazing detail and hopefully will replace mammography. The genius behind this is Dr. Peter Littrup who is also the pioneer physician for breast and prostate cryoablation, a technique used to freeze the tumor in place with liquid nitrogen. There will be more about cryoablation later in chapter 9.

FDA Approves 3-D SoftVue/Delphinus Breast Ultrasound Device, January, 2014

Breast Cancer News & Perspectives and Medscape Medical News reports that:

"The US Food and Drug Administration has granted a 510(k) clearance for a diagnostic imaging system called SoftVue from Delphinus Medical Technologies, Inc. that uses ultrasound technology to provide accurate operator-independent 3-dimensional images of the entire breast in one to two minutes. Patient-centric benefits include a lack of painful breast compression; women simply lie down on a comfort pad while the breast is suspended in a warm water bath, surrounded by a soft pliant membrane that accommodates all breast sizes and contours to the chest wall.

"The breast is lowered through a hole in the table so that the ring array can go all around to the chest wall, even to the axilla, and then you push a button and the entire breast is scanned in one to two minutes", states Peter J. Littrup, MD, chief medical officer at Delphinus, in an interview with Medscape Medical News.

Dr. Littrup goes on to explain that:

"The short scan is performed by a transducer ring comprised of more than 2000 elements that emit ultrasound signals in a sequenced 360 degree circular array around the entire breast. Images are automatically acquired in two mm increments from the chest wall and axilla, and can be stacked 'like slices of bread' for 3-D viewing or tiled for comparison with other studies."

Dr. Littrup, the developer of the technique states:

"For women with dense breast tissue, who are at much higher risk for developing breast cancer, the performance of mammography is at its worst. Consequently, many early cancers go undetected when they are the most treatable. Improved cancer detection for women with dense breasts would decrease the proportion of breast cancers diagnosed at later stages, which would significantly lower the mor-

tality rate. The emergence of whole breast ultrasound provides good performance for women with dense breast tissue, and may eliminate the current trade-off between the cost effectiveness of mammography and the imaging performance of more expensive systems such as magnetic resonance imaging or MRI."

Dr. Peter Littrup's new 3-D SoftVue / Delphinus Breast Ultrasound Device will hopefully be available to hospitals in early 2018. I suggest you ask your local hospital to explore getting this equipment for your area.

Breast MRI Scanning

MRI can have a positive impact in the breast management continuum ranging from risk assessment to diagnosis and treatment monitoring. MRI uses magnetic forces as a non-ionizing imaging technique rather than X-rays and is currently the most sensitive and accurate structural screening tool. MRI can show much more structural and vascular detail than conventional mammography. It is reported to have 90 to 98 percent sensitivity, but a specificity no better than conventional mammography. Its major problem is that it is prohibitively expensive at this time, thus limiting its widespread use as a regular screening tool. MRI also requires long exam times and intravenous contrast agents. There is a need for an equivalent low-cost alternative that I hope the new 3-D ultrasound will provide in future.

MRI cannot be used with people who have implanted metal devices or have tattoos with lots of blue or black ink that have metal in them. At the present time, it is used more for secondary screening of women with suspicious findings on other studies, or those with known genetic risk factors for breast cancer, such as carriers of the BRCA gene mutations.

PET Scans

PET scanning of breasts, using radioactive tracers, is a type of functional scanning. That means that it is looking at the metabolic activity in the breast. It can find some tumors. However, it misses most small tumors, and its resolution is poor. It has been used most for whole body scans to screen for metastases, and can also discriminate between tumor, fibrotic scar, and necrotic or dead tissue.

PEM or Positron Emission Mammography

There is a new type of PET scanning specifically for breasts using smaller detectors closer to the breasts, called PEM, or positron emission mammography. This technique can detect smaller tumors, does not need to be timed with the menstrual cycle, and can be used with biopsy procedures. It can still miss tumors that have a low metabolic activity, and false positive results can be seen in cases of fat necrosis (fatty tumors that have died, frequently seen after trauma to the breast), fibroadenoma, recent biopsy, and breast inflammation. PEM is already FDA-approved but is still finding its niche. It does use ionizing radiation.

Breast-Specific Gamma Imaging, or BSGI

Breast-specific gamma imaging, or BSGI, is another FDA-approved imaging technique similar to PET scanning. In this technique, a very short-lived radioactive tracer is injected into the blood and is absorbed by all the cells of the body. A special detector then can see concentrations of tracer in the breast tissues, without requiring breast compression. Higher concentrations are seen where there is more metabolic activity, such as with actively growing tumors. This is used primarily as a follow-up test after mammograms for women with dense breast tissue, suspicious areas on a mammogram, lumps that can be felt but not seen with mammography or ultrasound, breast implants, and scarring from previous surgeries. It also is finding its niche, and does use ionizing radiation. It would be expected to report false positives with metabolic activity not related to cancer, as well as to miss low-activity tumors.

Breast Tomosynthesis, or BT

A new type of mammography that creates three dimensional images, is called breast tomosynthesis, or BT. Although emerging technologies such as tomosynthesis and positron emission mammography may improve upon some of the limitations of standard mammography, they are unlikely to create a paradigm shift in performance because of their generation of ionizing radiation. Breast tomosynthesis is similar to CT scanning. This method is reported to increase sensitivity and specificity by 10% while at the same time decreasing the recall rates from current screening mammography by 43%. This method also decreases the amount of breast compression needed during the exam. Research is currently being conducted at Massachusetts General Hospital, the University of Iowa, and the AVL Cancer Hospital in Holland. Although its radiation exposure is considered to be low, it still uses ionizing radiation.

The Wonderful World of Breast Thermography also known as Medical Infrared (MIR), Infrared Thermography (IR), Digital Thermography (DIT), or Thermo-mammography

Breast thermography is the best risk detection tool available to modern medicine. In fact the FDA's 510k documents that were assigned to my military camera state that the IR camera is a "Risk Detection Tool".

I must admit that I am biased when speaking about breast thermography. I use it with my patients on a daily basis. I refer women for other imaging modalities when appropriate. I find that thermography is the best risk detection tool available to modern medicine for breast screening. Research suggests it is able to detect changes in the tissue prior to tumor development. IR can identify a suspicious area at less than 3 mm and it has to be larger than 3 mm for mammogram detection. It is non-ionizing with no radiation, so IR does not increase cancer risk and is 100% safe for young women, pregnant or nursing moms, or anyone who is concerned about radiation exposure. It helps to identify women who have estrogen dominance or hormone effects in their breast tissues. It provides a way to monitor therapies and interventions for both breast cancer survivors, as well as those hoping to reduce their cancer risk.

Advanced infrared thermography is the other non-ionizing imaging technique besides MRI. Women appreciate that there isn't any radiation. The infrared camera, coupled with a computer, detects heat patterns given off by the breasts and adjacent tissues. It does not require contact, compression, or venous access. Infrared imaging is based more on physiological and metabolic changes than structural changes, assessing the blood flow to the tissues, as well as the metabolic activity of the tissues.

How Infrared Thermography is Graded

Thermography has a grading system and it is known as the Hobbins Method of evaluation which is an internationally recognized system of grading the infrared images on a TH1 to TH5 range with 26 points available. This is a grading system similar to the better known Birads system that radiologists use to grade mammograms, ultrasounds and MRIs.

In thermography, the more points, the higher the reading. TH1s and TH2s are considered "Normal" with the lowest number of points. The TH3s are broken down into a weak TH3-, a "Borderline or Equivocal" TH3 and a strong TH3+. If there are additional points, it is graded as an "Abnormal" TH4 and the most number of points would give you a "Very Abnormal" TH5. This grading scale is named after Dr. William Hobbins, MD who is considered the "Grandfather of Medical Infrared".

To get a better idea of what this grading system looks like, I suggest you view my website www.ProtectYourBreasts.com and check out the "Protect Your Breasts" section where you can see the infrared images which will be illuminating for you.

If you are looking for an infrared clinic, it is important that you find one with a high-end military grade camera. There is more information later in this chapter about how to find an infrared clinic near you. These cameras will have nationally certified infrared technicians running them and a nationally accredited infrared thermologist who reads them based on the Hobbins Method and graded TH1 to TH5. These cameras and their computers should be able to change through several color palettes including a gray inverted palette that shows blood flow to areas of interest. They should also be able to print out large images that fill an 8 ½ by 11 photo paper sheet. Many of the cameras are now Dicam compatible so the images can be transferred around to other imaging centers. The radiologists use this Dicam system to send images to other facilities when they want to do comparison readings from center to center. This will hopefully educate radiologists on how they can utilize and compare thermography, which is a test of metabolic activity or physiology with their own structural studies.

Why Don't Radiologists Like Thermography

In my fifteen years of experience in utilizing thermography since 2005, one of the frustrations is trying to educate radiologists on what the technology does and how it could be useful as an adjunctive tool to help them find a "Target" and get women in for medical care sooner to improve their survival rate. Most of the radiologists have had no experience with thermography, so consequently they are suspect of a technology that is beyond their training. I refer to 42 different radiologists and imaging centers in Oregon, Washington, Idaho and California. In general there are only a handful of radiologists who have been interested in learning about thermography and have been willing to meet me or review images that I send electronically to them prior to the woman's structural studies. Some of these radiologists even call and want to consult with me as to what the thermogram is showing. This is a minority group. Most of them tend to be dismissive and occasionally rude. They will usually inform me that the mammogram or ultrasound is "Totally normal" and that my "Abnormal TH4 or Very Abnormal TH5" hyperthermic scan with blood flow leading to the palpable mass, according to the radiolgist is due to an error in the infrared technology and IR report. Then they usually tell me that they are an MD with "X number of years of experience" and that I "Am only a Nurse Practitioner" and that I have to be "Wrong". I now sweetly respond that I may in fact not be wrong, it is just that I am seeing a developing problem physiologically 3 to 5 years prior to mammogram detection at potentially less than 3 mm. That usually does not go over well with the radiologist.

I think the other issue here is in regards to the radiologist's concern that the woman's cancer was "Missed" by the structural studies and that the woman may sue the facility. I was told by my local hospital radiology department that "I should never say to the patient or record that the cancer was "Missed on structural studies" since they then felt that I personally or my technology had become a "Liability issue to them." I am able to document that "The cancer was undetected by structural studies". According to them, "Missed" refers to their error in diagnosis. "Undetected" is just stating fact.

Medicine is an imperfect art form. I can say that the women that I have seen where infrared did identify a suspicious area that was later biopsy proven; these women had no interest in starting a law suit against the radiology department. All of them were grateful that infrared was able to identify an area of concern earlier so they could get into treatment as soon as possible.

My interest is to provide the best care to the women that I serve. If that woman does have a palpable mass with blood flow to that mass and a very abnormal thermogram over 6-12 months with "Negative" structural studies, I may urge her to do a surgical excision so she does not continue to worry about the area. In the very near future I hope that this woman can go for cryoablation or cryosurgery for this suspicious finding instead. Cryoablation will be discussed later in chapter 9.

Just for fun my accountant and I recently looked into how much money this local radiology department made from my referrals to them over a ten year period, for the patients that I sent to them for mammograms, ultrasounds, MRIs and needle biopsies. Over the past ten years it looks as though I sent them approximately $985,500 in proceeds for just the imaging alone. The amount they charged the patient or their insurance for the needle and core biopsies came to more than that, but that amount was difficult for me to estimate. So I smile to think that I have made them more than a million dollars in profits, yet they never send any patients back to me to be evaluated by infrared thermography to assist their work up.

How Cancers Grow and What is Seen on Thermography

I have just mentioned the issue of blood flow leading to a mass and this requires some explanation. When cancers begin to grow in the breast, they develop their own blood vessels, causing an abnormal thermal pattern. When abnormal cancer cells first begin to cluster, they put up a heat signature. These early clusters may be the situation with hyperplasia with atypia, sometimes considered a pre-cancer.

I am most interested in the category of hyperplasia with atypia in which some cells become malformed and begin to accumulate within the milk duct. At this point, the cells are receiving their nutrition and oxygen from the capillary bed surrounding the area and they are slow growing. Research suggests that it takes about ten to twelve years for a cancer to grow to be palpable or be seen on a mammogram. Some experts believe that in this pre-cancerous stage your body has wonderful powers created by your immune system to alter what is going on in your body at a cellular level. Your body attempts to bring you back to a state of wellness. I believe this hyperplasia with atypia is the situation that I can see in the borderline TH3 infrared scans.

This is the area that the PBW program may have the greatest impact by being able to reverse the outcome. I also want to point out that three quarters of my whole patient population has borderline TH3 scans, which I feel are mostly due to the body burden of environmental toxins and foods that may have bovine growth hormone, etc. Women who follow the PBW protocol usually improve their infrared images about 65% of the time in six to twelve months. Now that is prevention!

Some heat changes, abnormal thermal patterns or hot spots can be seen even before a tumor has developed fully. A "thermal bullet," which is mostly seen in cases of DCIS (ductal carcinoma in situ), may be seen over a small palpable mass, which may be in the 3 to 4 mm range or about the size of a small lentil. The early DCIS seem to appear as this thermal island without large caliber vessels in the early lesions since the abnormal cells are still inside the duct. This is another advantage of using IR screening, to see if you can feel a small mass under the thermal island. Most women have difficulty identifying these lentil sized masses since they are quite small to actually feel. This is particularly the case if the woman has dense fibrocystic breasts with all sorts of lumps and bumps. If you can be guided by a colored image to palpate that region and then get an ultrasound or mammogram to find it, you will then have an early target.

Unfortunately, mammograms usually identify lesions that are more than 3 mm and if you have "Dense breasts" the visibility is decreased. One of the radiologists told me that targeted US is better for 5 to 6 mm masses but the technician would have to be directly over the mass to find it.

I send the imaging department a "Map" that states 3 mm mass palpated 2 inches from the nipple at 1:00 on the left, in the hopes they will find the early target. Unfortunately there is a geography problem since I scan the woman seated and the ultrasound is usually done lying down. So the area I want imaged, 2 inches from the nipple at 1:00, may now be at 3:30 and the tech may not be able to get this region into one of her four quadrant ultrasound images that she might send to the radiologist to read.

When these clusters of abnormal cells begin to enlarge, they release nitric oxide, which is a vasodilator that keeps the blood vessels dilated. The enlarging tumor mass requires a steady flow of oxygen and nutrition to increase its tumor doubling potential.

These areas of abnormal heat can be detected by infrared cameras and become more pronounced as the cancer advances. Infrared imaging and MRIs can also detect neoangiogenesis, large caliber blood vessels that begin to move across the chest and breast to feed the enlarging mass of cancerous cells in the case of invasive ductal or lobular cancers that usually display large arborizing vessels.

Another reason to find a high end military camera with nimble computer medical infrared software is to be able to change over to a gray inverted palette and to be able to take delta measurements. A delta temperature is the temperature difference between any two selected points. In this case I am evaluating a delta temperature or the difference from nipple to nipple on a Celsius scale. The nipple delta is usually over one degree C on an abnormal thermography scan. When a woman has an invasive ductile carcinoma or lobular cancer that may have begun to spread to surrounding tissues and lymph nodes, she may have delta temperatures greater than 2.25 to 2.75 degrees C and the whole affected side is becoming hyperthermic with increased blood flow and metabolic activity. The hottest sets of images I have seen were from two women who both had inflammatory breast cancer, which is very rare. They had delta temperature readings of over 3.25 degrees C. These rare inflammatory breast cancers are not detected on mammograms or ultrasounds.

Some research suggests that thermal changes may be seen three to eight years before tumors can be detected by clinical exam or mammography. I often refer to thermography as a poor woman's MRI since it is able to detect blood flow to tumors at a fraction of the cost of an MRI and without IV dye contrast that may be a problem if you are older and your kidneys cannot clear the contrast well.

You might now wish to visit www.ProtectYourBreasts.com to see an artist's rendition of what the cells are doing when they start changing. Also, please view the slide show in the "Protect Your Breasts / Save Your Breasts" area of the website to better see what I am talking about and actually see how the vessels are changing and enlarging in women with biopsy proven breast cancers.

An Overview of Thermography or Medical Infrared Imaging over Time

As an overview of thermography, I have taken this section from the research area of Dr. William Amalu's website. Dr. Amalu is my infrared interpreter or thermologist, friend, and mentor for over fifteen years. William is the President of the International Academy of Clinical Thermology, board member of the International Thermographic Society, and Medical Director of the International Association of Certified Thermographers, as well as an Associate of IEEE the Institute of Electrical and Electronics Engineers and the Engineering in Medicine and Biology Society. Dr. Amalu has been a national expert on infrared thermography for over 25 years and he trained under and is a protégé of the grandfather of clinical thermography, William Hobbins, MD, who started to look at IR as a tool over 30 years ago. Dr. Amalu writes:

> *"The large patient populations and long survey periods in many of the above clinical studies yields a high significance to the various statistical data obtained. This is especially true for the contribution of Thermography to early cancer*

diagnosis, as an invaluable marker of high-risk populations, and therapeutic decision making (a contribution that has been established and justified by the unequivocal relationship between heat production and tumor doubling time)".

"Currently available high-resolution digital infrared imaging (Thermography) technology benefits greatly from enhanced image production, standardized image interpretation protocols, computerized comparison and storage, and sophisticated image enhancement and analysis. Over 30 years of research and 800 peer-reviewed studies encompassing well over 300,000 women participants has demonstrated thermography's abilities as a risk assessment tool in the early detection of breast cancer. Ongoing research into the thermal characteristics of breast pathologies will continue to investigate the relationships between neoangiogenesis, chemical mediators, and the neoplastic process".

Dr. Amalu continues with:

"It is unfortunate, but many physicians still hesitate to consider thermography as a useful tool in clinical practice in spite of the considerable research database, continued improvements in both thermographic technology and image analysis, and continued efforts on the part of the thermographic societies. This attitude may be due to the fact that the physical and biological bases of thermography are not familiar to most physicians. The other methods of cancer investigations refer directly to topics of medical teaching. For instance, radiography and ultrasonography refer to anatomy. Thermography, however, is based on thermodynamics and thermokinetics, which are unfamiliar to most physicians, though man is experiencing heat production and exchange in every situation he undergoes or creates".

"Considering the contribution that thermography has demonstrated thus far in the field of early cancer detection, all pos-

sibilities should be considered for promoting further technical, biological, and clinical research in this procedure".

Infrared Thermography Has its Roots in the United States Military

Now I would like to provide a bit of historical context for infrared thermography. Modern infrared imaging has improved immensely in the last 50 years, both in terms of hardware improvements, enhanced software, as well as improved techniques for ensuring uniform quality of images.

Thermography has a long history, although its use has increased dramatically with the commercial and industrial applications of the past fifty years. Firefighters use thermography to see through smoke, to find persons, and to localize the base of a fire. Maintenance technicians use thermography to locate overheating joints and sections of power lines, which are a sign of impending failure. Building construction technicians can see thermal signatures that indicate heat leaks in faulty thermal insulation and can use the results to improve the efficiency of heating and air-conditioning units.

The early infrared cameras were created mostly for the military or for civil engineers. In the beginning of the Vietnam War in the 1970s, we were losing too many soldiers from snipers in the dense jungle regions. They put infrared cameras on the helicopters and if a warm silhouette of a body was seen, the soldier on the aircraft shot at the enemy below.

Modern Infrared technology benefited and evolved rapidly following millions of dollars of military money being spent on the surface to air missile program during the Gulf War under General Secord and more recently with "Smart Infrared Helmets" on medics in the Iraq War. The Flir camera that is used in my clinic had also been used for military applications for years.

The Research Behind Breast Thermography

All the military money spent on perfecting tools for defense had a trickle-down effect for Medical Infrared.

I have included pages of peer-reviewed abstracts and article links on my other website: www.InfraredBreastHealth.com Please go to the Physicians Area where you will find two sections of compiled abstracts and articles that you can read in their entirety if you feel so inclined.

There are over 800 peer-reviewed studies on breast thermography that exist in the index-medicus literature. On my Infrared Breast Health website, there are more than forty articles to review. I have also included some of the more interesting studies on my resource digital download that is over 1,000 pages and medically indexed. This resource guide is FREE to you as part of the comprehensive *Proactive Breast Wellness* program or the *Protect Your Breasts* book or eBook. You also receive the *Waves* relaxation program as part of my "Gift of Health" to you!

I will include just a few of the research articles here for you. The articles are also available to read on my IBH website in the research section if you want to learn more (www.InfraredBreastHealth.com).

Even as long ago as 1997, in an article by John Keyserlingk, MD, a long-term infrared researcher, the mean size of tumors undetected by mammography was 1.66cm, compared to smaller 1.28 cm tumors that infrared imaging was able to detect. In the same study, they found that the 85% sensitivity rate of mammography alone in non-dense breasts in menopausal women was increased to 95% when infrared was added.

"In a study of 10,000 women screened, Gautherie found that, when applied to asymptomatic women, thermography was very useful in assessing the risk of cancer by dividing patients into low- and high-risk categories. This was based on an objective evaluation of each patient's thermograms using an improved reading protocol that incorporated 20 thermopathological factors.

"From a patient base of 58,000 women screened with thermography, Gros and associates followed 1,527 patients with initially healthy breasts and abnormal thermograms for 12 years. Of this group, 40% developed malignancies within five years. The study concluded that, 'an abnormal thermogram is the single most important marker of high risk for the future development of breast cancer".

Breast Thermography Considered Adjunctive

Nineteen years after Keyserlingk's research, infrared breast imaging is slowly becoming more accepted by allopathic medicine as an adjunctive screening tool. Thermography in the United States is primarily being used in research centers and medical schools, but is slowly expanding to other health care centers. In the American Journal of Surgery, October, 2008, researchers at Cornell Medical School cited a study of the effectiveness of digital thermography in the detection of breast cancer in 92 patients who had been advised to have biopsies as the result of prior mammography or ultrasound. Infrared identified 58 of the 60 malignancies, with a 97% sensitivity. I use the same camera in my clinical practice as was used in this Cornell study. In other studies, infrared had a 90% and a 96% sensitivity and a 90% specificity. This rivals MRIs at a fraction of the cost and may help women evaluate their breast condition.

Again, these articles are available in the research area of my IBH website.

Thermography is useful for lobular cancers and inflammatory breast cancer. As previously noted, lobular cancers are missed or undetected over 70% of the time with mammograms. In my clinical practice, I have picked up many lobular cancers that were not identified with mammograms or ultrasound that were later biopsy-proven after a positive MRI and after I sent the woman to a surgeon. Thermography is also useful for screening for inflammatory breast cancer, which is rare but deadly. Increased thermal patterns are produced in both cases of lobular and inflammatory breast cancers.

Sensitivity vs Specificity

Let me give a bit of an explanation of the terms sensitivity vs specificity and predictive value from a medical and statistics standpoint. The statistics definitions are: sensitivity is the true positive rate and specificity is the true negative rate.

What is a Sensitive Test?

The sensitivity of a test (also called the true positive rate) is defined as the proportion of people with the disease who will have a positive result. In other words, a highly sensitive test is one that correctly identifies patients with a disease. A test that is 100% sensitive will identify all patients who have the disease. It's extremely rare that any clinical test is 100% sensitive. A test with 90% sensitivity will identify 90% of patients who have the disease, but will miss 10% of patients who have the disease.

A highly sensitive test can be useful for ruling out a disease if a person has a negative result. For example, a negative result on a pap smear probably means the person does not have cervical cancer. The acronym widely used is SnNout (high Sensitivity, Negative result = rule out).

What is a Specific Test?

The specificity of a test (also called the True Negative Rate) is the proportion of people without the disease who will have a negative result. In other words, the specificity of a test refers to how well a test identifies patients who do not have a disease. A test that has 100% specificity will identify 100% of patients who do not have the disease. A test that is 90% specific will identify 90% of patients who do not have the disease and 10% of patients who do have the disease.

Tests with a high specificity (a high true negative rate) are most useful when the result is positive. A highly specific test can be useful for ruling in patients who have a certain disease. The acronym is SPin (high Specificity, rule in).

Infrared Thermography Used in Medical Oncology

In addition to cancer screening, thermography may be used as a low cost, non-invasive, easily reproducible objective tool for guiding cancer therapy, as they do at the Cleveland Clinic. They are using infrared to help assess the response of tissues to chemotherapy by imaging their patients weekly, changing their treatment regimen if the thermal patterns are not improving.

The Cleveland Clinic was using thermography in its medical oncology clinic to monitor women weekly with IR as they go through chemo. If the IR thermal patterns increase, the physicians consider another type of chemotherapy instead of continuing the full course of the current type, only to discover that the tissues had not been responding favorably. By monitoring the physiological response to therapy throughout the process, they are able to make adjustments as necessary. IR also has no side effects, is 100% safe, and is pain free for the woman. It is a great way to monitor a woman's health and progress.

Forward Thinking Breast Surgeons are Also Considering Thermography

Robert Elliot, MD, PhD, is a breast surgeon and Founder and Director of the Elliot-Elliot-Head Breast Cancer Research and Treatment Center in Baton Rouge Louisiana. Their website is www.breastoncology.com/research-institute.html.

You will find a number of research papers generated by Dr. Elliott and Dr. Head's team on breast surgery and thermography in the research section of my other website, www.InfraredBreastHealth.com.

Dr. Elliott made the following comment about thermography:

> *"The use of computerized medical infrared imaging for breast cancer detection, diagnosis, and as a high risk and prognostic indicator leads to both earlier detection of breast cancer and increases the overall survival of breast cancer patients."*

I have spoken with Dr. Head, their research director, on several occasions. Dr. Elliott's team uses infrared thermography for the majority of their patient population as part of their workup. IR aides in the decision-making process about the extensiveness of the surgical approach. Many women in Baton Rouge cannot afford an MRI as part of their workup prior to surgery.

IR assists in providing neoangiogenesis information, which indicates the blood flow leading to the surgical target. MRI and infrared can see these large dilated vessels. MRIs generally cost around $3,000 to $3,500 depending on where you are living in the US and an IR exam runs in the $160 to $225 range. If you do not happen to have insurance, you are looking at a sizeable medical fee for an MRI. If the IR shows large-caliber, trans-quadrant, dilated blood vessels, then doing a simple lumpectomy may not be suitable. The woman may need a larger amount of tissue removed. If the cancer is a DCIS, (ductal carcinoma in situ), infrared images usually look like a thermal bullet of heat over the mass but the large, dilated vessels usually have not developed yet. This is helpful information for the surgeon so he or she can better plan the surgical approach. Of course, the surgeon will also be guided by ultrasound images and mammograms.

After surgery, the Elliot-Elliot-Head Breast Cancer Research and Treatment Center team uses infrared to safely monitor their patients' progress during healing or when using various cancer therapies.

Susan Lark, Holistic Physician Also Promotes Thermography

Susan Lark, MD, a nationally-known health researcher and educator, has long been a supporter of infrared technology and has also voiced some controversial concerns about mammograms. She feels that since mammograms emit radiation, they may increase the risks of the cancers that you are trying to avoid. She also feels that mammograms deliver a high rate of false positives that can lead to unnecessary surgeries. She also made a strong statement that I will now quote.

> *"Contrary to what most people believe, mammograms do not save lives. Recent research proves this convincingly.*

The fact is, a woman's chances of dying from breast cancer are exactly the same whether she has a mammogram or not. So they are much less helpful than women are led to believe. Studies show that Thermography can increase a woman's survival rate from breast cancer by 61 percent."

Consider Bringing a Cutting Edge Infrared Thermography Camera to Your Area

I predict that infrared breast imaging will become the preferred screening tool for breast cancer in women of all ages, with secondary MRI scans for those with suspicious infrared scans or by adding the soon-to-be-available 3-D SoftVue breast ultrasound from Delphinus Medical Technologies.

The United States is not yet embracing thermography whole-heartedly but Asia and the European nations are already using thermography as a first-line screening tool. In countries with socialized medicine that have more of an interest in prevention, the current recommendations are to have a baseline breast infrared scan at age 25, then at 30, 35, then annually after age 40. Infrared thermography is the best risk detection tool available to modern medicine.

Women have an infrared scan more often (perhaps every four to six months) if they have a BI-RADS 3 probably benign mammogram or ultrasound or a suggestion that the structural exam or the thermography was suspicious. As previously mentioned, radiologists use a BI-RADS rating scale of a BI-RADS 1 through BI-RADS 6. When the radiologist does not have a clear target or there are some questionable regions on the imaging, he or she suggests that the woman return for a six-month structural study recall. Women also are screened more often if they have an abnormal TH4 or TH5 infrared report, so they can see if the PBW protocol changes they are making are positively impacting their IR images. If the vasculature is getting worse and the radiologist still does not provide a target, I usually send these women to a surgeon for a biopsy or try to get an MRI paid for. Hopefully these women will be able to do cryoablation under an "Early Freeze Protocol" in the near future.

If you are a practitioner or a woman who feels that your town would benefit from a cutting-edge FDA-cleared military infrared camera for a thermography clinic in your area, please contact us through our www.ProtectYourBreasts.com website. The camera, computer, cables, medical software package, and camera stand that I have arranged currently can be shipped in 30 days with all the national and international export licenses in place.

If you start shopping for infrared cameras, you will want to have a camera and software that can do a variety of colored images, nipple Deltas, and that also include a gray-inverted palette that will show the vessels. You will also want to have a Celsius scale on a bar on the edge of the image and be able to enlarge the photo to a full 8.5 by 11 inches. Many of the low-end, old-technology IR cameras and software will not provide an inverted gray scale and they provide images that are only about two inches across. You do not want this infrared camera set up.

Another important consideration is who will interpret the IR images and create a report for your patients. Many of the nationally or internationally certified thermologists or infrared interpreters who have 15 to 25+ years of experience will only read images from high-end military cameras. It certainly is fair to ask the thermologist how long their training was, who trained them, and how long they have been reading infrared images. If they just finished a two-weekend workshop, you may need to research further.

You do not need to be a medical provider to become a Certified Infrared Thermography Technician (CITT), but working with a medical clinic will prove helpful so that there will be a medical provider who can order imaging studies, lab work, and have prescriptive authority to assist patients with hormone replacement therapy if they are estrogen dominant or menopausal.

I have been a Nurse Practitioner for over 40 years and I am also a Certified Infrared Thermography Technician since early 2006. I have been able to provide the complete package for my patients who often travel great distances, sometimes over several states to see me.

The Marriage of Infrared Thermography and Cryoablation

I also hope to create a marriage of technologies between infrared thermography and cryoablation that I pray will be available nationally and internationally in the very near future. Cryoablation will change the face of breast cancer treatment by freezing the breast cancer with liquid nitrogen delivered through a probe in a 35-40 minute office visit that is ultrasound-guided. All that is needed is a small amount of local anesthesia injected where the probe is inserted into the breast. You can watch a short video about this cryotherapy procedure on the cryoablation page on www.ProtectYourBreasts.com.

Adding thermography would assist the doctor prior to the freezing process to see the hyperthermic area that has blood flow leading to it. Then, six to eight weeks after cryoablation and six months after the cryoablation, the woman can have a 100% safe infrared scan to make sure there is no thermal activity, the vessels leading to the tumor have shrunk or disappeared, and the cancer mass is now cold and inert on the IR scan.

I will be covering cryoablation, this utterly fabulous method to treat breast cancer, in the next chapter. It is the most exciting technology that I have come across in my 40-year medical career. I am trying to bring cryoablation clinics to the Pacific Northwest at the time of this book's publication. Please add your contact information to my newsletter link and follow us on the PBW Facebook page so that I can send you breaking news on cryoablation and cryotherapy. Please visit: www.ProtectYourBreasts.com/newsletter/ and www.facebook.com/ProactiveBreastWellness/

Other Promising Tests for Detecting New Breast Cancers

There are a couple other tests or procedures that are not related to imaging, but I will include them in this section. I feel that they are exciting and have promise and may be available more widely in the near future. There are serum tests that can now be done to assess widespread disease or to detect recurrent breast cancer, but no tests currently are available to detect new breast cancers.

Nipple Aspiration

Nipple aspiration uses a small suction cup to pump fluid from the nipple that the pathologist can check for abnormal cells. This is known as atypical hyperplasia. This safe technique is also highly accurate and it can identify cancer up to 20 years before tumors show themselves. This test was recommended by Susan Lark, MD.

Saliva Protein Assay Test

There is also research being conducted on a saliva protein assay test. Scientists are identifying markers in saliva that may indicate that a woman has breast cancer. The testing was developed by a dentist who was originally trying to detect oral cancers.

Here is the link to a National Institute of Health abstract: http://www.ncbi.nlm.nih.gov/pmc/articles/PMC2763326/.

The abstract reads, in part:

> *"Serum tumor markers, such as carcinoembryonic antigen (CEA) and CA15-3 or CA27–29, are used in current clinical practice to assess widespread disease or to detect recurrent breast cancer, but not to detect new breast cancer. Many researchers are using a number of new technologies, such as proteomics or DNA/RNA arrays, to discover novel markers in the blood. While saliva is a source of easily accessible bodily fluids, there has been very little effort to study salivary fluid. We hypothesized that a profile of angiogenic and tumor markers in saliva could be complementary to the current methods used for breast cancer diagnosis. We observed that the levels of the above proteins in the saliva are elevated in breast cancer patients in comparison to normal controls. Thus, it is possible that saliva may serve as a novel avenue in the search for breast tumor markers."*

Hopefully women will be offered a saliva test as a breast cancer screening test they can take annually to get information. If anything is positive, then they can request structural studies or a surgical consult. These saliva protein assay tests may have a much better catch rate than mammograms do and the patient just needs to spit into a test tube annually. Just imagine the amount of radiation and false positive mammograms that could be avoided by a simple saliva test.

Why Family History and Genomics Matter – Breast Cancer BRCA Gene Testing

I would like to include some information here about BRAC Gene testing as an option for women. This information comes from Color Genomics at their website www.Color.com website. There is some exciting news that BRCA Gene Testing is now made affordable at $249 as a saliva test and you can order it yourself.

So what is BRAC gene testing all about? "For example, a BRAC1 mutation may increase the chances of breast cancer up to 81% and ovarian cancer up to 54% by age 80. Mutations in the BRAC1 and BRAC2 genes are rare, found in approximately 1 in 300 individuals in the general population and in 2% of the Ashkenazi Jewish individuals – but they significantly increase the chances of cancer. Mutations in other genes are more common, but have less of an effect on the risk of developing hereditary cancer."

> *"Detecting cancer early improves the odds of survival. Knowing that you have a mutation that increases your risk of developing cancer allows you and your health care provider to create a personalized screening plan, which increases the chance of early detection. The 5-year survival rates for the cancers covered by the Color Test increase dramatically when they are caught at an earlier and more treatable stage".*

Another recent merger of resources occurred in 2016 between Quest Diagnostic and Lab Corp and several other backers. They wish to provide all women 30 years of age and older, access to having their genetics tested through Color Genomics. They are trying to make this testing inexpensive and as easy as a saliva test. The head geneticist, Mary-Claire King, PhD, who discovered the BRCA1 gene, is involved in this project. Check out this website to learn more: www.Color.com. With this test, you will not have to deal with an expensive price tag of thousands of dollars and have to fight with your insurance company to get it paid for.

> *"There is strong evidence that family history is critical for defining risk. Beyond family history, we have the ability to sequence the genes known to carry high-risk mutations. Dr. Mary-Claire King, who discovered the BRCA1 gene, has advocated that all women age 30 and older should be screened for mutations that carry a high risk for breast and ovarian cancer."*

She's right. And at some point, why not add men, who unknowingly can pass along important BRCA mutations to their daughters.

> *"We didn't have a way to widely implement such a recommendation until a few months ago when collaboration, called "BRCA Share", was reported between the two largest central lab companies, Laboratory Corporation of America (Lab Corp) and Quest Diagnostics to include a new genetic testing company called Color Genomics. For $249, Color Genomics is offering, via a saliva sample, a sequencing of the BRCA genes along with 17 other genes that carry a high risk for familial cancer. For one year of mammography costs in the United States, we could now perform such genetic testing for over 56 million women. The unrelenting plummeting of the cost of sequencing – and a much more expansive approach of testing the whole genome (instead of just less than 20 genes) – is just around the corner."*

This was exciting news for me and I hope to start networking with groups who are interested in BRAC Genes and genetic testing. If one of their goals is to assist you and your health care provider to create a personalized screening plan, that should include this *Proactive Breast Wellness* Program and *Protect Your Breasts* book and eBook plus breast thermography imaging.

The "Angelina Jolie Effect" after Her Double Mastectomy

When Angelina Jolie announced her choice to undergo bilateral mastectomy in 2013, she wrote in an op-ed in The New York Times: "But today it is possible to find out through a blood test whether you are highly susceptible to breast and ovarian cancer, and then take action. Life comes with many challenges. The ones that should not scare us are the ones we can take on and take control of." Just a couple of years later, the "Angelina Effect" on heightening awareness and the US Supreme Court decision against Myriad Genetics BRCA testing monopoly have introduced exciting opportunities for adopting a new approach. We shouldn't be scared of it. The genetic testing doesn't even require a blood test anymore. We should take it on, study it, and exploit the progress in genomic science to develop an intelligent, evidence-based, and economically attractive, precise path forward.

I would like to bring up a word of caution to women who may want to become a follower of the "Angelina Jolie Effect" if they have a strong family history or happen to be BRAC Gene positive. They also need to remember that genes may be turned on or off and that their immune system has a huge impact on the outcome of disease prevention. Surgery may not actually be the answer to your breast cancer fears.

Having a Double Mastectomy Will Not Protect You 100% from Breast Cancer

A woman came to see me recently after she had had a double mastectomy after discovering she was BRCA gene positive and had a strong family history of breast cancer. She did not have any pathology from the biopsied samples from the removed breast tissue. She told me she was upset by her surgeon's comments at her last visit following her reconstruction surgery. She had asked the physician if the double mastectomy that she had just undergone would provide 100% certainty for not getting breast cancer in the future. Her doctor had shrugged and said that there is usually about 15% residual breast tissue remaining in the tail of the breast extending towards the armpit and along the chest wall. A double mastectomy could not remove all the breast tissue, so the surgeon could not give her a guarantee that she would never develop breast cancer in the future.

This woman said she wished that she had known about infrared thermography prior to her mastectomies. She was glad that she was able to come to see me and be instructed on what the *Proactive Breast Wellness* program had to offer her and her other family members. PBW could help to reduce her risk of breast cancer or its reoccurrence in other women with breast cancer.

Another Option for BRCA Gene Positive Women

In the summer of 2015, I was invited to meet Kathryn Murray, the head genetics counselor at Peace Health Hospital here in Eugene Oregon. Kathryn Murray is one of the first genetic counselors in the US and has practiced over 25 years since 1989 as a specialist in BRCA gene testing and testing for other genetic diseases. She has held positions at major medical teaching facilities on the East Coast and in the Midwest, with several publications of her research over several decades. She moved to Eugene to be closer to family and we are grateful for the medical expertise that she now provides in the Pacific Northwest.

A number of her BRCA gene positive women had also been to my thermography clinic here in Eugene and she was interested in discussing thermography as a technology. She also wanted to know what my *Proactive Breast Wellness* education program provided to decrease breast cancer risk. She wanted to see how this might assist her population of BRCA gene positive patients.

Murray discussed how women who now learn that they are BRCA gene positive were considering undergoing a double mastectomy out of fear. We discussed using infrared thermography to monitor these women in a 100% safe way. Infrared thermography is able to observe the physiological / metabolic activity in the breast as part of other approaches to follow these women since they were at greater risk to develop breast cancer. If the IR scans remain negative, these women would be encouraged to do an infrared examination annually and hence save them from choosing to undergo a double mastectomy and potentially removing two healthy breasts.

Murray also pointed out the statistical risk curves of developing breast cancer over time as a BRCA gene positive woman vs. the statistical curve over time of a US woman in the general population. She stated that the *Proactive Breast Wellness* program might well help decrease the risk curve for these women carrying a genetic marker because it could assist the at-risk women to become more empowered. Since genetics only contributes about seven percent to nine percent of your risk, there is a possibility that 91% to 93% of the risk may be altered by things that you can do to improve your health. The PBW program can teach women that they can do something, through diet, limiting environmental toxins where it is possible in their environments, getting their hormones adjusted, getting on a supplement program, and making other lifestyle and stress management changes. This gives a lot of hope to women, their daughters, and their families.

Kathryn Murray felt that all these positive actions that the PBW program and the *Protect Your Breasts* book would encourage, could alter the BRCA gene positive women's risk rates over time and might well extend the time into later in life that these women might develop breast cancer.

Here is another source that Kathryn Murray suggested to further your quest on BRCA gene research. Please look up *Facing Our Risk of Cancer Empowered* or FORCE at http://www.facingourrisk.org/index.php.

CHAPTER 9

Cryosurgery or Cryoablation: The Future of Breast Cancer Treatment

A Short History

Cryoablation, also called cryosurgery, cryotherapy or targeted cryoablation therapy, refers to the application of extreme cold to destroy diseased tissue, including cancer cells.

PubMed offers this background.

> *"The use of freezing temperatures for the therapeutic destruction of tissue began in England in 1845–51 when Dr. James Arnott described the use of iced salt solutions (about minus 20 degrees C) to freeze advanced cancers in accessible sites, producing reduction in tumor size and amelioration of pain. Improved freezing techniques were possible early in the 1990s when solidified carbon dioxide came into use and later when liquid nitrogen and nitrous oxide became available. Nevertheless, cryotherapy was a minor technique, used only for the accessible lesions of skin and mucosa. With the development of modern cryosurgical apparatus by Cooper in 1961, a resurgence of interest in cryosurgery was initiated and techniques for diverse clinical conditions, including visceral or abdominal cancer, evolved. After the initial widespread clinical trials*

matured in the 1970s, some applications of the technique fell into disuse while others became standard treatment. Late in the 1980s, further improvements in apparatus and imaging techniques have permitted increased clinical use in neoplastic disease, including visceral cancer."

Cryotherapy has been used for cervical abnormalities in females as standard of care for at least 40 years. Cryotherapy is used to destroy skin tumors, precancerous skin moles, nodules, skin tags, or unsightly freckles. With the improvement of imaging techniques and the development of devices to better control extreme temperatures, physicians are using cryotherapy as a treatment for patients with breast cancer as well as other forms of cancer including liver which usually metastasized from other organs, and cancer of the lungs, kidneys, prostate, and pancreas. From a technical perspective, breast cancers are much easier to freeze since the tumor is sitting in fatty tissues with very few large blood vessels or large nerve tracts to get in the way.

The cryotherapy technique can also be used as an alternative to surgery for women with breast fibroadenomas. Fibroadenomas frequently cause pain and can become quite large. They are usually more of a problem in younger women, but most women worry about a lump within the breast. Cryoablation is a simple approach to these concerns of fibroadenomas. An article by Dr. Peter Littrup et al entitled "Cryotherapy for Breast Fibroadenomas" in the journal Radiology, August 2004, concluded that "Cryotherapy of fibroadenomas is safe, effective and virtually painless done as an outpatient procedure as a treatment option with good cosmetics."

I have posted several clinical studies in the cryoablation section of my website www.ProtectYourBreasts.com. Please share this site with your friends, family and doctor. I have videos there as well.

Over the past ten years, I have been dealing with 42 radiology centers in Oregon, Washington, California, and Idaho. My favorite radiologist, Dr. Cindy Tortorelli, who is now at EPIC Imaging in Portland, Oregon, previously had been freezing fibroadenomas for over a decade at the Mayo Clinic where she worked in the women's breast imaging department. I hope that in the near future, Dr. Tortorelli will be able to bring more cryoablation equipment to Portland, Oregon, so I will have a trained radiologist available to whom I can send patients for fibroadenomas and breast cancers. As of January 2020, the Good Samaritan/ Legacy Health Surgical Oncology Department was the first to purchase cryoablation equipment in the state of Oregon!

How I Became Interested in Cryoablation and The Cryo Pioneers

I hope cryoablation will become a worldwide standard of care for breast cancer. The technology is also called cryosurgery, cryotherapy or cryoablation.

I was fortunate enough to work with two women who had this procedure done by Dr. Peter Littrup, an interventional radiologist who at the time was at the Karmanos Cancer Center in Detroit, Michigan. Dr. Peter Littrup is now at Crittenton Hospital in Rochester, Michigan, as of spring 2017, and I am in contact with him as well.

Laura Ross-Paul is the "Patient pioneer" of cryoablation and she received her cryotherapy treatment in 2003 at the Karmanos Cancer Center in midtown Detroit, Michigan, one of 41 National Cancer Institute's designated Comprehensive Cancer Centers in the U.S. and the only hospital in Michigan dedicated exclusively to fighting cancer. Laura is the first woman internationally in the modern era to have her breast cancer frozen. Years earlier, Dr. Peter Littrup had received FDA approval for a device that he first invented and used to freeze prostate cancer using liquid nitrogen. Alex Paul, Laura's husband, contacted Dr. Littrup and asked if they could come see Dr. Littrup and asked if cryotherapy could be used for the two biopsy proven breast cancers with which Laura had been diagnosed. Dr. Littrup said it had never been done before but it was a good application for cryoablation, and he told them to fly to Detroit. Thank goodness for out of the box thinking!

Laura Ross-Paul has co-written a book with her husband, Alex Paul, and her cancer physician, Dr. Littrup, titled *They're Mine and I'm Keeping Them*, which documents the story of how she and her husband bucked the system and found Dr. Littrup, whose advanced skill in the field of cryoablation ultimately saved her breast. Review and purchase her book by clicking on the book link above.

What is Cryoablation or Cryosurgery All About? Dr. Dennis Holmes Explains the Technology

I was fortunate to get to know Dr. Dennis Holmes, breast cancer surgeon, researcher, and a leader in the field of cryoablation based in Los Angeles. He was kind enough to review my entire book and has made excellent revisions to my cryoablation chapter and provides the following perspective.

"Now let us get back to discussing what cryoablation or cryotherapy is all about. Cryoablation has two main goals: 1) complete ablation or killing of the tumor to eliminate the need for surgery, and 2) stimulation of the immune system to evoke auto-immunity to the cancer. The degree to each of these goals is accomplished depends upon a number of factors that are not guaranteed and only partially understood."

"There is a large body of evidence that cryoablation is capable of killing various types of cancer. However, the key requirement for successful cryoablation is a well-defined tumor that can be accurately targeted. Unfortunately, the complete extent of a breast cancer might not always be detectable on mammography, ultrasound, MRI, or thermography. This is especially true for non-invasive breast cancer or ductal carcinoma in situ (DCIS), which is typically invisible unless it is associated with microcalcifications or a mass. DCIS co-exists with most invasive breast cancer and may also extend a few millimeters or more beyond the main cancer mass. There might also be small, undetectable areas of invasive cancer outside the main tumor. Unlike surgery, which permits microscopic examination of the surgical margins to determine if cancer extends beyond the visible tumor, cryoablation does not permit microscopic examination of the tissue surrounding the visible tumor. Consequently, when cryoablation is performed for breast cancer, doctors intentionally freeze an area 1–2 cm beyond the visible tumor with the hope that undetectable DCIS and / or invasive cancer in the perimeter of the main tumor will be ablated or killed along with the visible tumor—a result that cannot always be guaranteed."

> *"One of the major misconceptions with cryoablation is that it completely replaces the need for radiation or other treatments. Even with lumpectomy and clear margins, radiation is usually recommended to treat undetected residual disease in the surrounding breast, skin, or lymph nodes. In fact, the addition of radiation to surgery is generally associated with a 60% reduction in the risk of recurrence in the breast and lymph node area, and anti-estrogen medications may reduce the risk of estrogen-sensitive tumors by an additional 50%. Similarly, many patients treated with cryoablation would also benefit from radiation and*

anti-estrogen therapy. Women certainly have the right to refuse one or more of these additional treatments. However, they should be reminded that the primary intent of cryoablation is to replace surgery, and other measures may be needed to minimize their risk of recurrence."

"The second main goal of cryoablation is to induce an immune response that might provide immunity to the cancer and prevent growth of residual or future disease in the breast, lymph nodes, or elsewhere. This is very much a goal, but the extent to which this occurs in the average breast cancer patient has yet to be fully established. Most of the evidence supporting the immune benefits of cryoablation has been demonstrated in animal studies performed under controlled conditions which might not represent what happens in humans. Although the vast majority of animal studies demonstrate stimulation of the immune system by cryoablation, a few studies show immune suppression. There have also been numerous anecdotal reports of immune system stimulation in humans, resulting in regression of metastatic tumors following ablation of the primary tumors. However, there are also numerous examples in humans when regression of distant metastatic sites did not occur. What IS clear from these conflicting observations is that we still have a lot to learn about the natural human immune response to cryoablation. We also have a lot to learn about how to amplify this immune response, perhaps using drugs or immune system stimulants, to achieve a more predictable and sustained anti-cancer immune response."

"The unpredictable nature of the immune response to cryoablation, and specifically, whether or not it is strong enough to immunize a woman against her breast cancer, provides a cautionary note to those who hope and believe

that cryoablation eliminates the need for adjuvant therapy, namely anti-estrogen therapy, anti-HER2/neu targeted therapy or chemotherapy. Even when lumpectomy and radiotherapy are performed, we rely upon anti-cancer medications to kill or inhibit the growth of undetectable tumor cells that might have metastasized to other parts of the body. The same principle applies to cryoablation. In fact, the common misperception among patients that cryoablation replaces all other forms of adjuvant therapy (i.e., radiation and medication therapy) is one of the major factors that impairs acceptance of cryoablation by the larger medical community."

"Thus, until we have a better handle on how to predict the immune response to cryoablation, the safest way forward is for women not to abandon anti-cancer medications completely as a means of controlling distant cancer spread. This is not to say that anti-estrogen therapy and/or chemotherapy will completely eliminate the risk of recurrence. Cancers may evolve and develop resistance to these treatments, but the immune systemic is also imperfect. If the immune system were perfect, the cancer would not have developed in the first place. Therefore, the best strategy might be to combine the benefits of anti-cancer medications and cryoablation, along with other recurrence risk-reducing measures discussed in this book, to provide the most comprehensive cancer treatment."

I was really delighted that Dr. Dennis Holmes was willing to review my chapter on cryoablation. In our discussions, one of the things that he felt would be important on the topic of immune response was the material in my *Protect Your Breasts* book / eBook. He stated that anything that could improve the health of the "Host," which in this case is the health of the woman, would improve how her immune system functions:

eating organically, avoiding bovine growth hormone and toxins, natural estrogen blockade, a healthy lifestyle and stress management.

Now I would like to transition to materials by Laura Ross-Paul. As an example of a best-case scenario, here is a short overview of what we hope cryoablation will accomplish with regard to stimulation of an immune response. This is taken from *They're Mine and I'm Keeping Them*. Check out Laura Ross-Paul's book for yourself on my website.

She writes:

> *"The body's immune system is able to recognize the protein structure of the cancer cells when it cleans out the dead tissue, and in about half the cases of cryoablation, naturally creates an immunity to the cancer. The book also relates the success at FUDA Hospital in Guangzhou, China in treating a variety of Stage 4 cancers by combining cryoablation and advanced immune system therapies, which increase the frequency of the occurrence of the natural immune effect to approximately eighty percent or higher of the breast cancer cases."*

Her book goes on to describe the typical cryoablation procedure:

> *"Cryoablation is used in a variety of clinical applications using hollow needles or cryoprobes through which cooled, thermally conductive, liquid nitrogen is circulated. Local anesthesia is administered to the surface of the breast and then cryoprobes are inserted into or placed adjacent to tissue that is determined to be diseased in such a way that ablation will provide correction yielding benefit to the patient." "When the probes are in place, the cryogenic freezing occurs from the tip of the probe and by extension freezes the surrounding tissues containing the tumor."*

Dr. Dennis Holmes, a breast surgeon and cryoablation specialist, has provided the following information:

"Cryoablation kills cancers using two alternating freezing and thawing cycles which accomplish tumor kill via five mechanisms:

1. **Osmotic injury**
2. **Mechnical injury**
3. **Vascular injury**
4. **Apoptosis or programmed cell death**
5. **Immunogenic injury**

Osmotic injury

Rapid and sustained freezing of the tumor initially causes freezing of water and ice crystal formation in the extracellular space or the spaces between cells, which dehydrates the extracellular space. Dehydration of the extracellular space concentrates the electrolytes and proteins between the cells, which creates an osmotic gradient that forces water to flow from the interior of the inside the cells (which have yet to freeze) to the extracellular space to restore the water balance outside the cells. Forced withdrawal of water from within the cells causes the cells to shrink and crinkle, creating cracks in the cell membrane or cell wall. During the subsequent thaw cycle, ice crystals in the extracellular space thaw and dilute the electrolytes and proteins between the cells. This forces the excess extracellular water to flow back into the cells that are now relatively dehydrated compared to the extracellular space. This flow of water back into the cells causes them to swell and then rupture because the cell walls have been damaged from prior shrinkage. As it turns out, the killing effect of a long thaw cycle seems to be as important as the killing effect of a long, cold freeze cycle.

Mechanical injury

Although ice crystal formation is one of the earliest changes during the freeze cycle, colder, rapid and sustained freezing causes formation of large ice crystals inside of the cells, which directly damages intracellular structures, like the DNA-containing nuclei, energy-generating mitochondria, and intracellular cytoskeletons that help to maintain cell shape. With each subsequent cycle of freezing, the damaged tissue conducts the freezing with increasing efficiency, which progressively increases the diameter of the cryoablation zone.

Vascular injury

Cancer cells rely on blood vessels to deliver oxygen and nutrients and eliminate waste. During cryoablation, small and medium sized vessels within and surrounding the tumor are killed in very much that same way that cancer cells are killed. In addition, damage to the lining of the blood vessels causes clot formation in the vessels feeding the tumor, which further deprives the cancer cells of oxygen and nutrition, a combination of events that contributes to tumor kill. In addition, restoration of blood flow around the cryoablation zone after thawing releases chemicals called free radicals that reinjure the vessel lining which causes further clot formation. Taking aspirin within 10 days of cryoablation might inhibit platelets that are essential for clot formation, so this is not advised.

Apoptosis or programmed cell death

The tumor next to the cryoprobe in the center of the cryoablation zone reaches the coldest temperature, as low as –180°C. However, the temperature near the outer portions of the cryoablation zone and farther from the cryoprobe do not reach such a low, direct tumor-killing temperature. Nevertheless, "warmer" sub-lethal temperatures in the range of 6°C to –10°C are capable of activating enzymes within the cancer cells that destroy the intracellular proteins and DNA. This phenomenon, called apoptosis or programmed cell death, essentially causes the cancer cells to commit suicide. Programmed cell death from cold temperature has been exploited as a weight loss method by plastic surgeons, who now employ a new technology called CoolSculpting®, that uses cold temperatures in the range of 4°C to induce apoptosis of fat cells.

Immunogenic injury

Although the strength and duration of a generalized, systemic immune response remains to be fully understood, experimental studies show that abnormal cancer cell proteins are capable of inducing an immune response at the tumor site in three key ways:

1) uptake of abnormal tumor proteins by granulocytes, monocytes, and macrophages that stimulate formation of antibodies (and possibility immunity) that bind to cancer cells and target them for attack by T-cells;
2) uptake of abnormal tumor proteins by antigenic presenting cells like dendritic cells and macrophages that directly stimulate T-cells to attack the cancer as foreign cells;
3) killing of cancer cells prevents them from producing "checkpoint proteins" that bind to nearby T-cells and function as a brake on the immune system that prevents it from attacking the tumor. There is now a whole new field of immunotherapy focused on developing immune checkpoint protein inhibitor drugs to turn off the brake that some cancers place on the immune system."

Laura Ross-Paul's book describes the tumor checkpoint phenomenon in a different way:

> *"Cancer survives in the body by camouflaging itself from the immune system. After a tumor is frozen, the body absorbs the dead tissue. The protein structure of the tumor remains intact after freezing, so the immune system can "see" the cancer and recognize that it is a foreign body. When it does, this potentially triggers a complex immune process that often builds antibodies to the cancer. These antibodies might kill other tumors throughout the body. This is the Immune Effect."*

I have demonstrated this to my own infrared patients by holding the fist of one hand up against the palm of my other hand. I then tell the woman that the fist represents the cancer which is a parasite and living off the organ that it has invaded, represented in this case, by my palm. My body cannot "See" the cancer, and it continues to provide oxygen and nutrition to this parasitic cancer. However, once the cancer has been frozen with liquid nitrogen, the body and your immune system can recognize this foreign invader and destroys it.

Dr. Littrup has been doing clinical studies using this technology to freeze breast cancer tumors since 2003 using liquid nitrogen to freeze the tumor in place. This therapy completely conserves the breast without the need for surgery. Cryoablation kills the cancer and theoretically may kill satellite breast cancers in other regions IF an adequate immune response develops. If the tumor should return in the perimeter of the original cancer, for example in an area that was not previously detected and cryoablated, then cryotherapy may be repeated to treat the new area.

I have become friends with Laura Ross-Paul, and she and I are trying to network and raise awareness of this life and breast-saving technology. We are also trying to bring cryoablation to the Pacific Northwest at the time of publication of this book. I have expanded my website www.ProtectYourBreasts.com to have a whole section on cryoablation as well as interesting articles and abstracts.

I have also been sending women to other clinics that are providing cryoablation so they can get the care that they desire until we have more cryoablation units here in Oregon, Washington, and across the rest of the U.S. If you are reading this book and have breast cancer, you may contact me to do a medical consult via telemedicine to see if you would be a candidate for a cryoablation clinical trial going on in different clinics across the U.S. right now. Reach me at:

Contact@ProactiveBreastWellness.com

Information From the Fuda Hospital Brochure entitled "How to Treat a Cancer Patient"

The Fuda Hospital in Guangzhou, China, provides this brochure to patients. These quotes are authorized by a team of doctors and scientists at Jinan University School of Medicine and the Fuda Cancer Hospital. This is a direct quote from the brochure. I think this is helpful to see why cancer is considered by many to be a chronic disease.

> *"Cancer is a systemic disease with tumors as a local manifestation of the disease. Once cancer occurs in a person, cancerous cells may metastasize (spread) throughout the whole body. Surgical removal of the tumors in no way implies that one is cured of cancer. For example, breast cancer can relapse even if the original tumors were removed."*

> *"Like hypertension and diabetes, cancer is a chronic disease. The disease may take a few years to manifest itself, from its occurrence until the emergence of tumors. In some cases,*

cancer cells may exist in a stage of dormancy and never manifest themselves."

"Our immune system plays an important role in controlling the development of cancer. Cancer cells may either be killed by immune cells or if they are as strong as the immune cells, nothing happens in the body. However, if the amount of immune cells decreases, leading to a decrease in their activity levels, or if cancerous cells are able to evade the detection of immune cells (a process known as immune tolerance), then the cancerous cells will spread rapidly and become life threatening."

"Influenced by various factors inside and outside the body, a series of genes mutate continuously so tumors are formed. Though cancer patients may be suffering from the same cancer, their pathogenic factors and mutational genes differ. Every tumor has its specific biological features, or heterogeneity. Ignoring the heterogeneity is the main reason that cancer treatments often cannot achieve their ideal effects. It will work better if more personalized treatment is prescribed to deal with the heterogeneity."

"The complete cryoablation of the tumor is done to minus 160-degrees Centigrade or lower. Later the temperature is raised to 20 to 45 degrees C with warm packs. This is repeated two or three times resulting in the complete ablation of the tumor. After cancer cells have been destroyed by the cryoablation they are left intact. Dead cancer cells will release antigens stimulating the immune system to eradicate any remaining cancer cells and reduce recurrence of cancer."

This "Immune Effect" I feel is far superior to just surgery alone or surgery with radiation or chemotherapy which damages the immune system. Your own body is quite clever in trying to heal itself. The issue Dr. Holmes points out is that there has not been dedicated research to date on how often and in what percentage the immune response actually occurs following cryoablation.

He told me that he hopes that he and the other cryoablation clinics will start collecting that data in the next couple years.

Some Other Interesting Articles on Cryoablation

In order to try to keep up with new research as it is made available in the future, I will be posting articles and links on my website so you may review the current literature at www.ProtectYourBreasts.com. Please sign up for our newsletter and on our Facebook page so we may send you new research once it is available.

This interesting article in *Annals of Surgical Oncology* is posted on my website. The article was published on July 2016, and is entitled "Exploring the Success of Cryoablation Therapy in the Treatment of Invasive Breast Cancer." There were 86 women in the study, and 92% of them had a successful ablation of their tumors up to 2 cm. It showed 100% effectiveness in tumors 1 cm or less.

My Personal Thermography Observations of a Woman Pre- and Post-Cryoablation

I invite you to view the first known infrared images of a patient, Mary L., who came for a thermography scan prior to having cryoablation done on her left breast by Dr. Peter Littrup on 4-27-2010. Please visit my website at www.ProtectYourBreasts.com in the cryoablation section. There are YouTube and Webinar links for you so you can follow along with the images as I describe the case.

Mary L. Infiltrating Ductal Carcinoma Three Months Pre-Cryoablation

I personally came to be introduced to the cryoablation technology in 2010, prior to meeting Laura Ross-Paul. A woman named Mary L., who lived in the Portland, Oregon area, wanted to come to see me to do a thermography study. Mary came to me early in 2010 after being diagnosed in December 2009 by needle biopsy with an infiltrating ductal carcinoma Stage II tumor in her left breast at 12:00 that was two cm by two cm in dimension by breast MRI with and without contrast (1-29-10). Mary had a very abnormal thermogram with a two-degree Celsius Delta thermal shift over the mass and blood flow leading to the tumor that I was able to palpate.

The size of the tumor was also substantiated by a previous ultrasound done prior to her needle biopsy. A left axillary lymph node had a lobulated and thickened cortex. Pre-cryoablation, she had dimpling above the left nipple at 12:00 and a mass as noted above with increased caliber vessels leading to the area of her tumor. The red circle surrounds the region of the tumor, which was warmer (as indicated by the Celsius scale to the right if you are looking at the TED Talk slides on my website www.ProtectYourBreasts.com under the Cryoablation videos. (Please view these slides now so you can follow along).

Remember from an earlier section of this book that I mentioned that when infiltrating ductal carcinomas as well as lobular cancers achieve a certain size, the cancer cells start emitting nitric oxide, which is a vasodilator that keeps the blood vessels open so tumors have greater access to oxygen and nutrition, which then encourages tumor doubling times. You can see these vascular changes by following the link to the slides on my website in the "Save Your Breasts" section.

Mary had refused standard surgery, radiation, and chemotherapy, and she had been able to be seen in Detroit at the Karmanos Cancer Center by Dr. Littrup, after she had contacted Laura Ross-Paul to find out about this technology. Mary's cryoablation procedure took about 35 minutes in an office with an ultrasound machine. The cryoablation was done with local anesthesia. A hollow probe was inserted into the tumor, guided by ultrasound and liquid nitrogen flowed through the probe to create an ice ball extending two cm out beyond the tumor margin in a 360-degree freeze zone. Warm compresses were applied shortly afterwards to melt the ice ball. Dr. Littrup froze the tumor and any suspicious lymph nodes that were seen by ultrasound.

After the procedure, Mary went out for lunch with her daughter and later in the day took two Tylenol. Pretty amazing! Dr. Littrup told me that some women do not even take the day off and go back to their offices after the procedure.

Since cryoablation is using extreme cold, this freezing also acts as a cold cautery and any small blood vessels are shut off due to the freezing, so there is little bleeding, but perhaps some bruising. In addition, the freezing has an additional numbing effect, so many women have said that the cryoablation was much less uncomfortable than a needle or core biopsy.

Mary L. Infiltrating Ductal Carcinoma Eight Months Post-Cryoablation

I saw Mary again for a thermogram eight months after the cryoablation, and the mass was now large and spongy and the region was 4 cm by 6.5 cm across. On this exam, there was no thermal activity over the soft spongy mass, and the blood vessels that were observed three months prior to her cryotherapy procedure that were leading to the tumor were now absent.

If you now continue to view Mary's slides you can see the pointer views on the infrared images that demarcate the borders of the spongy mass, which was 4 cm by 6.5cm. The thickened area is blue and scanned cold or was hypothermic on IR.

At first, I was alarmed by the size of the soft spongy mass since it had doubled in one direction and tripled in the other direction. The hard mass previously had been 2 cm by 2 cm. However, I later learned from Dr. Dennis Holmes that the appearance of a larger mass at the cryoablation zone is explained by the fact that the iceball that typically forms during cryoablation is oval in shape, with the longest dimension formed along the long axis of the cryoprobe. Thus, the 4 cm (across) X 6.5 cm (long) dimensions of the cryoablation zone correspond to the volume of tissue, including the tumor and surrounding margins, that was treated with cryoablation.

Mary L. Two Years Post-Cryoablation

I saw Mary again two years after the cryotherapy and the residual tumor was now only 1.5 cm and had become a thermally inactive, cold, inert mass of scar tissue without any blood flow or neoangiogenesis leading to the area shown in the red circle on the post cryoablation slides. Resolution of the 4 cm X 6.5 cm mass comes about through a natural process of healing, which brings neutrophils and macrophages to the cryoablation zone to clear away damaged tissues. The initial healing response also attracts fibroblasts that eventually fill the cryoablation zone with collagen. The spongy mass shrinks about 80% in size leaving a small bit of scar tissue. Scar tissue on infrared scans cold since there is no thermal activity. Mary was also instructed to follow the *Proactive Breast Wellness* protocol. These cryoablation results were amazing to me! Please share the slides and information on my website with as many people as possible!

Why Aren't We Hearing About Cryoablation?

You must be saying to yourself, "Why on earth have I not heard about cryotherapy or cryoablation from my doctor or oncologist? Why haven't you seen information on the news? If cryoablation works so well at killing off breast cancer cells, why does no one know about this?"

Cryotherapy to treat malignant breast tumors is still considered experimental even after 17 years since Laura's first case in 2003 and thousands of women treated in China and other countries internationally and even though there is very little risk of harming anyone using this technology. The ice ball created around the tumor simply melts.

I personally feel the reason cryoablation is not being embraced is that it works too well and it would be taking money away from the "Cancer machine" by which physicians make more money when people are ill. There is little incentive to do a 30 to 50-minute office visit with ultrasound to freeze a cancer that might never come back again. U.S. medicine is an illness-based system, not a prevention-based system. Women are the pawns on the allopathic medical chess board.

I recently conducted a local survey here in Eugene, Oregon, when a fee-for-service patient of mine without any insurance wanted to know what a simple mastectomy might cost her and her family. She had a very abnormal thermogram and I had begun to send her through the system to get structural studies done, a biopsy, and a surgical consult. When she asked me how much it would cost, I did not know, so I started calling offices at the hospital to find out. It was eye opening for me.

I called the following offices: radiology to get the costs for mammogram and ultrasound; pathology to find out about the cost of needle and excisional biopsy samples. Then I called one of the local surgical groups to find out about the costs for the surgical consult prior to surgery, the surgical procedure itself, and post-op visits. Then I called the anesthesia department to get the pre-surgery anesthesiology visit charge and cost for the anesthesiologist's services during surgery. Then I called outpatient day surgery and asked also what it would cost for hospital facility fees if there was an overnight stay, plus post-op care in the recovery area, IVs, medications, etc. After all these calls, I discovered a simple mastectomy in Eugene, Oregon, ranged between $57,000 and $57,500! These fees may be higher in other regions of the U.S. I was shocked and amazed to know how much this would cost this farmer's wife who was home schooling her kids, and who currently had no insurance!

As a postscript in this case, I want to let the readers know that I also contacted the hospital social services department, and after several phone calls, I was able to get this woman enrolled in the Oregon Health Plan / ObamaCare so that her upcoming breast cancer treatment would not bankrupt her and her family.

Unfortunately, this financial forecast of what breast cancer costs a woman is not yet complete. Now these previously mentioned medical / surgical fees do not take into consideration what might come next for this woman if she were sent to medical oncology for chemotherapy or radiation oncology or, worst case scenario, to both departments if she had an invasive cancer with positive lymph nodes. This woman might also be put on estrogen blockers like Tamoxifen and be subject to the costs and medical oversight that go along with that. This was harder for me to estimate, but several of my client cancer survivors who had gone that route told me that, conservatively, that might total another $50,000 or

$60,000 or more on top of the surgery. You might easily be up over $110,000 to over $120,000 to treat your breast cancer! You can now see why I have been so passionate about promoting "Prevention IS the Cure!" after learning the financial strain as well as the emotional and physical suffering a woman and her family go through after being handed a breast cancer diagnosis.

Will Insurance Companies Pay to Freeze Your Breast Cancer?

Depending on whether you can get into a cryoablation clinical trial in this country, you might currently be looking at $2,800 to $7,500 for your short cryo out-patient office visit which includes the cryo probe cost. Several of the cryo-clinics are still trying to bill insurance for the procedure. Since cryoablation is still "investigational/ experimental" for breast cancer patients, insurance companies may not want to pay for it currently, which I think will start to change. Insurance companies might pay $2,800 for the fibroadenoma CPT code, but you cannot use the fibroadenoma code for a breast cancer even if it will likely take the same amount of time to do as an office visit with the same equipment. The procedures to treat breast cancer and fibroadenomas are not exactly the same, but very similar.

This lack of attention by insurance companies has begun to anger me and I hope there are a few women who are reading this book who are willing to start taking some action to change this insurance ruling. The insurance companies' position to not recognize cryoablation for breast cancer severely harms women and prevents us from getting the care for our breast cancers that we want and need.

I think we as women need to approach some feisty militant women's groups that will take action and force this into the spotlight. I think it also could be framed as a human rights/ women's rights issue. A man can appear at the office of a urologist pretty much anywhere in the country and have his prostate cancer frozen by cryoablation and the insurance company pays for the procedure using the CPT code for freezing his prostate cancer. At the time of the third edition of the publication of this book in January of 2020, I am told that Medicare may be considering some new CPT codes for cryoablation for breast cancers. Historically once Medicare starts to embrace new CPT codes the other insurances begin to follow.

Currently they have a CPT code for freezing fibroadenomas but not for freezing a breast cancer, so the local insurances are for the most part not recognizing cryoablation yet, but I think this is on the cusp of a national change. They have been paying to freeze cervixes for over 40 years, but not breast cancer.

If men can have their prostate cancers frozen, why can't women have their breast cancers treated by the same technology that works so well for the men? Breast cryoablation now has a 17-year history since the first case in 2003. Why should it still be "Investigational"? The Chinese are setting up clinics all over their country and have done thousands of successful treatments.

Just two months prior to this book's publication, I learned that insurances in five states had begun to pay for breast cryoablation some of the time. These states are: Florida, Alabama, Texas, Michigan and Georgia. The insurances that are paying are: Medicare, United Health Care, Cigna, Aetna and Blue Cross/ Blue Shield. This procedure will save the insurance companies thousands of dollars that they are currently paying out for "Standard of care costs for breast cancer." So my hope is that once there are more cryoablation clinics available to more women in more states, there will be more insurances paying for this treatment. I think the other point is the huge difference in what the insurance company has to pay out for treating one case of breast cancer. I imagine they might decide that $2,800 to $7,500 looks a lot more cost effective than the cost of lumpectomy or mastectomy. Having more women demand these services through their own insurance carriers, I think will also promote change.

Dr. Holmes recently provided this information regarding insurance:

> *"Fortunately, effective January 2020, a new Category III CPT code (0581 T) goes into effect for cryoablation of breast cancers. The "T" in the code indicates that this is a temporary code created as a means to track the frequency of cryoablation procedures performed for breast cancer. Temporary codes do not have an assigned reimbusement value, which means that reimbursement, if any, is determined by the health plan. As with most T codes, the utilization of the code is tracked over a period of 2–3 years before Medicare assigns a reimbursement value to the code that becomes a reference value for use by other health plans."*

Minimally Invasive Breast Cancer Cryotherapy Largely Ignored in U.S.

I have taken a couple portions from the Breast Cancer News article March 29, 2016, by Charles Moore after interviewing Laura Ross-Paul. This article is also available on my website. This Breast Cancer News article was also the most reposted article in all of 2016 on their site, so you can see that there is tremendous interest in this! Laura and I were delighted that we are beginning to get some traction in the journals, but we obviously need more exposure in the media. If you are reading this and feel that you or an organization that you know may assist in championing this, please contact us! Find me at: Contact@ProactiveBreastWellness.com This may require a "Grassroots women's movement" to promote this technology.

A Real Life Example of Barriers to Adoption of Cryoablation

The following is a letter to the editor written by Dr. Dennis Holmes in response to a November 2019, *Desert Sun* newspaper article regarding a surgeon in Palm Springs, California, who was placed on probation by the California Medical Board related to offering cryoablation or "tumor freezing" to women seeking an alternative to surgery for early stage breast cancer.

> *As a breast cancer surgeon, researcher and patient advocate, I feel it necessary to challenge the negative impressions that the article creates regarding cryoablation, the surgeon, and the significant number of women seeking alternatives to "traditional" surgical treatment.*
>
> *Although cryoablation is new to most readers, the procedure has served a role in the management of cancer for decades. For example, cryoablation has long been used to treat pre-cancerous growths of the cervix and is now increasingly used for treatment of early stage prostate cancer. I began performing breast cryoablation in 2003, initially as a treatment of benign breast tumors called fibroadenoma, and later beginning in 2009 for early stage breast cancer as part of a national clinical trial sponsored by the American College of Surgeons.*
>
> *The American College of Surgeons trial found cryoablation to be 100% effective at killing invasive breast tumors that*

were 1 cm or smaller and 92% effective for tumors up to 2 cm. As a result of the lessons learned from that trial, two additional national trials were launched evaluating cryoablation as an alternative to surgery for early stage breast cancer. Currently, the early results of both trials are promising and I am honored to serve as lead principal investigator of one of them, the FROST Trial (http://clinicaltrials.gov/ct2/show/NCT01992250).

Internationally, the most promising breast cancer cryoablation experience comes from Japan where a respected surgeon has treated more than 300 women with estrogen-sensitive breast cancers 1.5 cm or smaller with cryoablation, radiotherapy, and anti-estrogen therapy. This method has achieved a local control rate of 99% at 6 years average follow-up, and rivals what we can achieve with surgery. However, unlike surgery, cryoablation is a relatively pain-free procedure that can be performed through a 3 mm skin nick under local anesthesia as a 1-hour office procedure with expedited return to normal activity and no long-term changes of breast shape or volume.

Based on growing international experience, I am certain that cryoablation will one-day become a standard option for U.S. women with early stage breast cancer and for some women with more advanced breast cancer. This view is supported by Medicare's recent decision to establish a CPT (billing) code for breast cancer cryoablation and as well by the recent National Institute of Health suggestion to evaluate cryoablation as a treatment of Stage 0 breast cancer (ductal carcinoma in situ), an effort that I am currently undertaking. The challenge for breast surgeons and breast cancer researchers such as myself is to determine which patients and which breast cancer types are most appropriate for cryoablation.

The primary issue raised by the California Medical Board was "informed consent." Informed consent is essential for everything we do as cancer specialists, whether it's lumpectomy, mastectomy, radiation, chemotherapy, or other treatments. Each treatment can reduce cancer recurrence, but none is guaranteed to prevent recurrence. To varying degrees, each is also capable of causing physical or emotional harm that can impair short-term or long-term quality of life. The goal of informed consent is to ensure that patients are aware of these factors and possible alternatives so that they can determine which treatment regimen suits them best. As it turns out, compared to their doctors, patients tend to be more willing to accept risk and explore novel treatment options. However, as surgeon-innovators, we must also temper our enthusiasm to offer patients new treatment advancements by ensuring that they are fully informed about what is known and more importantly, unknown about the innovations we offer.

Criticism of the disciplined surgeon must also be judged in the context of a long history of surgeon-innovators and patient advocates who sought to make breast cancer surgery less disfiguring and less harmful to women. For example, if not for the advocacy and independent research efforts of Umberto Veronesi, an Italian surgeon, and Bernard Fisher, an American surgeon, women across the globe might still be subjected to radical mastectomy with removal of the entire breast, chest muscles and underarm lymph nodes. Radical mastectomy was the standard breast cancer operation for all stages of breast cancer as little as 40 years ago. Though criticized by the medical community-at-large and ostracized by surgical societies, the leadership provided by Drs. Veronesi and Fisher made it possible today for most women to be offered lumpectomy and radiotherapy instead of radical mastectomy. However, ultimate credit goes to the communities of women around the world who demanded different and better options for treating breast cancer. Today's physicians are facing the same call-to-action. At the end of the day, most major advancements in cancer care are driven by physicians and patients seeking something better than the status quo.

Cryoablation is not the only place where the surgeon challenged the status quo. Readers might also be surprised to learn that this same surgeon played a seminal, but similarly controversial role in establishing tamoxifen as a treatment option for breast cancer. His early advocacy for tamoxifen stimulated national research efforts that ultimately established tamoxifen and similar medications as the preferred anti-cancer medication for women with estrogen-sensitive breast cancer. The human impact of this innovation is immeasurable.

My first status quo challenge began in 2005 with my efforts to eliminate the side effects and burden of breast radiotherapy with the use of single-dose intraoperative radiotherapy (IORT), a procedure that reduced the usual 6-week course of radiation after lumpectomy to a brief 30-minute dose of radiation given during surgery immediately after lumpectomy. After facing years of criticism from the radiation oncology community but tremendous support from patients, my decade-long endeavor to make IORT a standard option for women has been vindicated by long-term data supporting its safety and effectiveness, increasing adoption by radiation oncologists, and coverage by Medicare and most health insurance plans. I now serve as President of the Targeted Intraoperative Radiotherapy Collaborative Group, a national organization of surgeons, radiation oncologists, and physicians committed to expanding access to IORT.

It is safe to say that most physicians are motivated by their sworn professional obligation to "first do no harm" and by the desire to achieve the best possible outcome for their patients. However, it is no longer acceptable for physicians to be the sole judge of what is best for individual patients and to impose their own value-system on their patients. The new standard is "patient-centered care," which the Institute of Medicine defines as "providing care that is respectful of, and responsive to, individual patient preferences, needs and values, and ensuring that patient values guide all clinical decisions." Thus, for patients wishing to avoid traditional surgery, radiotherapy, or chemotherapy, it is therefore the challenge and responsibility of physician-innovators and advocates to develop a range of treatment options that allow patients to select therapies appropriate for their tumor biology, tumor extent, physical anatomy, and willingness to tolerate risks and side effects. It is in this context that I support ongoing efforts to expand access to cryoablation including launching the following informational website: www.cryoablation.com.

In many ways, I feel that the reaction to cryoablation mirrors the early days of lumpectomy and IORT. However, I am confident that the next 10 years will see cryoablation emerge as an established option for women with breast cancer. For this to happen, we must continue to monitor the outcome of ongoing trials and develop new trials for early and later stage breast cancer. Patients must understand that cryoablation is not intended to be a substitute for all other cancer therapies. Much like lumpectomy and mastectomy, cryoablation works best when supplemented by radiotherapy and/or drug therapy, as appropriate. Physicians must not hold cryoablation to a higher standard than we hold other cancer treatments. If a woman undergoes lumpectomy but later declines recommended radiation, we don't insist that she return to the operating room for a mastectomy lest we fire her from our practice—at least most of us don't. If a woman accepts tamoxifen but refuses chemotherapy despite its promise of additional survival benefit, we physicians still try to help her achieve the best possible outcome that can be achieved with tamoxifen alone. When the roles are reversed and the physician becomes the patient, we also expect our healthcare providers to respect our right of self-determination.

At the end of the day, our highest responsibility is to equip patients with the knowledge required to make informed decisions about a range of imperfect treatment options. This practice will empower them to make healthcare decisions that best suit their physical and emotional needs from both a survival and quality of life perspective.

Dennis R. Holmes, M.D., F.A.C.S.
Breast Cancer Surgeon and Researcher
Los Angeles, CA

Cryotherapy Benefits

In Charles Moore's article in *Breast Cancer News*, Ross-Paul contends that:

"In America, cryoablation is seen as a treatment that needs to be proven effective before it is considered a safe alternative to mastectomy and lumpectomy. FDA trials have been undertaken in the last 13 years, but the size of the trials has been limited due to financial constraints. As a result, when a doctor advises their patient who has breast cancer, cryoablation is considered as an unproven, experimental alternative to the much safer and statistically proven surgery."

"Without statistical proof through trials," she said, "cryoablation won't be used. But if cryoablation isn't used, there

will be no statistics. This has doomed cryoablation in the U.S. to forever be an experimental treatment. To get around this dilemma, we believe that prevention is the key. Through early detection, women are finding something suspicious in a mammogram. Since it is not yet identified as cancer, they are told to wait and see if it develops. If it doesn't, after a long time of fearful waiting, there is a joyful sigh of relief. If it is cancer, however, at that point, cryoablation is not considered and only surgery is advised."

Laura Ross-Paul and I have been upset by this.

Meeting Laura Ross-Paul and Considering the Perfect Marriage of Thermography and Cryoablation

In April 2016, I was finally privileged to meet Laura Ross-Paul after I had begun to delve into the cryoablation literature on her website and after reading her book, *They're Mine and I'm Keeping Them*. In fact, she had become so excited about what I was doing using my infrared camera and the *Proactive Breast Wellness* program that she wanted to experience what I had to offer first-hand. She felt that what I was doing was so important in the realm of breast health and breast cancer prevention that she brought the whole Ross-Paul Clan down for a clinical day of thermography. She invited her two sisters, her daughter, and her niece from Portland, a two-hour drive to provide infrared exams for all of them. I also went over the *Proactive Breast Wellness* program with all of her relatives. If you wish to see some photos from their field trip go to www.ProtectYourBreasts.com/blue-breasts-healthy-breasts/.

After this meeting, Laura and I began to spend a lot of time networking and brain storming on the phone and through emails to see how we might be able to bring cryoablation to the Pacific Northwest and beyond. She also introduced me to Dr. Peter Littrup, so I began to have these discussions with him as well and gain his insights. Alex Paul, Laura's husband and co-author of their book, also provided some historical perspective and practical suggestions on how to move cryoablation forward.

The "Early Freeze Protocol" and What Women Want

As Laura, Alex, and I continued our discussions, it became clear to all of us that the medical establishment and the FDA move at a snail's pace. It had been 17 years since Laura became the first woman internationally to have had her breast cancers treated successfully by freezing them in 2003. What we discovered was there were major hurdles regarding who would put up funding for clinical studies if the physicians felt that they would lose money when the woman did not go through the current standard of care of surgery, radiation or chemotherapy. If there weren't large-scale clinical studies here in the US and if there weren't statistics, cryotherapy would be doomed to being experimental as a breast cancer treatment.

Maybe there was another way to think about this. I first came up with some parallel thinking in regards to the way physicians currently treat a suspicious finding on a Pap smear. I shared my idea with Laura and Alex and we began to brainstorm to see how we might be able to present cryotherapy to physicians in a more palatable way. This was the start of what we now call the *Early Freeze Protocol.*

This is what I gave as my example to Laura and Alex during our brainstorming session. If a woman is going to see her OB/GYN for her annual Pap smear and later receives a call from the physician that there are some "suspicious findings" (specifically, a precancerous condition called cervical dysplasia) on the Pap report, the doctor would suggest that she return to the office for a cone cryo of the woman's cervix. This is a simple office procedure that freezes the cervix with liquid nitrogen after which the woman returns in six months for another Pap smear to make sure that everything has resolved. The woman is not being treated for cervical cancer; she is being treated for a "suspicious finding" on the Pap smear. This has been done for over 40 years and is well-accepted by physicians as a preventative approach for pre-cancerous Pap smears.

Why couldn't this same approach be used in the case of a suspicious finding on a "probably benign BI-RADS 3 or a suspicious, low-grade suspicious BI-RADS 4A reading" after a mammogram, ultrasound, or MRI? These women are currently told, "We are not too sure about this suspicious finding on your structural study" and the radiologist suggests a needle biopsy or a six-month recall. The imaging centers also do not give the woman any educational information about what she can do to improve her health in that six-month recall period during which she is now dreadfully concerned. My *Proactive Breast Wellness* program/*Protect Your Breasts* book/eBook should be offered to these frightened women.

In addition, if the imaging center were to do an infrared thermography on all the suspicious findings cases on structural studies, then the physician would have additional information to help determine if the area is sinister or not. Remember that fibrocysts which are common, and lipomas, which are fatty tumors; they both scan "cold" on thermography, which would decrease unnecessary biopsies or procedures. If the infrared instead showed an abnormal TH4 or TH5 thermogram with a hyperthermic focus and blood vessels leading to a palpable mass, then the *Early Freeze Protocol* could be implemented, using cryotherapy to address the suspicious finding. For expediency, a needle biopsy of the finding could be performed immediately before cryoablation to document the histology of the suspicious finding and treat the finding all in the same office visit. In fact, needle biopsy technology has been developed that could detect cancer immediately upon insertion of the needle into the growth.

Documentation of the histology or biopsy report is essential to both correlating the imaging finding; confirming a benign, premalignant or malignant condition; and determining whether or not the pathology requires adjuvant therapy in addition to cryoablation, such as lymph node biopsy, radiotherapy, hormonal therapy, immunotherapy, or in some cases, even chemotherapy.

Statistically, only 80% of needle biopsies performed today yield a non-malignancy diagnosis, a statistic that could likely be improved with the use of thermography. Thus, with the *Early Freeze Protocol,* most women would not be treated for breast cancer but preventative action would be undertaken on a suspicious finding or pre-malignant growth just like physicians are currently doing for Pap smears and using liquid nitrogen to freeze the woman's cervix. Ross-Paul and I maintain that if this new protocol is used in enough patients, the potential of a naturally occurring immune effect will start to show itself. Over time, a statistical base will demonstrate that women treated through early, preventative cryoablation then develop far less breast cancer than those who simply wait, and if they add thermography as a "Risk detection tool" combined with cryoablation.

The remaining women with small biopsy-confirmed breast cancers would benefit from this minimally invasive breast cancer treatment that does not alter the appearance of their breast.

Furthermore, analysis of their needle biopsy tissue could be used to determine if any additional treatment is needed.

I personally would like to see this clinical trial done and track the women into the future and see what happens to them over time with continued structural studies and add thermography to their follow up visits at 8 weeks, 6 months and one year post cryoablation.

Cryoablation is obviously inexpensive compared to surgery and results in low morbidity. This should be a win-win for everyone!

Laura Ross-Paul gave our *Early Freeze Protocol* presentation at the Fuda Cancer Hospital in Guangzhou, China, (which used to be called Canton), at the 5th International Cancer Forum on Cryoablation and Stem Cell Research held on July 2, 2016. The forum was organized by the International Society of Cryosurgery, the Asian Society of Cryosurgery, Fuda Cancer Hospital, Jinan University School of Medicine, and the First Affiliated Hospital of Shenzhen University. The organizers had invited over 200 experts and peers from around the world, including America, the U.K., Japan, Australia, and other authorities.

Laura's presentation of our material was well-received by the researchers and her Chinese hosts. My thermography slides of Mary L. were included as part of her presentation to demonstrate pre- and post-cryoablation metabolic tissue response and to promote our ideas about the *Early Freeze Protocol*. I was also invited to attend with her, but sadly, I would not have done well on a long 19-hour flight since I am rather claustrophobic. Ross-Paul said, "I appreciate the forum organizing committee's inclusion of a patient pioneer to speak alongside the doctors and researchers." This was Laura's second speaking engagement at this forum.

The focus of the 2016 forum was on treatment of cancer by cryosurgery, irreversible electroporation (IRE), immunotherapy, and stem cell treatment for cancer. The *Early Freeze Protocol* is our proposed approach for dealing with "something suspicious" in the breast found through structural studies and thermography.

Please go to my website in the cryoablation section of videos to experience my slides and Laura Ross Paul's presentation at Fuda Hospital in 2016 for yourself. I have posted a shorter version of my "Ted Talk Application" in the same cryo video section where I discuss what you are seeing on the slides of Mary L and a short overview of cryoablation as a technology.

If you wish to learn more about the Fuda Hospital programs which at the time of publication of this book, they have satellite offices in the Philippines, Indonesia, and Australia. You may contact the hospital directly at Consultation1@FudaHospital.com

Laura's book, *They're Mine and I'm Keeping Them,* is available through my bookstore in both hard copy and eBook versions. Click on her book link above.

Ross-Paul also maintains a web page at keepingthem.com and Facebook page at Facebook.com/keepingthem.

I also ask that you sign up and click on my own Protect Your Breasts website Newsletter link and sign up on my Facebook page so that I will be able to keep you up to date on breaking news and research.

I personally pray that the breast cryoablation or cryotherapy techniques will be embraced by all surgeons and radiologists in the very near future. Women are waiting for this breast-conserving technology that holds such promise.

I Want You to Get Cryoablation Equipment For Your Town

Since I first learned about breast cryosurgery in 2010 after doing a thermography scan for Mary prior to her cryosurgery, I knew I had to bring this technology to the Pacific Northwest and beyond. Before the publication of my third edition I had been frustrated because I had been sending my Oregon and Washington breast cancer patients off to California, Arizona and Michigan. In order to speed up the process and to help women find a cryoablation clinic closer to where they live, I had tried a different approach. I became a cryoablation sales agent for both Sanarus and IceCure! The sales agent positions lasted less than two years but this was an excellent learning experience to be able to have access to all the most recent publications and be able to connect with physicians that were interested in cryoablation in different parts of the country. I want this equipment available if I ever needed it or if my daughter ever had a problem in Seattle. I want my friends and patients to have access to this breast saving technology. I wish to actively work to get this equipment to surrounding towns where women can access it more easily and not have to fly around the country to get care!

So if you are a woman reading this and you know a radiologist or breast surgeon in your town who you think might consider obtaining cryotherapy equipment, please speak with them and have them reach me through my website or at: Contact@ProactiveBreastWellness.com

I will be able to send them materials that they will need to know to set up a cryoablation clinic of their own! The doctors can also provide my book to their cryoablation or surgical patients. You can also forward this information about my book and cryoablation to your Facebook friends and networks. The more women who know about this the better!

Find a Cryoablation Clinic: Need Help Finding a Cryo Clinic? I Have Become the First Cryoablation Nurse Practitioner Navigator

Since I have been involved with breast cryoablation since 2010, I decided to take on a new role to assist women with breast cancer or fibroadenomas to find a clinic that can potentially treat them. The first step is to contact me by email for a medical phone consult/ telemedicine appointment. Reach me at: Contact@ProactiveBreastWellness.com You can send me your recent imaging reports, biopsy report, breast history information and demographic sheet that I can send you. I can then assist you in sorting through your particular case to see if I can triage you to an appropriate cryoablation clinic. In some situations, I may recommend you receive care through your local surgeon if cryoablation does not seem to be the best option for your care. Otherwise, I can then assist in presenting your case as the Cryoablation Nurse Practitioner Navigator to get you to a treatment location as soon as possible and to educate you about the process. The physicians appreciate the pre-screening and it saves time for their staff to get you in for care sooner. See page 274 to learn about Navigator services and if you qualify.

Dr. Dennis Holmes and The FROST Trial

Please check out the websites (www.drholmesmd.com and www.cryoablation.com) for Dr. Dennis Holmes. I have been sending a large number of my clinical patients to him in Los Angeles for cryoablation. He has also become a mentor for me in this new emerging field of breast cancer care. I am very grateful to him for his time and encouragement and the expert care that he has offered my women when they have gone to see him in LA.

Dr. Holmes is the national principal investigator of the FROST Trial. Go to the Cryoablation videos on my website to view his discussion of the FROST Trial. He is also leading a national effort to promote cryoablation research and patient access. The FROST Trial, which stands for Freezing Alone Instead of Removal Of Small Tumor, is a clinical trial offering cryoablation to women with estrogen sensitive invasive breast cancer 2 cm or smaller and normal appearing lymph nodes. The FROST trial is sponsored by Sanarus Technologies, a manufacturer of cryoablation equipment, and provides cryoablation free of charge to clinical trial participants. For patients able to pay, Dr. Holmes also offers cryoablation outside of the trial to selected women with larger breast cancers and for those with non-invasive breast cancer or ductal carcinoma in situ (DCIS). Dr. Holmes and his office will also help you coordinate your post-cryoablation care with your local healthcare providers to help you receive comprehensive care, which often calls for medication therapy and/or radiotherapy, as well as appropriate imaging follow-up.

Please also check out this video link for Dr. Belinda Barclay White's website. She and I have become friendly over the phone and I have been trying to send patients to her as well since she is closer to Oregon than Peter Littrup, MD in Detroit, Michigan. Here is a link to her website at Arizona Breast Net in Scottsdale, Arizona: www.breastnet.net/cryoablation/

An additional consideration for women who are exploring cryoablation, is whether or not, if given the option, you would seek cryoablation by a radiologist who would perform the procedure as a stand alone treatment, or by a breast surgeon who not only performs the cryoablation procedure, but would provide a comprehensive discussion of the surgical altenatives to cryoablation as well as the additional therapies that might be appropriate for your specific cancer type.

The breast surgeon also commits to providing ongoing follow up care, coordination of care with your local healthcare providers, and supervision or facilitation of ongoing imaging follow-up. These latter points are very important, because many local doctors and radiologists are unfamiliar with cryoablation or the imaging appearance of cryoablated breasts, and are therefore reluctant to advise patients regarding their care. As a result, some cryoablation patients are left to figure these things out on their own.

I have been collecting a library of clinical articles on breast cryoablation that I can send physicians to review. I feel that within the coming years this will be the primary option women will want to choose if they have early stage breast cancer or a "Suspicious finding" on breast Imaging.

I will be calling insurance companies to make them aware of CPT codes to help through the acquisition process. The new breast cancer cryoablation CPT code is 1051 T. At the time of publication, there is no track record for paying this CPT code. However, I hope that insurance companies will soon reimburse this code at a fair rate to encourage surgeons to offer cryoablation to their patients. The insurance companies will come to see how much money they will save doing cryosurgery vs "Standard of care"! The women of course will start demanding that their insurance carriers provide this therapy as part of their plan benefits. I feel this will happen once more women recognize cryoablation as another and better treatment option. If you seek cryoablation by a radiologist, be sure that they or another healthcare provider can help you access comprehensive cancer management and ongoing follow-up.

My New Services as a Cryoablation Nurse Practitioner Navigator for Prospective Patients. Do You Meet the Criteria?

You are probably wondering, what are the parameters for a woman to qualify to have their tumor cryoablated. This is a short overview and I council women one-on-one at my thermography clinic, or by doing phone medical consults with potential cryoablation clients.

It has become obvious to me as more women contact me off my website that these women need a Cryoablation Nurse Practitioner Navigator to assist them in finding a cryoablation clinic that may be able to help them.

You may find this information below helpful on your quest to learn more about cryoablation. The two main manufacturers of cryoablation equipment are Sanarus and IceCure. What I have found strange on these websites is that the cryo clinic locations are not always that obvious for "Master Googlers." Since I was a sales agent for both these companies, I have been compiling lists of physicians.

You can also visit the ICECURE equipment website: icecure-medical.com or Sanarus at www.Sanarus.com

The Sanarus Visica® System is FDA Cleared for Ablation of Cancerous or Malignant Tissue and Benign Tumors

- Reimbursed using CPT 19105

- Over 4,000 cases in the U.S. have been done with this equipment.
- Z1072 study single arm multi-center study in 19 large hospitals by NCI (National Cancer Institute) found:
- 100% effective for tumors less than 1cm
- 92% effective for tumors greater than 1 cm. There was some erroneous probe placement, which is why the study states 92%. The trial demonstrated 100% ablation within the ablation zone.

What you want to know:

Ideal cryoablation candidate

- Lesion size less than but not greater than 4 cm for fibroadenomas and 2 cm for malignancies
- Your lump needs to be visible by ultrasound.
- 3–5 mm of space between lesion and surface of the breast.
- Patients who are not good candidates for surgery and/or general anesthesia.
- Patients concerned about cosmetics and scaring. Excellent cosmetic effect: one 3 mm incision regardless of tumor size which fades to a freckle sized scar over time.
- Patients with anxiety about surgery and general anesthesia.
- The diagnosis must be confirmed by biopsy.
- Recommended 3–6 month post-cryoablation follow up visit.
- Necrotic tissue can show up in mammography until fully resolved so it is important for patient to tell imaging specialists that she has had cryotherapy.

The palpable lump that results from cryoablation may take 2–3 years to disappear completely depending on the size of the cryoablated tumor, tumor location in the breast, closeness to the skin, and woman's breast density among other factors.

- Laura Ross-Paul cautioned me to not allow a biopsy of this area while you are healing. The area will shrink down by about 80%.
- Bruising and swelling may occur but will diminish over time.
- Lesion can be potentially palpable for up to two years or more post-cryoablation depending on the original size.
- Instructions post-cryoablation are similar to a core biopsy: to avoid strenuous activities (e.g. jogging, weightlifting, swimming) for a brief time.

So as you can see with this new technology, there are variations as to what is being provided and a range of parameters which may need some unraveling.

As an example some of the clinics only want to treat women who are 60 or 65 years of age with a certain size tumor to be in their clinical trial. That makes sense for publishing a study. They want all the subjects of the clinical trial to be the same age and certain size tumor or tumor type for their study. So what happens if you are 48 or 58? It means that you need to be able to contact a cryoablation clinic where the physician treats women "On and Off Protocol" and not just participating in the clinical trial that has set parameters. As the "Cryo Navigator" I may be able to stream line this process for you. In the course of your medical consult with me, it may become clear that you have a larger more extensive tumor, you may be advised that you may not be a good cryoablation candidate. This will then save you time if you have been trying to find cryoablation clinics on your own and then trying to call all over the country to find a clinic that may treat you. In that case it may be best to work with your local surgeon and medical community to obtain the care that you need for your breast cancer treatment. Following the protocols in my book will still help you and your immune system to begin to support your healing journey towards improved health.

Here is some other information that my "Cryoablation Navigator" patients have found helpful.

Currently, I suggest to my patients to get all their recent imaging such as mammograms, ultrasounds, MRI if (done), imaging reports and biopsy information, (if done) all on a CD from the hospital. I also suggest they ask for a second CD of this material that they hand carry. Since I am sending people around the country right now, the physician in the cryosurgery clinic usually wants to review these images and reports prior to you arriving to make sure you may be a good candidate for that center. I can also assist in triaging your particular case and assist you in getting you to a center quicker.

I have also found that some physicians are bolder than others for what they will treat or the size of the mass or clinical presentation. Some of these physicians are in a national clinical study with 20 centers, and they may only treat patients that fall into the parameters of the study. Others will treat women on and off the study protocol. This is why it is a good idea that you have your personal information on CD so you can duplicate the CD if you need to send it to a different clinic.

It would help if you could go to an active national clinical trial site but that may require travel. As this all moves forward, things will become easier. New technologies sometimes have growing pains, but I think this is just what women have been waiting for!

If you are a woman with a breast cancer diagnosis and you are trying to figure out if your case would be appropriate for cryoablation or not, you may contact me as your Nurse Practitioner Navigator through my email to set up a paid medical consult. Please also let me know what time zone you are calling from and a phone number. If you would also scan and send me by email your ultrasound report which will give me the size of your tumor in centimeters or millimeters, your biopsy report or tumor type and your age and where you live. We can arrange a medical phone consult time by email. Contact@ProactiveBreastWellness.com

Stay in Touch and Help Me Save Lives

Remember to sign up on my Newsletter link at www.ProtectYourBreasts.com/newsletter and on my Facebook Page at www.facebook.com/ProactiveBreastWellness/ so that I will be able to keep you up to date on breaking news and research. I personally pray that the breast cryoablation or cryotherapy techniques will be embraced by all surgeons and radiologists in the very near future. Women are waiting for this breast-conserving technology that holds such promise. We really need help to spread the word about cryoablation. Please share information about my book with friends and family and on all your social media sites.

We found out that the more positive reviews on Amazon and Barnes & Noble, the higher the ranking on their search engines to get us to the goal of having our book visible on page one or two in the breast cancer section.

As of April 1, 2019 Amazon wiould not allow me to advertise on Amazon anymore because "The subject of the book is not suitable for all audiences." This I found curious since half the population are women, and most are concerned about breast cancer. Amazon also said that, "Cancer is a serious condition, so my book cannot be advertised through Amazon." I countered that if a woman goes to Amazon, types in "Book, then breast cancer," there is a huge number of books that are being advertised, even though "Breast cancer is a serious condition," so I wonder if the cryoablation section to "Freeze and Cure Breast Cancer" is what the Amazon marketing department does not want women to hear about. I need some militant women to spread the word to other women or other women's organizations to help educate.

Finally after eight months of trying to find out from Amazon "Why" they were preventing me from advertising my book, an Amazon supervisor finally said I needed to change the front of the book and title to say: "Freeze Your Breast Cancer with Cryoablation." It used to say "Freeze AND CURE Your Breast Cancer with Cryoablation" and for me to add some more rose petals on the cleavage of the stern looking woman on the cover!

Before Amazon made this decision, I was advertising on Amazon, and the book could be found on the top of page two. Now the book might be found on page 23 with 20 books per page and my book is displayed after baseball caps with pink ribbons! After finally getting their tip about getting rid of the offensive language of "Freeze AND CURE" and redoing the cover which means extra expense for me so that my fabulous publisher can redo things so I can jump through the Amazon political hoops. I hope to now be able to get the word out to women who need to know how to protect their breasts!

The positive comments on Amazon and Barnes apparently still help me to raise my book's visibility to a first or second page. Please make a comment on Amazon or Barnes & Noble for me. Also, please tell women about this directly and have them promote the book through their own social media sites. I'm now providing autographed copies for less than Amazon if they contact me through the website Store: www.ProtectYourBreasts.com/store/

I hope you can help me save more breasts and lives!

CHAPTER 10

Putting It All Together

Getting Started Making a Difference in Your Health and the Health of Your Whole Family Plus Your Community

So, you are now approaching the end of this *Proactive Breast Wellness* program and the *Protect Your Breasts* book or eBook. I wouldn't be surprised if you are feeling overwhelmed with the amount of information and choices you have to make to improve your breast health. That is understandable, especially if you have read or listened to the PBW program in a short period of time. The good news is that there are many things you can do to decrease your risk of breast cancer or its reoccurrence.

With respect to this program, another bit of good news is that there is a summary checklist at the end of this chapter in the eBook version or you can obtain the free data disc or free digital resource download from the website Store and print the checklist and worksheets from the worksheet section of this book to help you recall healthier choices. This checklist will assist you by systematically listing the actions that you can take immediately and later you can also go back and address other actions or make health changes in the future.

Remove Stumbling Blocks When Making New Health Choices

This brings us to the discussion of what might keep people from making changes in their lives for improved breast health. Let's address some of these potential stumbling blocks.

A first challenge might be that you are feeling overwhelmed and powerless, with all these poisons floating around our earthly home that can't be avoided. To that I would say several things. One is that we can decrease our individual exposure to some of these items, some of them drastically. Another is that people have been lobbying for a safer environment with respect to some of these toxins, such as banning of some plastics in Europe and some parts of the United States and decreasing the use of some pesticides. There is a scientific and political movement to improve our environment. Our personal choices, as well as our governmental and industrial choices, can make a difference for the better. We don't have to be fatalistic about exposures that have already occurred. We can be proactive about the future for ourselves and our children.

For those of you who wish to take action and try to promote change, we have included a list of organizations on the free data disc or free resource download in the resource section and links on the my website in the "Take Action" section. You may find organizations that you wish to assist financially or by signing petitions to be sent to decision makers. Preventing GMO seeds (genetically modified) being planted in your region and having GMO foods labeled as such in grocery stores should be a right for consumers to know where their food is coming from and how it is treated. GMO foods have been banned in Europe and other countries are following suit. Writing letters and getting involved with organizations that are trying to influence change locally and protect your family's food would be a benefit at this critical time.

A second stumbling block could be financial concerns. Some of the expenses will be one-time costs, such as replacing kitchenware. Others can be ongoing expenses, such as supplements or buying organically. Some may not require any expense at all, such as stopping microwaving in plastic containers or storing in plastic. Because of limited financial resources, some people may need to pick and chose a few items at a time, adding more as money becomes available. It is very reasonable to use up current stocks of items in your pantry or freezer before replacing them with safer items. People with limited resources are eager to know what efforts will have the greatest positive impact on their health.

To help with those decisions, the summary checklist is somewhat organized into those things that are most effective in reducing breast cancer risk or decreasing recurrence rates, and those that may be less dramatic in their effects. For instance, before going totally organic in your grocery cart, as a first priority you can choose to avoid the fruits and vegetables on the "dirty dozen list" with the highest risk of pesticide or herbicide exposure. Another concept to keep in mind is that breast cancer can be very expensive with loss of income and medical costs. When you consider this and balance it against organic food shopping, prevention is much cheaper in the long run.

A few women may think that their fate is already determined and that their efforts won't make any difference. To them I would be sympathetic and encouraging, pointing out that following the *Proactive Breast Wellness* program/*Protect Your Breasts,* is likely to improve their health in many ways that may or may not include the avoidance of breast cancer. Every little bit helps, even if the cards of fate seem to be stacked against you. The *Proactive Breast Wellness* program is designed to be empowering for women to be more positive in their goal towards better health.

Remember the PBW program has also been shown to be heart healthy and women usually loose 15 to 30 pounds over a six to twelve month period. Please view the "Protect Your Breasts" section on the website to actually see how a woman's breasts improve on the PBW protocol! Loosing that stubborn belly fat and regaining energy and a sense of general wellbeing fits the PBW goal of restoring a woman's health and encouraging prevention-based behaviors.

Another stumbling block can be that people just don't like the idea of taking lots of pills or supplements. It is true that the entire protocol, including all of the recommended supplements, constitutes a formidable piece of kitchen shelf real estate, not to mention mouthfuls. In the PBW protocol, I have added food sources instead of supplement pills that you may wish to try instead.

However, some of the items in the protocol probably contribute more than others to improved breast health, and other aspects of health are likely to improve such as menopausal symptoms, bone density, cardiovascular health, and thyroid function. On the PBW supplement protocol list, I have added stars so that you will know that three stars means most important, two stars means important, and one star means helpful. If I were to list the things that I think would make the biggest improvement for the least expense, they would be: use a bioidentical progesterone if appropriate; start sprouting organic broccoli seeds or take DIM or Indole-3-Carbinol; supplement vitamin D3 adjusted to your lab levels to reach your optimal level of vitamin D3, which should be over 55, and I would prefer your lab result to be in the 70 to 75 range; start taking a digestive enzyme and a probiotic with

50 billion organisms and 14 strains or add more fermented foods to your diet. Try adding more organic green juicing and smoothies to your health routine, which will really improve your health, start an exercise program, and learn a meditative technique. Simple but really important.

Start to supplement your diet with omega-3 fatty acids from fish or krill, or eat a handful of raw walnuts or chia seeds on a daily basis. Ensure adequate iodine levels and be sure your thyroid function has been evaluated. I have included a hormone checklist and instructions on how to do a temperature journal in the printable section of the free resource materials available on the website or in the worksheet section of the book and eBook so you can further monitor your thyroid and other hormone symptoms over time to share with your provider. Consider a whole food multivitamin or add organic green smoothies to your diet. Increase your consumption of vitamin C and magnesium. Get your weight to a healthy level. Start an exercise program and improve your stress management. A woman can reduce her risk of breast cancer by 65% if she exercises three times a week for thirty minutes!

While you are making these healthy changes on the PBW protocol, at the same time you are learning to avoid environmental toxins and changing to a diet that contains more organic foods. This is especially important in the meat or dairy department to avoid bovine growth hormones and the extra antibiotics and GMO grain that have been added to the food of conventionally-raised meat and dairy animals.

Get 20% Off All Your Quality Supplements and Save Money

To address the concerns of having to take too many supplements and the cost of the additional bottles on your shelf, my program provides 20% off all your supplements through the Protect Your Breasts website in the "Supplement" section when you are following our lifesaving protocol. We have partnered with Emerson Ecologics on their Wellevate platform where we created a virtual patient dispensary. Emerson is a distributor for hundreds of brand name manufacturers. You may see products that your naturopath or MD had suggested to you but now you can purchase them for 20% off the retail cost you have been paying. You can easily browse my favorite supplements from my protocol but you can also access the full range of what Emerson has to offer and still get the 20% discount if you have entered through my website portal. I created this portal so you will be able to receive high quality supplements in the correct dosage that you require without a lot of additives or fillers. These are the same products that your naturopath, nutritionist or MD orders. Friends and family can take advantage of this 20% off discount as well. Check out how much you will be able to save!

For more information, go to our website www.ProtectYourBreasts.com to the NEWSLETTER section to register your interest in upcoming products that will be added to the nutritional protocol and you will be sent a free quarterly newsletter regarding new research that will improve your health as articles are published in future. We will bring these important articles to your home via email newsletters to help you safeguard your health.

Some women find themselves with clinicians who are resistant, uneducated, or even mocking of their efforts to decrease their breast cancer risk through efforts such as those in this program. Many traditional medical providers have never been trained in preventative medicine, and are instead narrowly focused on diagnosing and treating pathology with pharmaceuticals. However, more and more practitioners are being exposed to these concepts in healthcare, and many of the preventative therapies are being ushered into the realm of traditional practitioners. A good example is the recent emphasis on screening for vitamin D3 deficiency and treating to levels higher than were previously thought to be adequate.

I expect this shift will continue to occur, and these preventative regimens will not be restricted to naturopaths, herbalists, chiropractors, and other complementary medicine and integrative or alternative practitioners. If you find that your clinician is not open to learning more about these things, you may need to find another consultant. Many of the MD/DO clinicians who are educated in these matters are listed as anti-aging, environmental, or functional medicine physicians. We have included links to some of these websites on the free data disc/free resource download so you may find a practitioner who is more willing to work with you and has more of an interest in prevention.

Occasionally women will find resistance in their own families. Their partner or children may not appreciate the new dietary items, such as seaweed in their brown rice. Their favorite plastic water bottle may have disappeared. There may be a new financial strain on the family budget. Organic food will help to safeguard the whole family's health. Just consider that if you wish to prevent your family becoming ill or developing chronic diseases, many of these medical problems are showing links to eating conventional foods with bovine growth hormone and antibiotics, processed foods, gluten and GMO foods. I tell people that it is cheaper to pay the grocer or the farmer than to have to pay for treatment of a major illness. The best recourse is gentle education of your family, perhaps by letting them read the PBW book/eBook. Small, gradual changes are more likely to be accepted. Your reward may not come until years later, but you can be confident that you are helping to protect your family members as well as yourself.

There may be other impediments to embarking on this *Proactive Breast Wellness* program. You have, however, already taken the first step by reading the *Protect Your Breasts* book or eBook. Congratulate yourself for beginning your empowered journey towards making a positive difference in your health. If you have daughters or granddaughters, share this program with them. Remember "Prevention Is The Cure!"

How to Receive Your FREE Resource Material and 45-Minute Relaxation Program

The next step is to access the FREE data disc or FREE resource download from my website Store if you chose the PBW book/eBook version. Look at the file called Using This Disc or Resource Download and scan the table of contents. I encourage you to print out the supplement protocol, as well as the summary checklist and the other work sheets. I have added many of the worksheets to the end of this chapter in the book and eBook. This will give you something to refer to as you consider your next phase in making changes on the *Proactive Breast Wellness* program.

I have included my *Waves of Serenity* 45-minute progressive muscle relaxation/guided beach imagery as a CD/DVD or digital download as part of your *Protect Your Breasts* book or the *Proactive Breast Wellness* program as a FREE gift on the website Store. Use password code **PBWBOOK** to access your FREE digital download of *Waves of Serenity* and the resource download. If you prefer these to be sent to you in CD form, please click that box for the people who purchased the book or eBook so we may mail them to you. There will be a small $3.00

postal charge for shipping these CDs within the United States. Other shipping is available for foreign postage. I designed this as a comprehensive program, so please remember to access these FREE components of my program and book.

Waves of Serenity helps to decrease stress, insomnia, anxiety, pain, and will also help to improve your blood pressure if you practice these relaxation techniques 20 minutes once or twice a day. You can also explore yoga classes or other forms of meditation. Try out different things and see what fits best with your interests. Your family might also like to participate in your new exercise or meditation programs as a family activity. Some women just want some special time for themselves. See what works for you.

This *Protect Your Breasts* book with the *Proactive Breast Wellness* program can also be given as a "Gift of Health" to a loved one from our website Store with your own greeting attached.

Thank you for reading the *Protect Your Breasts* book/eBook and joining me on this journey towards health. I hope that I have empowered you to make changes that will improve your health and the health of your family.

I turned 69 this past year and I believe I have become an activist, though I had never considered myself as an activist before. I needed to take action after working for over 16 years with an infrared camera and actually seeing what happens to breast tissue when exposed to herbicides and estrogen mimickers.

I met with the Lane County Commissioners and members of the Eugene Health Department. I brought a breast surgeon with me. We showed them the power point on herbicides and pesticides that is available on my website in the "Protect Your Breasts" section. The surgeon told these officials that there are no safe herbicides or pesticides. We were able to stop the roadside spraying here in Lane County, Oregon. We want to expand the information to a state-wide level and beyond.

If your community is threatened by toxic exposure and toxic trespass, I give permission to show the images in the "Protect Your Breasts" section of the website to decision makers and community groups in your area. I am trying to educate more people about these environmental hazards in order to make a positive change in all our communities and to protect our families.

I see this world at a critical juncture with escalating cancer rates, childhood and adult diabetes, and chronic diseases we did not see in the past generations at such levels. So much of this is related to our food choices, environmental toxins, and a food supply that is becoming controlled by big agriculture that favors genetically modified crops. We are threatened by global warming, 5G and a shrinking domestic economy. It is a challenging time for all of us.

Women are the keepers of the hearth. We nurture and care for our children and families. We educate and set examples. In many ways, women are the change makers. My goal and hope is to touch the lives of women who also see the negative trends and who wish to empower themselves so they can make better choices and in turn they can affect the lives of their children and their grandchildren.

Women stand strong together, we care, we nurture, we support. Please share this information about the *Proactive Breast Wellness* program and *Protect Your Breasts* with all your friends and family on Facebook and social media. Empower as many people as you can to start taking charge of their own health.

Thank you for accompanying me on this journey towards health and healing.

Remember – Prevention IS the Cure!

Worksheets

CONTENTS

Overview for the Worksheets

You have taken the first step to improve your breast health and reduce your risk of breast cancer or its reoccurrence by using the *Proactive Breast Wellness* program! These changes will also help protect the health of your whole family!

Here is how you can start using the supplemental resources and research materials. Please print out the following materials from the Getting Started Section so you can follow along with the narrative and the *Protect Your Breasts* books. It is important that you print these sheets as part of the protocol. It will help you stay focused and encourage you as you make progress towards improving your health. You can make copies of the work sheets and then date them so you can see how your symptoms are improving over time. Keep a copy of the original so you can use it over and over again.

The Getting Started section includes the following:

1. Putting It All Together Checklist

For the *Proactive Breast Wellness* Program/*Protect Your Breasts* by Ingrid Edstrom, FNP, M.Ed., Updated September 2020 Third Edition

I will help you get organized and give you a step-by-step way for you to start making changes. You can check them off as you accomplish these changes. Your family may be able to assist so they are able to learn about healthy choices and changes also.

2. The *Proactive Breast Wellness* Nutritional Supplement Protocol

Print out this supplement list so you will be able to compare what you are currently taking and have the dosages readily available. This will make it easier to shop or order off my Virtual Dispensary. You will also be able to take the supplement list to your medical provider, if he or she is interested.

If you are a woman who has felt confused about whether you are taking the right supplements or dosages to improve your health, I have taken the guess-work out of this problem for you. I have spent seven years researching the protocol and then had two holistic nutritionists, three MDs, and several NDs, plus two nationally-known compounding pharmacists review my *Proactive Breast Wellness* protocol.

3. Instructions on How to Use Progesterone

This list assists you on deciding how much and when to use topical progesterone. Menopausal women have a different schedule than women that are still cycling.

4. Hormone Replacement Therapy Symptom Checklist

Use these easy checklists over time to monitor your progress.

5. Abnormal Hormone Symptoms for Females by PCCA

Ever wonder why you are not feeling "balanced"? Review these symptoms to try to narrow down what may be wrong. Then you can share this with your provider and do some labs or arrange to receive your home hormone test kits from ZRT Labs or Dutch Labs.

6. How to Do a Temperature Journal

This is very helpful for you and your physician to monitor your thyroid function. As you make changes, you can then check the temperatures every 6-8 weeks and it is totally free. Combined with your thyroid labs, you can more easily monitor your progress towards a better functioning thyroid.

7. How to Take Liquid Iodine and How Much

This worksheet will assist you on ways to start and use iodine.

8. How to Do an Iodine Patch Test

This easy test will show you if you are deficient in iodine. Remember 90% of Americans are. As you change your iodine dose, you can periodically do the patch test.

9. The Benefits of Certain Foods

I found this to be an interesting list of the healing potential that different foods have. This list may help you make better choices if you have identified some specific health challenges.

10. The EWG Shoppers Guide for Pesticides

This guide by The *Environmental Working Group* (EWG) is an American environmental organization that specializes in research and advocacy in the areas of toxic chemicals. This guide lists the chemicals that may be in your food if you are not eating organic produce. There are also apps available from the Cornucopia Institute and the EWG that you can load on your smart phone to make shopping easier and safer.

11. How to Access my Virtual Dispensary to Receive 20% Off All Your Supplements

We have given you instructions on how to set up your own account to order from my Virtual Dispensary on my website www.ProtectYourBreasts.com. There are access codes on my website in the supplement section to make this easier. You can print the instructions when you are ready to order. Or you can call Emerson Ecologics to order your supplements. You need to identify yourself as a person following my PBW protocol in my book in order to get the 20% off all of the supplements that I currently use are also on the PYB Virtual Dispensary. As new products become available, I will post them on my website so you can stay current. This makes it easy for you to compare what you are currently taking with the PBW protocol.

Just click on the picture of the supplement bottle and it will drop down to show you all the ingredients. Emerson Ecologics is a large distributor of high-end supplements and nutraceuticals. Your doctor or naturopath probably has a wholesale account with them already so you will be saving 20% off anything that you are currently purchasing retail. Emerson Ecologics carries products from more than 385 manufacturers, so you will probably find the products you are currently taking for a lot less. You will also see that in purchasing higher quality supplements through my site or Emerson Ecologics, you will avoid purchasing lesser quality products that have a lot of fillers, additives, or are sourced from places that do not do their due diligence on product testing, safety, and quality. Since MDs, NDs, and nutritionists purchase from Emerson Ecologics, you know that they will offer you the quality that these other health care providers expect and trust.

12. Other Books and Organizations You May Find Helpful

I have added other resource lists that include recommended books or websites that you might find interesting and to expand your research towards better health and vitality.

We also have over 90 books listed on my website in the Resources section that will help guide your journey towards health and vitality. I broke the books down into different sections and categories to assist you in finding the book that you need. These books are all favorites of mine and I have them on my bookshelves. We encourage you to purchase books by these authors who may be of interest to you through our Amazon link. I have personally met many of the authors at various conferences over the years.

I added a Take Action section on my website that will quickly link you to other organizations to expand your knowledge base. You will find links that will help you choose less toxic cosmetics and body care products. You will learn which seafood has more heavy metals or contaminants. Just for the record, avoid all farmed fish. There is an assortment of website links of sister organizations with whom we anticipate working more closely in the future. We have also included various newsletter sources from other organizations that you might enjoy and wish to subscribe to.

13. Receive Your Two Free Gifts as Part of the Comprehensive *Proactive Breast Wellness* Program and your *Protect Your Breasts* book or eBook Purchase

As part of the third edition PBW program now as *Protect Your Breasts* available as an eBook or soft cover book, I encourage you to receive these two FREE gifts as part of the PBW comprehensive program. I have included the *Waves of Serenity* relaxation CD/DVD/digital download as part of the mind-body portion to improve your health. I have also included a free data disc/resource digital download.

14. How to Use the *Waves of Serenity* Relaxation CD/DVD/Digital Download:

I created *Waves of Serenity* for people who did not previously have any experience with relaxation or meditation techniques. I have used this tool for years with my patients who had insomnia, chronic pain, elevated blood pressure or cortisol levels, were approaching hospitalization or surgery, or who simply wanted to unwind at the end of a hectic day. There is no religious affiliation so any one will feel comfortable using *Waves*. You can listen to a clip of *Waves* on the home page of the Protect Your Breasts website. It starts with a progressive muscle relaxation and then transitions to a guided imagery of a beach walk with ocean sounds and harp along with the soothing narrative. Please listen to *Waves* daily and start incorporating these relaxation techniques throughout the day.

Advanced meditation practitioners also enjoy *Waves*. Great for children and teens too!

15. Acknowledgement to the Authors and Resources on the Resource Download/Disc

The PYB staff has compiled research and references over the last seven years that we felt might enhance your knowledge base. We gathered a selection of the articles together on the free data disk/ digital download for your use. It is our hope that this will provide a starting point for your own research at the library, on line, or in bookstores. Our staff tried to make the selection of materials based on current research in the medical literature that, by its nature, is constantly changing. We also have offered an integrative medicine viewpoint that encourages prevention of diseases and health promotion as a goal. We have provided the data disc and download in PDF format for the articles used as well as web links. We have tried to provide the sources, links, and websites of the articles on the free data disc/download so that you may view the original source materials and the authors to give them full credit.

Recent health polls suggest that 65% to 72% of adult Americans are already utilizing or are interested in complementary or integrative medicine with supplements, nutrition, acupuncture, chiropractic, massage, mind/body techniques, and other modalities.We acknowledge that the resources provided are a starting point due to the vastness of the breast cancer topic and may not address all the issues or include all the authors who are expert in this field.

16. Please Write a Review and Sign Up for Your Quarterly Newsletter

PYB will be providing a quarterly newsletter to people who have purchased the PBW program or purchased *Protect Your Breasts*. This newsletter will provide literature and medical updates as they become available. This way we can keep people appraised of breaking research in a timely manner after the book is out. Sign up on the "Newsletter" link on my website. We hope to also keep you updated on cryoablation and any new supplements that are improving breast health as the research is made available.

17. Help Get the Word Out About Cryoablation and Post a Review on Amazon and Barnes & Noble

Help women save their breasts! I would love some reviews and assistance on social media.

18. Cryoablation Nurse Practitioner Navigator Services

Turn to the worksheet section to learn more about having your breast cancer frozen and find a clinic to treat you!

1. Putting It All Together Checklist

For the *Proactive Breast Wellness* Program/*Protect Your Breasts* by Ingrid Edstrom, FNP, M.Ed., Updated September 2020 Third Edition

Reduce your dietary exposure to xeno-estrogens

Food choices

- Organic meats
- Organic dairy products
- Organic fruits and vegetables
- First non-organic food to eliminate: strawberries.
- Second non-organic foods to eliminate: bell peppers, spinach, cherries, peaches, Mexican cantaloupes, celery, apples, apricots, green beans, grapes from Chile, red raspberries, and cucumbers.
- Filter water instead of buying plastic bottled water.
- If possible, choose foods that are not packaged in plastic.
- Avoid BPA plastic-lined cans.

Food preparation

- Stop microwaving food in plastic.
- Replace plastic nonstick cookware with metal or ceramic.
- Replace plastic cookware, colanders, spoons, and spatulas with metal, ceramic, or wood.

Food storage

- Discard all water bottles that are not BPA free.
- If plastic containers must be used, choose BPA-free types one, two, or five, and don't store them in a hot car or put hot liquids or foods in them. It would be best to avoid ALL plastics, BPA free or otherwise.
- Replace plastic water bottles with stainless steel or glass.

- Replace food storage containers with stainless steel or glass.
- If using plastic wrap, use Glad brand, and do not have it rest against the food. A better choice, put a ceramic plate on top of the bowl.
- Use brown waxed paper. Avoid other gray waxed papers.

Acid-alkaline diet

Purchase and use one of these books:

- *The pH Miracle: Balance Your Diet, Reclaim Your Health* by Robert Young, PhD, and Shelly Redford-Young or
- *The Acid Alkaline Diet for Optimum Health: Restore Your Health,* Christopher Vasey, ND
- Consider the use of an alkalinizing supplement or magnesium or add one teaspoon of Bragg's Apple Cider Vinegar or lemon to your water.

Other general dietary recommendations

- Increase dietary omega-3 fatty acids.
- Wild salt-water fish (other than shark, mackerel, and swordfish) or use Nordic Fish or Krill oil, 2000 mg per day or 1.5 ounces of walnuts or walnut oil or chia seeds
- Increase iodine intake (seaweed from Maine or Iceland, iodized Celtic sea salt).
- Avoid food additives such as nitrites, bromine, artificial sweeteners, artificial colors, preservatives.
- Natural preservatives such as vitamin C (ascorbic acid) and vitamin E (tocopherols) are OK.
- Avoid soda pop.
- Minimize caffeine and chocolate.
- Use cold pressed virgin olive oil or organic coconut oil over other oils.
- Limit use of phytoestrogen-containing foods such as non-fermented soy, flax, black cohosh, dong quai, hops,

red clover and hemp. Marijuana and these hemp products, I feel are estrogenic and avoid or limit use..

- Limit alcohol usage (not more than one to two organic alcoholic drinks per day for women). None would be better or an occasional half glass of organic wine.

Nutritional supplements

- Multivitamin with CoQ-10
- Vitamin D3 5,000 units daily as minimum supplement, 8,000 IU in Pacific NW
- Higher dose of Vitamin D is usually needed to reach a target blood level of 65 to 70 on a 32–80 scale, 80–85 if normal Vitamin D is 30–100 scale.
- Levels need to be monitored with blood tests at six months and adjust dosage as necessary.

Estrogen binders

- Indole-3-Carbinol, 400 mg per day or
- DIM complex, 100 to 120 mg one to two tabs per day is preferred or
- organic broccoli sprouts, 25 to 50 sprouts per day raw

Calcium and magnesium and other vitamins

- Calcium citrate, calcium maleate, or hydroxyapatite, 500 mg per day at bedtime. Do not exceed 500 mg daily from all sources.
- Magnesium citrate, or magnesium glycinate, work up to 500 to 750 mg per day in divided doses.
- Black current seed oil, two capsules per day
- Alternative: borage oil, or evening primrose oil
- Vitamin C, at least 1200 mg per day, 2,500 mg preferred or to bowel tolerance.
- **Iodine:** If hypothyroid, monitor thyroid labs and Temperature Journal. See the Iodine sheet and review Chapter 2 on

how to use Lugol's 2% liquid iodine.

- Atlantic Seaweed powdered: ¼ teaspoon equals three mg of iodine

Progesterone

- Bioidentical / USP / Micronized Progesterone supplement: paraben-free compounds recommended

As directed by your clinician, or see How to Use Progesterone sheet. Usual initial topical dosage for Menopausal women, 40 to 50 mg, total per day, best to use approximately 20 mg twice a day. Maintenance dosage 15 to 20 mg per ¼ teaspoon per day after testing results stabilized or if you are a cycling woman.

For example, Pro-gest USP Cream, one quarter teaspoon applied twice a day for Noncycling / menopausal women apply three weeks on, one week off each month or take Monday–Friday twice a day and off the weekends which is easier to remember.

For Cycling women, apply days 12 through 28 each month, ¼ teaspoon or one pump daily topically to thin skin.

Another product Natural Progeste Cream by Metabolic Maintenance is 20 mg USP / paraben free progesterone per one pump. (These are available on my website.)

Other hormone and environmental issues

- Avoid synthetic estrogen and synthetic progesterone / progestin products. This means no hormonal contraception or synthetic estrogen hormone replacement.
- Avoid hormone pellets as they markedly increase vascular activities in the breasts. If you have a suspicious region and increased blood flow, you will have tumor doubling.
- Choose a clinician experienced in use of bioidentical

hormones.

- Estriol is the preferred estrogen (rather than estradiol or estrone).
- Have your estrogen, progesterone, free testosterone, DHEA, and cortisol levels monitored.
- Testosterone supplements should be avoided by those with breast cancer or at high risk of breast cancer.
- DHEA is not recommended. It converts to other hormones.
- Reduce environmental toxic exposures.
- Stop using tobacco and avoid tobacco smoke or vaping.
- Decrease pesticide exposure (including herbicides and fungicides).
- If you must use herbicides, use protective equipment, and minimize their use (for example, applying the agent to the cut stem rather than spraying the entire plant).
- Stop using pesticides altogether in your personal environment (preferred).
- Lobby neighbors to avoid pesticide and herbicide use.
- Lobby city, county, and forest agencies to avoid pesticide and herbicide use.
- Minimize exposure to exhaust fumes, especially diesel fumes.
- Minimize exposure to solvent fumes.
- Avoid products with parabens.
- Avoid products with petrochemical additives (mineral oil, Vaseline-type products).
- Avoid chemical static eliminators, dryer-sheets, fabric softeners in laundry.
- Alternatives include Maddock's Static Eliminator dryer sheets.
- Avoid unnecessary X-ray procedures.

- Discuss necessary breast imaging with your clinician.
- 5G and Electromagnetic Radiation Exposure. Go to SolutionsForHumanity.Net for lists of positive actions to take to protect your family. Put your cell phone on airplane mode or turn it off and get a land line. Do not wear the phone up against your body. Get a modem or fiber optic computer connection. Turn off the Wi-Fi in your home. Do not get a wireless base unit system for your house. Do not sleep with your cell phone near your bed. Do not wear your phone in your bra when exercising or over your heart. Do not watch movies on a laptop computer on your lap over ovaries or testicles. A caution for the men and boys in your life. Increased sterility may be the outcome. There is so much you can learn to do by checking out the website for SolutionsForHumanity.Net

Breast care

- Avoid tight fitting clothing across the breasts.
- Eliminate brassiere underwires.
- Consider regular dry brushing and lymph massage of the breasts.
- Don't wear sports bras all day or at night time.

General health concerns

- Reduce obesity.
- Increase exercise, brisk walking for 25 minutes at least three to four times per week
- Consider genetic counseling and testing if there has been early or prominent breast cancer in siblings or parents.
- Establish a relationship with a trusted and knowledgeable clinician.
- Be sure your thyroid function is tested and normalized

with your clinician, especially if you are using iodine supplements.

- Practice stress management.
- Consider meditation, relaxation techniques, yoga etc.
- Listen to my *Waves of Serenity* once or twice a day!

2. Nutritional Supplement Suggestions For Improving Breast Health

Protocol developed by Ingrid L. Edstrom FNP, M.Ed., Copyrighted as part of the Proactive Breast Wellness program.

Updated September 2020 for the Third Edition

This protocol is not a substitute for working with your own primary care physician. If you do have cancer, it is important that you work closely with your oncologist. This protocol was created for improving a woman's general health as well as breast health. Our cancer patients utilize this protocol as well as other supplements not listed here for immune support. We help customize a nutritional support program for women who are also working with their physician teams. The *Proactive Breast Wellness* (PBW) program below is directed towards health promotion with a disease prevention focus. We have written "or" next to different products to give you different choices or food equivalents. Visit the Virtual Dispensary at www.ProtectYourBreasts.com to view product ingredients so you may more easily compare with your current supplements.

All of these supplements are also available on the website Virtual Dispensary with a 20% discount. We have put stars next to items to rank their importance.

Items with three stars are considered most important for the protocol to be effective. Items with two stars are important. Items with one star will be helpful.

We use a number of products by Innate. They are nutriceuticals from fruits, vegetables and herbs. Most are organic and GMO-free. We have also noted the dosages that are optimal. If you are taking inadequate amounts, consider changing brands. **Sign up** on the PYB website in the Newsletter section to be notified when our new products become available and you will receive updates on supplements we have added to the protocol and the latest research.

mg = milligrams

mcg = micrograms

IU = international units

Vitamins

*** **<u>Food Multi III</u>** by **INNATE,** two tablets three times a day or try organic juicing.

*** **<u>B complex</u>** by **INNATE,** one tablet twice a day.

*** **<u>C Complete Powder</u>** by **INNATE,** one to two scoops daily (goal is over 2,500 mg daily for heart health) **<u>OR,</u>**

*** **<u>Vitamin C 400</u>** by **INNATE,** two to three tablets daily. Increase vitamin C to bowel tolerance. Good antioxidant and helps decrease colds and flu.

*** **<u>Vitamin D3,</u> 8,000 IU** daily in the Northwest if lab results are over 55. (Dosage of **5,000 IU everywhere else but you may require more after testing.**)

If lab results are 20 to 30 take 10,000 IU by mouth daily and 50,000 IU by injection monthly for **four months and recheck**.

If can't do shots, start 25,000 IU one tab two times per week of D3 by **Metabolic Maintenance** and **recheck lab work every four months**.

If levels are below 20, take 25,000 IU, one tab three times per week and **recheck in 60 days**. If levels are 32 to 45, take 10,000 IU daily and **retest in four months**. Once you get to optimal range of 55 to 75, take 4,000 to 5,000

IU daily for maintenance if you live in a sunny climate.

If you have a chronic health condition or have breast cancer concerns, get your lab values over 65 and below 95. **Having your vitamin D at an optimal level at the time of surgery or biopsy increases your survival rate by 65%.**

Important: A good goal is 70 to 75 if the lab range normal is 32 to 80. If your lab range is 30 to 100, then an optimal goal is 80 to 90. **Lab test kits are available on the ZRT/Dutch Lab websites for you to check your levels at home and share with your physician.**

Take your vitamin D3 with some healthy organic fat (olive, avocado, or coconut oil) for better absorption. If you are of Northern European decent consider vitamin D3 as sublingual drops, they will absorb better.

*** **Liquid D3** by **Rx Vitamins** 2000 IU per one drop

*** **Vitamin D3** by **INNATE**, which includes 450 mcg K1 and 50 mcg K2

OR

*** **Vitamin D3**, 5,000 IU by **Metabolic Maintenance** and **also add vitamin K2 (see below) for better absorption.**

*** **Vitamin K2**, 150 mcg by MK-7 **Bio Tech** **or** eat organic natto or dark greens.

Minerals

***Calcium citrate** by **Douglas**, two 250 mg tabs at bedtime (500 mg daily). New research advises avoiding higher doses due to cardiovascular plaque and micro-calcifications in the breast.

Calcium maleate is also well absorbed. Avoid using calcium carbonate due to poor absorption.

***Magnesium citrate by **Allergy Research Group**, 170 mg four to five tabs daily in divided dosages (needs 500 to 750 mg total daily) (Softens stool, good for constipation)

OR

***Magnesium 300 powder or tablets by **INNATE**, 300 mg per scoop daily (Goal is 500 to 750 mg daily in divided dosage.)

***Magnesium glycinate, 125 mg by **Metabolic Maintenance** (this is less loosening than magnesium citrate). Take two tablets twice a day and one at bedtime to get in the 700 to 750 mg range.

*Rebuild Plus Osteoporosis Form by **Metabolic Maintenance** if bone support is an issue.

Adrenal support

***Adrenal Response by **INNATE**, two tablets daily in the morning. If you do not feel overly stressed, omit this but it helps with adrenal fatigue and poor thyroid function.

Antioxidants

***Theracurmin by **Integrative Therapeutics** or sprinkle turmeric on foods.

***CuraPro by **EuroMedica** 375 mg capsule

***CurcuPhen Extra Strength by **EuroMedica** 902 mg capsule (better for joint pain or more severe conditions).

*** Resveratrol with piperine by **Metabolic Maintenance**, one 200 mg capsule daily with meals or **grapeseed oil**, one teaspoon daily

OR

*** Paleo Reds by **Designs for Health**, one scoop daily

Estrogen Regulators

***Organic broccoli sprouts. Note: **If you eat these plus Resveratrol, you may omit I-3-C and DIM in tablet form. Kills off breast cancer stem cells. Don't cook them.**

Ultra I-3-C by **Douglas Labs, one 200 mg tablet twice per day with meals (400 mg total)

OR

DIM-Avail / **dindolylmethane by **Designs for Health**, 100 mg 120 mg one to two tablets per day

Digestive Wellness

***Eat fermented foods like raw sauerkraut, organic kefir and yogurt, and kombucha. They are loaded with probiotics.

***Similase digestive enzymes by **Integrative Therapeutics**, take one cap before meals or eat slices of organic papaya or pineapple, or make a strong fresh organic ginger tea. These foods have digestive enzymes in them.

***Flora 50-14 clinical strength probiotics **(50 billion organisms and 14 strains)** by **INNATE**, one tablet daily after food (refrigerate). Do not take with hot beverage.

OR

Mega Probiotics by **DaVinci (five billion organisms and nine strains), two to three capsules daily (refrigerate)

Oils and Fatty Acids

Black currant seed oil by **DaVinci, two capsules per day. Contains linolenic acid, 640 mg, gamma linolenic, 80 mg, and alpha linolenic 150 mg

OR

Evening primrose oil by **Barlean's (organic) or Metabolic Maintenance, 1,300 mg (same amounts of EFAs)

OR

Borage oil by **Barlean's (herbicide and pesticide free), 1,000 mg daily

The three oils above help with tender breasts, dry eyes, and dry skin.

*****If estrogen dominant, use fish oil or krill oil, or Carlson's cod liver oil with lemon** one teaspoon daily. (If indigestion occurs, take in capsule form and freeze them, and take with juice. Fewer burps.)

ProOmega by **Nordic Naturals**, two per day. **Don't** take large amounts of fish oil if on Coumadin. It is a blood thinner. Check with your doctor.

Vegetarians may eat **1.5 ounces of walnuts** a day or **chia seeds** for their Omega 3s.

If estrogen dominant, avoid extra flax or non-fermented soy or tofu. Miso and tempeh are OK.

Progesterone

*****Progesterone**, 40 to 50 mg daily total. **Must say the following: USP, micronized or bio-identical.**

Apply ¼ teaspoon or 20 mg topically to wrists and forearms **then** apply and massage into thin skin or breasts. If you put it on your hands, you will wash off a portion of the dose. **For menopause**, apply twice a day for three weeks on and one week off

OR

Monday through Friday twice daily. Don't use on the weekends.

If cycling, use twice a day starting on day 12 through 28 then stop using it until your next cycle on day 12. (First day of flow equals day one.) Some women can later decrease to using progesterone just at bedtime since it also helps sleep. **ZRT/Dutch Lab hormone test kits may also help you test your levels to find out what hormones you may need, if you are deficient.**

Over-the-counter (OTC) progesterone Pro-Gest by Emerita, paraben free/ or Natural Progeste Cream by Metabolic Maintenance/paraben free. See instructions above, the progesterone sheet or Chapter 5. These dosages may need to be adjusted during treatment. If the OTC says only "Natural Progesterone from Wild Yam," **don't buy it**. It must say pharmacy grade **(USP), Micronized, Bio-identical, and a dosage in milligrams** per some amount.

Iodine (Review Chapter 2 and the How to Take Liquid Iodine sheets first for correct dose)

Iodine you only require 150 to 200 mcg/micrograms or 0.2 mg/milligrams a day.

***__**Iodine and seaweed**__, increase Celtic sea salt and seafood.

** Eat seaweeds from Iceland, Norway, and Maine to avoid contaminated Asian seaweeds. **One quarter teaspoon powdered seaweed equals three mg iodine.** You can easily use less since it is powdered. Eat sea vegetables such as nori, Sea Crunchies, wakame, kombui, hijiki and dulse. They have large amounts of iodine and they tend to alkaline your system. They are also loaded with trace minerals. Source: Sea Seasonings Organic Dulse Granules, Maine Coast Sea Vegetables, www.seaveg.com

OR

If you have thyroid problems and are on thyroid replacement therapy, then review Chapter 2 on iodine, do some testing and check with your physician before starting iodine.

Some conditions require more iodine. Work with your physician. Keep a temperature journal to monitor your metabolic activity. If your morning temperature is below 97.8, you may be hypothyroid. **ZRT and Dutch Labs provide iodine and thyroid test kits for further clarity.**

Lugol's 2% solution by **J. Crow or half strength**. Available on my website. One drop equals three mg. Dilute in a glass of water. Start slowly and increase after one week to two drops. Can take smaller amounts as liquid by dividing a glass of water in half with one drop in glass equaling 1.5 mg. This may still be too much. Seaweed may be a better choice.

Immune Support

***__Cellular Immune Support (mushroom blend)__ by **Gaia Herbs** - one scoop daily. Check my website for other protein powders.

Fiber

***__Organic Acacia Fiber__ by **NOW**. Try chia seeds, one teaspoon daily in liquid or rice, oat, wheat bran, or psyllium for fiber instead of flax seed, if estrogen excess is a problem. Do not use wheat if gluten intolerance may be an issue.

Lymphatic Drainage Massage

May be helpful for thickened areas. **A one hour DVD is available on the PYB website.** There is also a Free 5 minute YouTube on the website. **No underwire bras or aluminum antiperspirants.**

Compare and save at www.ProtectYourBreasts.com.

GET 20% OFF ALL YOUR SUPPLEMENTS FOR YOU & YOUR FAMILY ON OUR WEBSITE!

3. How to Use Bioidentical Progesterone Topically

(Directions: Ingrid Edstrom, FNP, M.Ed.)

Bioidentical Progesterone in an Oil Base

I usually mix up the progesterone solution by stirring or shaking the bottle you get from the compounding pharmacy so the powder that sinks to the bottom is stirred up. You can then see how much one drop looks like with the dropper and put the drops on your wrist and then from there massage into thin skin like your breasts, inside your arms, thighs, neck, behind your knees, or elbow creases. Probably avoid the abdomen since it slows down bowel motility and most of us have too much padding in that area.

You may also shake or stir the solution and then use a finger to apply the drops to the thin skin areas once you feel comfortable with dosage size. I would also rub the drops in with your forearm or wrist because if you have it all over your palms you will wash off most of your dose. We do not wash the wrists so often and it will have a chance to absorb. (When a woman is nine months pregnant, she produces about 800 mg of progesterone a day. The dosage of compounded progesterone or over-the-counter progesterone is only 15 to 20 mg per dose, so it is quite safe if you get a bit more or less onto your skin.)

For menopausal women, use four drops on your skin in the morning after your shower and another four drops topically before bedtime. It will also help you sleep and usually improves your moods. You become more mellow. You can transfer about a week's worth to a larger mouth small jar later so you can get all of it out with your finger when the jar is low. Use colored glass or tape on some pretty paper to avoid sunlight. The progesterone in oil can sit happily for at least 45 days on a counter at room temperature, but I usually put the stock bottle back in the refrigerator until I need more.

You can use it Monday through Friday and then discontinue on the weekend. Or you can use it three weeks on and one week off. Most of us do better remembering the Monday through Friday regimen. The dosage usually is 40 to 50 mg per day. If written as micronized progesterone, 40 mg per eight drops in organic jojoba oil, you will use four drops in the morning and four drops at bedtime. I prefer organic jojoba oil because it is less greasy and does not stain clothes a lot. It is stable at room temperature and does not need a preservative. If cost is an issue, ask the pharmacist if it is less expensive in olive oil, then have your provider change your prescription.

For cycling women, start on day 12 and continue through day 28, and then stop during your period. Count the first day of bleeding as day one of your cycle. Younger women may only use progesterone once a day since they are still making some of their own progesterone. We usually discuss your particular situation during the office visit. When you are cycling, you are usually making 15 to 20 mg per day. If the prescription is written as 40 mg per eight drops and you are only using four drops, it is five mg per drop or 20 mg. If you use three drops it will be 15 mg.

Over-The-Counter Progesterone

The progesterone purchased in the store or online must say USP (US Pharmacy grade), micronized or bioidentical progesterone and it should say exactly how many milligrams of progesterone you will be getting per quarter teaspoon for example.

If the bottle says, "Natural progesterone from wild yam" but doesn't tell you the dosage per ¼ teaspoon or doesn't say

USP, micronized or bioidentical progesterone, then do not purchase the brand. It will likely be a progesterone precursor that you will not be able to absorb. Also, completely avoid any product that has parabens in it (for example ethyl parben or methy paraben). These chemicals are preservatives and cause cancer. They are put in many cosmetics and over-the-counter products.

Remember that you can get 20% off your over-the-counter progesterone or any of your other favorite supplements through the Protect Your Breasts website.

4. Hormone Replacement Therapy Symptoms

Do you have these symptoms?

	Absent	Mild	Moderate	Severe
Fibrocystic breasts	______	______	______	______
Weight gain	______	______	______	______
Heavy or irregular menses	______	______	______	______
Dry skin and hair	______	______	______	______
Hot flashes	______	______	______	______
Anxiety	______	______	______	______
Depression	______	______	______	______
Night sweats	______	______	______	______
Vaginal dryness	______	______	______	______
Headaches	______	______	______	______
Irritability	______	______	______	______
Mood Swings	______	______	______	______
Breast tenderness	______	______	______	______
Sleep disturbance	______	______	______	______
Cramps	______	______	______	______
Fluid retention	______	______	______	______
Breakthrough bleeding	______	______	______	______
Fatigue	______	______	______	______
Loss of memory	______	______	______	______
Bladder symptoms	______	______	______	______
Arthritis	______	______	______	______
Harder to reach climax	______	______	______	______
Decreased sex drive	______	______	______	______
Hair loss	______	______	______	______

Patient Name: ____

Date:____________

Use this as your master and make copies. Do a morning axillary temperature for six days. Add up the temperatures and divide by six for an average. If you are under 97.8 axillary, you are probably hypothyroid. Now check against the other hormone symptoms listed. Make changes according to the PBW protocol and in six weeks check your symptoms and temperature again to monitor. This is free for you to do and you will gain valuable information as you track changes over time.

5. Abnormal Hormone Symptoms for Females by PCCA

(Professional Compounding Centers of America)

Low Thyroid Function /Hypothyroidism

If you have half to three quarters of these symptoms, you need to consider thyroid support or thyroid replacement.

- Fatigue (especially evening)
- Low stamina
- Cold extremities
- Low body temperature
- Weight gain
- Low pulse rate or blood pressure
- Dry skin
- Intolerance to cold
- General aches and pains
- Low libido
- Depression
- Anxiety
- Scalp hair loss
- Swollen, puffy eyes
- Brittle nails
- Poor concentration
- Iodine deficient
- Headaches
- Memory lapses
- High cholesterol
- Heart palpitations
- Constipation
- Infertility
- Fibromyalgia

Low Cortisol

- Fatigue
- Allergies
- Cravings for sweets or salt
- Irritability
- Chemical sensitivities
- Symptoms of hypothyroidism
- Symptoms of low progesterone

High Cortisol

- Same symptoms as low cortisol, and additionally:
- Bone loss
- Sleep disturbances
- Depression or anxiety
- Elevated triglycerides
- Low libido
- Hair loss

Testosterone Deficiency

- Fatigue, prolonged
- Mental fuzziness or memory problems

- Decreased libido
- Depression or blunted motivation
- Muscle weakness
- Diminished feeling of well being
- Heart palpitations
- Thinning skin
- Bone loss
- Vaginal dryness or Incontinence
- Fibromyalgia
- General aches and pains

Testosterone Excess

- Acne
- Male-pattern hair growth
- Loss of scalp hair
- Deepening voice
- Clitoral enlargement
- Insomnia
- Irritability, moodiness, aggressiveness

Estrogen Deficiency

- Hot flashes and night sweats
- Sleep disturbances and low libido
- Heart palpitations
- Vaginal dryness, atrophy or painful intercourse
- Depression and memory lapses
- Foggy thinking
- Bone loss
- Yeast infections
- Headaches
- Dry skin

Estrogen Excess

- Weight gain and water retention
- Cravings for sweets
- Low thyroid symptoms
- Heavy, irregular menses and uterine fibroids
- Nervousness, anxiety, irritability
- Fibrocystic breasts, breast swelling, and tenderness
- Fatigue and mood swings

Progesterone Deficiency

Many symptoms of estrogen excess, including:

- Weight gain
- Swollen breasts
- Mood swings, anxiety, depression
- Headaches or fuzzy thinking
- Joint pain
- Irregular menses, infertility, cramping
- Acne
- PMS
- Low libido

Progesterone Excess

- Somnolence or feeling really sleepy the next morning if you took too large a progesterone dose at bedtime
- Mild depression
- Exacerbates symptoms of estrogen deficiency
- Gastrointestinal bloating
- Candida and yeast exacerbations
- Breast swelling

6. How to Do a Temperature Journal

Doing a temperature journal is really easy to do and free!

This is a way you can monitor your metabolic activity and thyroid function easily at home.

Put a thermometer next to your bed with a pen and paper. Upon awakening and before you get out of bed and start wandering around, put the thermometer under your tongue or armpit for five minutes. Take the temperature reading always in the same place, i.e. under tongue vs. armpit. Collect your temperature upon awakening for five or six days. If you skip a morning, don't worry about it. Doing five or six readings over several different days will get you a better temperature average than just doing three readings. You can stop checking your temperature after the fifth or sixth day. You just want a snapshot in time of what your body is doing.

Now, calculate an average temp of the five or six readings by adding up all the readings that you took and divide that number by the number of days you checked your temperature.

If your average temperature is below 97.8 you are probably hypothyroid and you may need labs and possibly thyroid replacement therapy or thyroid support.

You can refer back to the Hormone Replacement Therapy Symptom List and the PCCA thyroid symptoms list (Worksheet 4 and 5). I would keep the original and make copies so that you can write on them and make your own symptom checklist and date it. This will help you track improvements.

I would also do a complete thyroid panel as a base line. You can then easily monitor your body's response in about six weeks after taking some iodine, B complex twice a day or Thyro Complex, which is referred to as thyroid support.

If later you are started on thyroid replacement therapy, then you can monitor how you are doing on that as well by checking your temperatures every six to eight weeks. You can then do another of your own symptom checklists and date it in six weeks so you can monitor your progress over time. You may note that your symptoms that might have been severe are now moderate or mild or perhaps now absent.

Your physician might wish to do free T3, free T4 and TSH tests every six months if you are on thyroid replacement therapy. Ask to have all three tests done, not just the TSH.

You can have the thyroid labs done locally through your physician. If you have concerns that you have a thyroid nodule, have your provider include two more tests. Add a baseline TPO AB (Thyroid Peroxidase Antibody) and a Thyroglobulin Antibody to the thyroid panel. You can also receive a hormone test kit through ZRT Lab or Dutch Lab.

These temperature journals can be done more often to assist you and your provider in monitoring your symptoms and response to therapy over time. They give a lot of information and it is free to do.

7. How to Take Liquid Iodine and How Much

Taking iodine is important and the following suggestions that I made in Chapter 2 under Supplements including iodine will assist you in determining what dosage may be the best for you. This is an individual matter. There is a lot of in-depth information in Chapter 2 and what dosage is suggested based on several parameters. Please review that section now.

Ninety percent of Americans are low in iodine, so it is safe to assume you are deficient also, unless you are eating wild caught ocean seafood and seaweed or sea vegetables three days a week.

On the next Worksheet #8, there are instructions on how to do an iodine patch test, which will be an easy experiment to find out how deficient your body might be.

Starting low and slow works best with iodine because if you have not been taking iodine or eating a lot of seafood, your iodine receptor sites will have become filled with chloride, fluoride, and bromine, which look similar to iodine chemically. Chloride, fluoride, and bromine are all halogens that are toxic chemicals. These iodine receptor sites are mostly located in the thyroid and secondly in breast tissue. If a person has been exposed to other halogens such as bromide, fluoride and chloride in the environment, these halogens will be displaced by iodine in the receptor sites as you start your iodine supplementation. These halogens are toxins and if too large a quantity is released into the circulation too quickly, they can make a person feel ill for four days as you detox and you get rid of the halogens. If you add iodine very slowly, at a low starting dose this does not occur.

Here are a few sources of halogens that you may have had contact with in your environment: bromide from hot tubs,

Gatorade, Mountain Dew, or bread with bleached flour. Fluoride is frequently present in city water or toothpaste. Chlorine sources are also from city water or swimming pools.

To start I suggest you get a bottle of Lugol's 2% solution (half-strength Lugol's) from J. Crows which is on my website Virtual Dispensary. Another option is Atlantic seaweed. Please refer to that section in Chapter 2 to discuss how much seaweed or liquid iodine to take.

If you have tender or fibrocystic breasts, you can apply one drop of the 2% Lugol's to your breast topically. Please again check Chapter 2 for more details.

Physicians should treat the patient and their symptoms not just the lab values. If your labs are borderline low but you also show up at your doctor's appointment with your symptom and temperature journal worksheets, the physician will be more willing to add a pharmacy thyroid replacement option if the glandular product still has not made marked improvements in how you are feeling or your symptoms. I have gone over the thyroid glandular support option in Chapter 2 in more detail.

8. How to Do the Iodine Paint (Patch) Test

Use tincture of iodine, the original, orange-colored solution, not the clear solution. Since iodine may be hard to obtain since it can be used in the preparation of methamphetamines. You can ask your compounding pharmacist to obtain it or you can order the Lugol's 2% liquid on my website Virtual Dispensary. (We also have this listed on the PBW Supplement section so you can learn more.)

Before going to bed, paint a three inch by one inch rectangle patch of iodine onto the underside of the forearm or on the inner thigh or abdomen. Note the color of the staining of the skin.

In the morning, upon rising, note the color of the area where the iodine solution was applied. When the body is really low in iodine it rapidly absorbs the iodine directly through the skin. Remember that 90% of Americans are usually iodine deficient.

If the stain is gone or almost completely gone after eight hours, this will indicate iodine deficiency and the need for iodine supplementation or increase iodine through diet.

If the stain is still there on your painted patch and the same size the next morning, you probably are taking enough iodine.

You may slowly increase the iodine dose for three to four weeks, and then repeat the iodine paint test. Reduce the dosage immediately if your symptoms get worse at any time following an increase in dose. Go back and refer to Chapter 2 for instructions on using iodine and seaweed.

9. Benefits of Certain Foods

Share this List with Everyone

Apples: protect your heart, prevent constipation, Block diarrhea, Improve lung capacity

Apricot: Combat cancer, Control blood pressure, Save your eyesight, Shield against Alzheimer's, Slow the aging process

Artichokes: Aid digestion, Lower cholesterol, Protect your heart, Stabilize blood sugar, Guard against liver disease

Avocados: Battle diabetes, Lower cholesterol, Help stops strokes, Control blood pressure, Smooth skin

Bananas: Protect your heart, Quiet a cough, Strengthen bones, Control blood pressure, Block diarrhea

Beans: Prevent constipation, Help hemorrhoids, Lower cholesterol, Combat cancer, Stabilize blood sugar

Beets: Control blood pressure, Combat cancer, Strengthen bones, Protect your heart, Aid weight loss

Blueberries: Combat cancer, Protect your heart, Stabilize blood sugar, Boost memory, Prevent constipation

Broccoli: Strengthens bones, Saves eyesight, Combats cancer, Protects your heart, Controls blood pressure

Cabbage: Combats cancer, Prevents constipation, Promotes weight loss, Protects your heart, Helps hemorrhoids

Cantaloupe: Saves eyesight, Controls blood pressure, Lowers cholesterol, Combats cancer, Supports immune system

Carrots: Save eyesight, Protect your heart, Prevent constipation, Combat cancer, Promote weight loss

Cauliflower: Protects against prostate cancer, Combats breast cancer, Strengthens bones, Banishes bruises, Guards against heart disease

Cherries: Protect your heart, Combat cancer, End insomnia, Slow the aging process, Shield against Alzheimer's

Chestnuts: Promote weight loss, Protect your heart, Lower cholesterol, Combat cancer, Control blood pressure

Chili peppers: Aid digestion, Soothe sore throat, Clear sinuses, Combat cancer, Boost immune system

Figs: Promote weight loss, Help stops strokes, Lower cholesterol, Combat cancer, Control blood pressure

Fish: Protects your heart, Boosts memory, Combats cancer, Supports immune system

Flax: Aids digestion, Battles diabetes, Protects your heart, Improves mental health, Boosts immune system

Garlic: Lowers cholesterol, Controls blood pressure, Combats cancer, Kills bacteria, Fights fungus

Grapefruit: Protects against heart attacks, Promotes weight loss, Helps stop strokes, Combats prostate cancer, Lowers cholesterol

Grapes: Save eyesight, Conquer kidney stones, Combat cancer, Enhance blood flow, Protects your heart

Green tea: Combats cancer, Protects your heart, Helps stop strokes, Promotes weight loss, Kills bacteria

Honey: Heals wounds, Aids digestion, Guards against ulcers, Increases energy, Fights allergies

Lemons: Combat cancer, Protect your heart, Control blood pressure, Smoothe skin, Stop scurvy

Limes: Combat cancer, Protect your heart, Control blood pressure, Smoothe skin, Stop scurvy

Mangoes: Combat cancer, Boost memory, Regulate thyroid, Aid digestion, Shield against Alzheimer's

Mushrooms: Control blood pressure, Lower cholesterol, Kill bacteria, Combat cancer, Strengthen bones

Oats: Lower cholesterol, Combat cancer, Battle diabetes, Prevent constipation, Smoothes skin

Olive oil: Protects your heart, Promotes weight loss, Combats cancer, Battles diabetes, Smoothes skin

Onions: Reduce risk of heart attack, Combat cancer, Kill bacteria, Lower cholesterol, Fight fungus

Oranges: Support immune systems, Combat cancer, Protect your heart, Straighten respiration

Peaches: Prevent constipation, Combat cancer, Help stops strokes, Aid digestion, Help hemorrhoids

Peanuts: Protect against heart disease, Promote weight loss, Combat prostate cancer, Lower cholesterol, Aggravate diverticulitis

Pineapple: Strengthens bones, Relieves colds, Aids digestion, Dissolves warts, Blocks diarrhea

Prunes: Slow the aging process, Prevent constipation, Boost memory, Lower cholesterol, Protect against heart disease

Rice: Protects your heart, Battles diabetes, Conquers kidney stones, Combats cancer, Helps stop strokes

Strawberries: Combat cancer, Protect your heart, Boost memory, Calm stress

Sweet potatoes: Save your eyesight, Lift mood, Combat cancer, Strengthen bones

Tomatoes: Protect prostate, Combat cancer, Lower cholesterol, Protect your heart

Walnuts: Lower cholesterol, Combat cancer, Boost memory, Lift mood, Protect against heart disease

Water: Promotes Weight loss, Combats cancer, Conquers kidney stones, Smoothes skin

Watermelon: Protects prostate, Promotes weight loss, Lowers cholesterol, Helps stop strokes, Controls blood pressure

Wheat germ: Combats colon cancer, Prevents constipation, Lowers cholesterol, Helps stop strokes, Improves digestion

Wheat bran: Combats colon cancer, Prevents constipation, Lowers cholesterol, Helps stop strokes, Improves digestion, Avoid if gluten intolerant

Yogurt: Guards against ulcers, Strengthens bones, Lowers cholesterol, Supports immune system, Aids digestion

10. Shopper's Guide to Pesticides in Produce
Environmental Working Group

EWG'S 2020
DIRTY 12™

1. Strawberries
2. Spinach
3. Kale
4. Nectarines
5. Apples
6. Grapes
7. Peaches
8. Cherries
9. Pears
10. Tomatoes
11. Celery
12. Potatoes

EWG'S 2020
CLEAN 15™

1. Avocados
2. Sweet Corn
3. Pineapple
4. Onions
5. Papaya
6. Sweet Peas (Frozen)
7. Eggplant
8. Asparagus
9. Cauliflower
10. Cantaloupe
11. Broccoli
12. Mushrooms
13. Cabbage
14. Honeydew Melon
15. Kiwi

11. How to Access my Virtual Dispensary to Receive 20% Off All Your Supplements

We have given you instructions on how to set up your own account to order from my Virtual Dispensary off my website www.ProtectYourBreasts.com. There are access codes on my website in the supplement section to make this easier. You can print the instructions when you are ready to order. Or you can call Emerson Ecologics/Wellevate to order your supplements. You need to identify yourself as a person following my PYB protocol in order to get the 20% off. All of the supplements that I currently use are also on the PYB Virtual Dispensary. As new products become available, I will post them on my website so you can stay current. I encourage you to also sign up for our newsletter so we can notify you of new products and research. This dispensary makes it easy for you to compare what you are currently taking with the PYB protocol.

Just click on the picture of the supplement bottle on my dispensary and it will drop down to show you all the ingredients. Emerson Ecologics/Wellevate is a large distributor of high-end supplements and nutraceuticals. Your doctor or naturopath probably has a wholesale account with them already so you will be saving 20% off anything that you are currently purchasing retail. Emerson Ecologics carries products from more than 385 manufacturers, and about 4,000 products, so you will probably find the products you are currently taking for a lot less. So if you like a product that is currently not on my "Favorites" list, then scroll down further and you can access the whole Emerson/Wellevate line and still get the 20% discount when you come through my website.

You will also see that in purchasing higher quality supplements through my site and Emerson Ecologics, you will avoid purchasing lesser quality products that have a lot of fillers, additives, or are sourced from places that do not do their due diligence on product testing, safety, and quality. Since MDs, NDs, and nutritionists purchase from Emerson Ecologics, you know that Emerson/Wellevate will offer you the same quality that these other health care providers expect and trust. You can share my dispensary with family and friends to improve their health also!

12. Other Books and Organizations You May Find Helpful

I have added other resource lists that include recommended books or websites that you might find interesting and to expand your research towards better health and vitality.

We also have over 90 books listed on my website in the Resource section that will help guide your journey towards improved health. I broke the books down into different sections and categories to assist you in finding the book that you need. These books are all favorites of mine and I have them on my bookshelves. We encourage you to purchase books by these authors who may be of interest to you through our Amazon link. I have personally met many of the authors at various conferences over the years.

I added a Take Action section on my website that will quickly link you to other organizations to expand your knowledge base. You will find links that will help you choose less toxic cosmetics and body care products. You will learn which seafood has more heavy metals or contaminants. Just for the record, avoid all farmed fish.

There is an assortment of website links of sister organizations with whom we anticipate working more closely in the future. We have also included various newsletter sources from other organizations that you might enjoy and wish to subscribe to.

13. Receive Your Two Free Gifts as Part of the Comprehensive *Proactive Breast Wellness* Program and your *Protect Your Breasts* book or eBook Purchase

As part of the third edition PBW program now as *Protect Your Breasts* available as an eBook or soft cover book, I encourage you to receive these two FREE gifts as part of the PBW comprehensive program. I have included the *Waves of Serenity* relaxation CD/DVD/digital download as part of the mind-body portion to improve your health. I have also included a free data disc/resource digital download. Enter password code **PBWBOOK** (all capitals and no spaces) at the Free Resources section on website Store. If you prefer, I can mail you *Waves* and the data disc CD for a $3.00 shipping fee from the website Store.

14. How to Use the *Waves of Serenity* Relaxation CD/DVD/Digital Download

I created *Waves of Serenity* for people who did not previously have any experience with relaxation or meditation techniques. I have used this tool for years with my patients who had insomnia, chronic pain, elevated blood pressure or cortisol levels, were approaching hospitalization or surgery, or who simply wanted to unwind at the end of a hectic day. There is no religious affiliation so any one will feel comfortable using *Waves*. You can listen to and view a clip of *Waves* on the home page of the website. It starts with a progressive muscle relaxation and then transitions to a guided imagery of a beach walk with ocean sounds and harp along with my soothing narrative. Please listen to *Waves* daily and start incorporating these relaxation techniques throughout the day.

If you prefer the gorgeous beach scenes, get the *Waves* as a DVD. The CD and DVD of *Waves* are also available from my website as a "Gift of Health" for a friend or family member who needs to "wiggle their toes in the sand" for a bit.

Advanced meditation practitioners also enjoy *Waves*. Great for children and teens too!

15. Acknowledgement to the Authors and Resources On the Resource Download/Disc

The PYB staff has compiled research and references over the last seven years that we felt might enhance your knowledge base. We gathered a selection of the articles together on the free data disk / digital download for your use. It is our hope that this will provide a starting point for your own research at the library, online, or in bookstores. Our staff tried to make the selection of materials based on current research in the medical literature that, by its nature, is constantly changing. We also have offered an integrative medicine viewpoint that encourages prevention of diseases and health promotion as a goal. We have provided the data disc and download in PDF format for the articles used as well as web links. We have tried to provide the sources, links, and websites of the articles on the free data disc / download so that you may view the original source materials and the authors to give them full credit.

Recent health polls suggest that 65% to 72% of adult Americans are already utilizing or are interested in complementary or integrative medicine with supplements, nutrition, acupuncture, chiropractic, massage, mind / body techniques, and other modalities. We acknowledge that the resources provided are a starting point due to the vastness of the breast cancer topic and may not address all the issues or include all the authors who are expert in this field.

16. Please Write a Review and Sign Up for Your Free Newsletter

THANK YOU FOR READING

Dear Reader,

I hope you were able to get as much out of *Protect Your Breasts* as I intended you to. I also hope all the articles on the FREE digital download were enlightening and the *Waves of Serenity* relaxation program was soothing and allowed you your own "Mini Vacation"!

Reviews are a huge help to authors and they assist other women who are seeking answers to their breast challenges and solutions for their breast health. Knowing what you thought will benefit all these other women and it helps me to get my book out into the public eye. These reviews will also inform women about breast cryoablation~ the future of breast cancer care! I need every woman to help me spread the word about freezing and curing breast cancer so we may be able to save breasts and lives!

I would encourage you to sign up for my newsletter to receive more information on cryoablation and other breast health articles as the research comes out. I can also send you notices if there is a big sale on supplements or new supplements are added or exchanged for a different dosage or manufacturer, so you can keep your breast wellness protocol updated.

I invite you to get on my email/newsletter list at www.ProtectYourBreasts.com/newsletter/

I promise not to share your email with anyone and I will be complying with GDPR- General Data Protection Regulation which is a new European law that provides privacy and spam protection at a higher level than before.

Wishing you health and healing!

—Ingrid Edstrom

17. Help Get the Word Out About Cryoablation on Amazon and Barnes & Noble

I need to ask a favor of you that will not only help me as an author but more importantly spread the word about cryoablation and the life and breast saving information in my book to many more women. If you are so inclined and you appreciated *Protect Your Breasts,* please write a review of my book on Amazon and also place a comment on Barnes and Noble and spread the word through your social media channels.

Amazon had cancelled my ads because they felt that cryoablation is too controversial. A head Amazon Marketing person named Tony Sabel, claims that Protect Your Breasts is "Inappropriate for all audiences" and "Cancer is a serious condition." Hence they would not allow me to advertise my book to get it back up to the top of page two for a whole year. I found their reasoning inaccurate, in that half the world's population are women and many are concerned about breast cancer so how is my book "Inappropriate for all audiences?" There are hundreds of books on Amazon about cancer and many are still being advertized.

In the end, the language Amazon found offensive was "Freeze and Cure Your Breast Cancer." I have changed the third edition to say "Freeze Your Breast Cancer with Cryoablation" and they wanted more petals covering her cleavage on the cover!

If men can have their prostate cancers frozen with liquid nitrogen and the insurance companies pay for this accepted standard of care, then women should be able to have their breast cancers frozen and save their breasts. More women should be insisting that this procedure be made available to them. Perhaps these other books are promoting "Big Pharm" and the large and powerful "Breast Cancer Machine" that makes a lot of money for the industry and they quite frankly like breast cancer care the way it is now. Perhaps you found some of this information rather disturbing!

Nevertheless, if you and others post positive reviews, then this may possibly help a bit to restore my search ranking on Amazon and Barnes & Noble. If there are more comments, my book will bubble up so that other women may find my book and learn about the important option of cryoablation and a more prevention based approach for their breast care. By spreading the word about cryoablation and information about "Prevention IS the Cure", you help expand options for other women.

Wishing you improved health,

—Ingrid Edstrom, FNP, M.Ed.

18. Cryoablation Nurse Practitioner Navigator Services

You are probably wondering, what are the parameters for a woman to qualify to have their tumor cryoablated. Please also review the earlier sections on pages 271 and 274 for further information.

I counsel women one-on-one by doing phone medical consults with potential cryoablation clients.

If you are a woman with a breast cancer diagnosis and you are trying to figure out if your case would be appropriate for cryoablation or not, you may contact me as your Nurse Practitioner Navigator through my email to set up a paid medical consult.

Please also let me know what time zone you are calling from and a phone number. If you would also send me some information like the size of your tumor in centimeters or millimeters, biopsy report or tumor type and your age and where you live.

Please scan the radiologist's written report for the ultrasound, mammogram and MRI, if done. I have also been attempting to bill insurance for this telemedicine visit, so please send me your insurance type with the group number and your date of birth.

Most women who utilize my "Navigator" services also want to do a telemedicine consult to go over questions they have from reading my book. They usually want some more direct personal guidance on the cryoablation procedure and to improve their immune system. In that case, scan and send me a list of your current supplements or medications, and any recent laboratory tests. I also want to know if you are menopausal and for how long? Please tell me if you were on hormone replacement recently and the dosage you were on and what type. Most doctors take women off hormone replacement therapy when they learn they have a cancer diagnosis.

We can then arrange a telemedicine phone consult time by email. Reach me through the link on my website or email:

Contact@ProactiveBreastWellness.com

Special Thanks and Gratitude

I am eternally grateful to the PYB staff and our consultants and I wish to personally thank them for their dedication, tireless efforts to persevere, detail-oriented editing, proof reading, photography, sound studio creations, and business guidance. Without your skills and expertise, *Protect Your Breasts* would not be available to the women who have been waiting for guidance to reduce their risks of breast cancer or its reoccurrence. Through your efforts as the PYB Team, you have helped to replace fear with empowerment and have mobilized concern into action. The PYB Team has provided education and support for the women and their daughters as well as for their partners and families who love them. I thank all of you for believing in this project and for wanting to make a difference by participating in the process.

I wish to personally thank all my infrared patients with whom I have been privileged to have participated in their journey towards health. Our latest marketing slogan, modeled after the "McDonald's Golden Arches," is "Over 10,000 breasts served." My thanks to all the women who shared their stories with me about their health challenges and triumphs. It has been an honor. I have appreciated your input and suggestions on how to improve my book over the years and all the networking to help spread the word among other women and organizations. My sticky note collection on what to follow up on is enviable.

I wish to personally thank the following medical consultants and reviewers of the *Proactive Breast Wellness* program who contributed so much to the creation of my third edition entitled *Protect Your Breasts*.

Max Chorowski, MD, FACOG. Max Chorowski is an Assistant Clinical Professor of Gynecology and Clinical Instructor of Psychiatry at the Tufts University School of Medicine. He is one of the first gynecologists in the country to integrate traditional and alternative therapies for gynecological problems. I worked with Max in his clinic when I was living in Massachusetts. My fondest regards Max for being a stellar mentor who always cheered me on and wanted to know what I thought. You always challenged me to do more. Thank you for improving the manuscript and my clinical practice.

Jim Paoletti, Pharmacist, FAAFM, FIACP, FACA. Jim Paoletti is a clinical consultant and educator in private practice. Jim has over 30 years of experience with bioidentical hormone therapies in clinical practice. Jim served previously as Director of Provider Education for ZRT Laboratory and as consultant and Education Director for Professional Compounding Centers of America in Houston, Texas. He is a graduate and former faculty member of the Fellowship of Anti-Aging and Functional Medicine. Jim has lectured extensively and internationally on all aspects of Bioidentical Hormone Replacement Therapy (BHRT) to medical practitioners and consumers. I thank Jim for reading the whole manuscript and adding all the red ink while on airplanes as he traveled to the next medical conference.

Dennis R. Holmes, MD, F.A.C.S. Dr. Holmes is an internationally-renowned dedicated breast surgeon and cancer researcher who has held the position of Breast Center Medical Director at several hospitals in Los Angeles County. Dr. Holmes has also served as Chief Breast Surgeon and Medical Director of the Los Angeles Center for Women's Health and as Chief Breast Cancer Surgeon and Breast Cancer Research Committee Co-Chair at the University of Southern California (U.S.C.) Kenneth Norris Comprehensive Cancer Center.

His former role was as Program Director of the U.S.C. Keck School of Medicine and John Wayne Cancer Institute's Breast Surgery Fellowship Programs. Widely respected by colleagues for his innovative approach to breast cancer care, Dr. Holmes has gained worldwide acclaim for his pioneering research in intraoperative radiotherapy and cryoablation (tumor freezing). He currently serves as National Co-Chair of the TARGIT U.S. Registry clinical trial and as National Principal Investigator of the FROST Trial, a clinical trial evaluating the use of cryoablation instead of surgery for the treatment of early stage breast cancer.

I am deeply indebted to Dennis for becoming my breast cryoablation mentor. He reviewed my whole book and helped me revise Chapter 9 on cryoablation twice and just in time for this third edition. I have been sending many of my clinical patients to him for cryoablation therapy. As a breast surgeon, I appreciate his encouragement of my book and how it will improve women's health and decrease breast cancer risk. I look forward to future years of collaboration.

Gordon Enns, MD. Gordon has been a general medical practitioner for 36 years, working in college health and emergency medicine at Ashland Community Hospital in Ashland, Oregon. Gordon was the first editor and proofreader of the *Proactive Breast Wellness* program. I want to thank Gordon for his friendship and the weeks of sitting shoulder to shoulder looking over the first manuscript and challenging me to get the medical research documented correctly. His battle cry was, "Show me the abstract." After the proof reading, the best complement that I received from this wonderful allopathically-trained physician was his statement, "PBW changed the way I am going to practice medicine." He promptly threw out all his Tupperware, plastic cooking utensils, and started buying organic food for himself and his family.

Carol Peterson, RPh, CNP. Carol is a registered compounding pharmacist, with a background in nutritional therapy, and she was the Director of the Women's International Pharmacy Education Department for many years. She is available to provide Compounding Pharmacist Coaching to my patients and readers of my book. https://thewellnessbydesignproject.com/meet-carol/

The following is an excerpt from a review she wrote on the *Proactive Breast Wellness* Program: "Thankfully, a comprehensive compilation of what we currently know about keeping our breasts free from disease, including breast cancer, is available as an engaging multimedia presentation. The *Proactive Breast Wellness* program is her Magnus Opus and a labor of love." I thank Carol for believing in my project. She also interviewed me for a two-hour spot on a New York City Public Broadcasting radio station as part of their fundraiser. The program reached five states in New England.

The following PYB Team members made the cogs in the larger wheel actually work. I wish to thank the diligence and hard work of the following folks.

Smita Deshpande, B.A. Economics, M.A. Public Administration, MBA. Smita Deshpande is a skilled and innovative professional with over 11 years experience in general administration and human resource management. When she ran a large Ashram in India, she interacted with decorum to meet the standards and needs of people from 40 different nations with her flair for understanding culture and connecting with people from diverse backgrounds. Smita had my office running like a Swiss watch and is the main reason that the 1,028-page resource/data disc got finished. I am very grateful for her cheerfulness and dedication to detail.

Carrie Janes, B.A., Nutritional Therapy Practitioner I wish to thank Carrie Janes, BA in Health Care Administration, and a nutritional therapy practitioner. Carrie had worked daily in my infrared clinic for five years. She helped support individuals going through the *Proactive Breast Wellness* program and she provided nutritional counseling to women with other challenging health concerns. I am eternally grateful for her organizational skills and sense of humor as she also ran my clinical practice flawlessly.

Tammera Karr, Ph.D. I also graciously acknowledge Tammera Karr, PhD, for some of her general comments on health and nutrition over the years. Tammera is a Holistic Nutritionist, founder of Holistic Nutrition for the Whole You, and board member of the National Association of Nutritional Professionals and the American Association of Integrative Medicine Accreditation Commissioner.

Barbara Bernadette, BA, EA (Enrolled Agent), Chief Financial Officer. Barbara Bernadette is a keynote speaker and author who founded a new paradigm based on techniques and tools she has used in creating her own personal portfolio and asset base. I am grateful to Barbara for having her hand on the rudder of my business for many years until her retirement.

Robin Klemm, Ph.D. In addition to her doctorate, Robin holds a BA in history, an MA in Art History, and an MBA from the University of Massachusetts, Amherst. She earned her doctorate in Managerial Science and Applied Economics from The Wharton School at the University of Pennsylvania. Her dissertation on financing emerging companies established the thread that would continue throughout her career. Following a faculty position at Wharton, Robin partnered in founding Optimus Consulting, a strategic consulting firm specializing in innovative and entrepreneurial challenges. One of Robin's passions is helping women's businesses succeed. To that end, she was advisor to the Wharton Women

Association, founding investor in the Women's Venture Capital Fund, board member to several women's business forums, and angel investor and advisor to countless women-owned companies. I am grateful to Robin for believing in PYB and my efforts. She personally tested the program by coming for an infrared scan, then did the whole PBW program individually with me. She was delighted with her health improvements!

Mackenzie England, BA, Digital Arts, Multimedia Graphic Arts, and Audio Engineering. Mackenzie joined the PYB team in the fall of 2006, initially as the primary web master for Infrared Breast Health. Working together, we redesigned the entire site and branded both Infrared Breast Health and the *Proactive Breast Wellness* Program. I am grateful to Mackenzie for doing all the recording of the PBW audio book/digital download and the audio engineering of the *Proactive Breast Wellness* Program. He is a musician at heart and he is the creator of the PBW musical theme that transitions the audio chapters.

Todd Garrison, BA, Computer Science and Web Designer. Todd has patiently assisted in custom-coding my website through three renditions. I am very grateful for his assistance over the years with Broadmedia Partners.

Cardinal Marking, Chloe Peterson, Morgan Janes, Morgan Starkey and Emma Routley, University of Oregon Interns. Special thanks to our PYB interns who have taken on the task of assisting with social media and launching the PYB third edition on Amazon and Barnes and Noble.

Special thanks to the staff at **Luminare Press** who helped to shepard me through the publishing process. Much appreciation goes to **Tim Hicks**, who with painstaking care, proof read the document and put in all the Oxford commas that were missing.

Additional gratitude is extended to my "Angel investors"- **Terri O'Dell** and **Pete Rosza**. My "Angels" believed in my mission and provided funds to assist me in making *Proactive Breast Wellness* and *Protect Your Breasts* a reality. Pete Rosza, who runs Healing Matrix, a Non Profit also helped me set up The Breast Cancer Education Fund to help raise donations so I can educate and empower more women.

Besides my amazing staff both past and present, I want to thank my daughter Kristin Edstrom, a children's librarian in the Seattle Public Library system. Kristin has tirelessly been cheering me on through the publishing process. She recently remarked to someone that, "Her mother had become an activist at 60." Better late than never! She also eats organically and has become an intense food products label reader. I am grateful that one woman who teaches a daughter or a granddaughter might create a positive outcome for generations to come. That was the PYB objective!

I am also grateful for IRIS, my infrared camera, for changing my medical viewpoint. Through her lens, you can see the present, have a glimpse of the future, and monitor progress and the environment you reside in.

My gratitude to all of you for your support and believing that...

Prevention IS the Cure!

—Ingrid Edstrom

ABOUT THE AUTHOR

Ingrid L. Edstrom, FNP, M.Ed., CTT

Ingrid Edstrom is the Founder and President of Proactive Breast Wellness, LLC and the Author of *Protect Your Breasts* and the *Proactive Breast Wellness*™ program. She has become a thought leader in the pursuit of breast cancer prevention. Ingrid developed and has been providing the *Proactive Breast Wellness* program for her patients on a one-to-one basis since 2006. She also created and owns Infrared Breast Health, LLC, based in Eugene, Oregon. Ingrid became nationally certified as a Clinical Infrared Thermography Technician, CTT, in 2007.

Ingrid's clinical practice has established a correlation between toxic exposure to herbicides, pesticides, and bovine growth hormone resulting in abnormal thermography scans.

Ingrid was instrumental in halting roadside herbicide spraying in Lane County, Oregon, and endeavors to alert the public and medical professionals to the dangers of estrogen mimickers and their contribution to rising cancer rates.

Ingrid has been nationally certified as a Family Nurse Practitioner since 1978 following her Bachelors in Nursing from the University of Rhode Island in 1974, with a minor in clinical nutrition. She is not a stranger to being in a pioneering role as one of the early nurse practitioners during her 40-year career or as an infrared thermographer. Now, she is promoting cryoablation as the future of breast cancer care.

She is skilled in business and community networking and has an extensive health teaching background. Ingrid was awarded a Masters in Health Education from Boston University in 1981.

Ingrid has long-term experience in mind-body and preventive medicine. During the early 1990s, she pursued various clinical training programs at the Mind Body Medical Institute through Harvard, and the New England Deaconess/ Beth Israel Hospitals in Boston under the direction of Herbert Benson, MD.

The *Waves of Serenity* relaxation CD/DVD/ Digital Download was developed as a companion tool for her mind-body practice and the PBW program. *Chill Out Naturally* is an educational program that she created and implemented in six high schools in Western Massachusetts.

Remember – Prevention IS the Cure!

Made in USA - North Chelmsford, MA
1189186_9781944733285
11.02.2020 1543

The Lovers

REBEKAH FAUBION

Berkley Romance
New York

BERKLEY ROMANCE
Published by Berkley
An imprint of Penguin Random House LLC
penguinrandomhouse.com

Library of Congress Cataloging-in-Publication Data

Names: Faubion, Rebekah, author.
Title: The lovers / Rebekah Faubion.
Description: First edition. | New York: Berkley Romance, 2024.
Identifiers: LCCN 2023053576 (print) | LCCN 2023053577 (ebook) |
ISBN 9780593640869 (trade paperback) | ISBN 9780593640876 (ebook)
Subjects: LCGFT: Lesbian fiction. | Romance fiction. | Novels.
Classification: LCC PS3606.A857 L68 2024 (print) | LCC PS3606.A857 (ebook) |
DDC 813/.6—dc23/eng/20231127
LC record available at https://lccn.loc.gov/2023053576
LC ebook record available at https://lccn.loc.gov/2023053577

First Edition: September 2024

Printed in the United States of America
1st Printing

Title page art: Desert sun background © MD.Riaz Parvej / Shutterstock
Book design by Alison Cnockaert

For anyone who loves rom-coms but never saw themselves on-screen:
Here, you are the star.

And for my soulmate, Nathan. You are my favorite adventure.

The Lovers

Chapter One

Kit

Shuffling the deck is more than a nervous habit. The weight of the cards in my hands, the *swish swish swish* as they slide into each other, rearranging themselves based on the rhythm in my soul; it stops the spiral I so easily trip right into. I trust them more than I trust myself, and maybe that's part of my problem.

One flies out and turns over against the steering wheel.

Strength, a major arcana card, and not one I pull for myself often. It's a card that's all about flexibility, letting go of the status quo to transform again, truer and clearer than in the past. It's about courage, passion arising to spontaneously flow, washing through all your dead or dying places.

Okay, Universe, no need to paint with such a heavy hand.

It's only brunch.

Mom's birthday brunch, to be precise.

A Larson family tradition five years running. Location: the Polo Lounge, a Hollywood icon. The idea: my father's. Like he plucked it right out of one of his favorite movies and planted it in our life for cinematic flair—his favorite kind. He really loves a gesture—grand or mini, doesn't matter.

If Tom Hanks would do it to the tune of Jimmy Durante, so would Dad.

The Polo Lounge is located inside the Beverly Hills Hotel, a stunning pink palace right off Sunset Boulevard that is impossible to visit without feeling like the main character in a golden age romantic comedy. Even if you're wearing an off-the-rack dress du jour instead of couture and taking selfies alone instead of walking hand in hand with a hot, bronzed movie star to the *flash flash flash* of paparazzi light bulbs.

Last year I brought Gavin, the sculpted-from-marble veterinarian I was dating at the time. He was already on his way out of our relationship, but at least I had some arm candy for the photo op.

This year, I was supposed to bring my live-in boyfriend, David. The reservation is still set for four people, the split so fresh I hadn't had time to change it. It's going to get awkward when I have to sheepishly say "just three." Mom and Dad will look at me with wide eyes and furrowed brows and ask if everything is okay, and I'll have to tell them, "Yep, all is absolutely peachy. I'm just single and momentarily without a home again."

For the second time this calendar year.

I snap the mirror on my car visor closed and smack my glossy lips together.

David Young was everything I thought I wanted.

On paper, anyway.

He was quick-witted, tall, dark, and handsome, with long, perfect fingers, and hair the color of ink. He was also getting *that look* in his eye. The one men get right before they drop down on one knee with something sparkly. You'd think that a believer in rom-com-style happy endings would be gunning to put a ring on it, but the directive handed down from my screenwriter-in-progress father was not simply to "get married and settle down."

It was to "find love, the kind that lasts forever," just like Meg Ryan in *French Kiss*.

It was to "never settle for less than a guy who gives speeches," like Hugh Grant at the end of *Notting Hill*.

It was to "be the ingenue in your own life."

I liked David. We had the kind of chemistry that makes sex good, kissing great, and conversation easy, but he could go days without texting and I'd almost forget I was dating him until he called, *hey babe*, and asked me out for sushi or to go to some new swanky club. Because David liked the aesthetic of a manic pixie dream blond on his arm, and I liked how easy it was to be that blond when I was with him.

He also had the hookup with a lot of celebs I was hoping to convert to clientele. Celebs and semi-celebs who can pay more so I can hopefully work smarter, not harder.

Dad, however, *really* likes David. A lot more than me. Dad likes that he's a good dresser and is polite and smart, but he likes David's industry connections even more. Dad is a perpetually sleep-deprived orthodontist by day, and a screenwriter on the brink of his next great script by night. David is a successful TV exec. They talk about the biz, and in Dad's mind, that talking might one day lead to pitching, which could possibly lead to his big break.

On some level both Dad and me using David for his clout is what made me realize the relationship needed to end. Dad, however, wasn't let in on that train of thought, so I need to make sure he is at least one pink sangria in before I break the news.

The valet attendant, Robbie—a slim, nervous-looking barely-adult with a bright shock of red hair he's tried to tame with too much gel—passes in front of my car. Again. I told him I needed to use the Wi-Fi to finish my upload, so he let me idle in the drive.

But he's getting antsy.

My computer chimes to alert me the upload is complete. I check all the details one final time before closing the laptop. It's one of my "Choose Your Own Tarot Adventure" videos, which is just my way of doing a tarot card reading for the masses. It's a signature video on my channel, and always gets me dozens of new inquiries for private readings.

My subscribers hold firm at one million, slowly growing now that the initial publicity from my Kardashians appearance has calmed down. Before, I was Mystic Maven Kit Larson, YouTube personality and high-end event entertainer; now, I'm that, *plus* the woman who predicted Kim's most recent dating scandal.

My bestie, Nina, coined the name Mystic Maven in college when I got into tarot as a way to help curb my growing battle with anxiety and panic attacks. It stuck like glue, and before I knew it, I was giving readings at sorority parties, before finals, any time anyone wanted to know if their crush liked them back.

I stow my computer, pack up my tarot deck, and climb out of the car, waving Robbie over with a smile. He beams as he takes my keys, and I press a Hamilton into his palm as a thank-you. I flip my sunglasses up like a headband and check my watch. Mom and Dad are due any second.

Should I wait here for them?

Should I go ahead inside and get in front of this "reservation for four" drama?

My phone buzzes. I don't have notifications turned on for any of my apps—a mental health boundary my therapist and I set up after my channel reached five hundred K. It's a text from Nina. I told her about splitting with David before I begged to crash on her couch last night.

> consider this a hug from the universe and a reminder that fate doesn't give us anything we can't handle

Nina is an actress, mostly bit roles on TV and a few in movies, but with lucrative prospects on the horizon and a lot of faith in her divine path; she's going places. I may be the one with the spiritual brand who gives spot-on readings, but she's a lot better at discerning her intuition for herself than I am. When it comes to my own inner compass, I get lost more often than I get where I'm trying to go.

I send her a heart emoji plus the sparkly stars I associate with cosmic magic.

"Kitten." I hear my mom's nickname for me and look up to see she's stepped out of the driver's side of her Mercedes and is dropping the keys in the hands of the other valet attendant.

Seeing her driving herself to her birthday brunch, where she always, without fail, ends up on the other side of toasted, is an unnerving plot twist. Mom is a mediocre driver at her most sober. This does not bode well. I'm about to ask what's up when she reaches me, smacks air kisses to both cheeks, and tugs me in, saying, "Let's grab a selfie together before your dad arrives."

She attempts her normal toothy smile, but her newly "refreshed" (code: Botoxed) face is still a little light on dynamic movement. She raises her phone and begins searching for an angle that flatters both of us—mostly her—and settles on an above, left-of-center position. Her good side, but it's the side I part my hair toward, which means my cheek is shadowed by a curtain of blond waves.

She pulls the phone back to examine the shots. "The light is atrocious, but we can add some filters. Make it work." I regret encouraging Mom to get on social media. She needed it to build her life coaching biz, but she uses it to stalk me—tag me and then passive-aggressively prod until I reshare—almost as much as she uses it to sell her coaching programs and packages.

Dad's Mini Cooper pulls up next. Just a few minutes behind Mom. Were they coming from different locations? On her birthday?

The moment Dad steps out, I see tension etched into every one of his normally *relaxed to the point of sleepy* facial features. He shoves a hand in his pocket to pull out some cash for a tip, pushing his wire-rimmed glasses up his nose, and walks over with stiff shoulders. His eyes flick to Mom and then me before he leans in for a quick hug.

"Hey there, cupcake," he says, his voice tight. It's easy to read the energy racing back and forth between them. Easy and *uncomfortable*.

I swallow a few times. Clear my throat.

Keep it breezy, Kit.

"Did you have an emergency at work?" I ask Dad, letting my eyes trail to his car, which is now pulling away, driven by Robbie.

"They never call me on my day off," he says. It's not an answer. "You know that."

"Right," I say, no less confused.

My parents are the Nancy Meyers embodiment of Dad's long-deferred Hollywood dreams, right down to the kitchen in their South Pasadena Spanish Colonial and eccentric elderly neighbor with an Oscar hiding in his cluttered, dusty office. I'm the twenty-something daughter perpetually in need of guidance (and financial assistance) that they are somehow still ridiculously proud of anyway.

We each have our role, and we're all really fucking good at playing them.

We never go off script.

Am I somehow responsible for this improv session?

I rack my brain. They couldn't know about the breakup yet—it just happened. But neither one of them has asked about David, either. They may be too pissed at each other to notice my missing significant other.

"Shall we?" Mom asks, but she doesn't wait for our answer. Her chunky espadrilles hit the red carpet that forms the pathway into the hotel. She doesn't look back at either of us; Dad doesn't get any less chilly.

My parents have had plenty of spats over the years, and a lot of them have taken place in that Nancy Meyers kitchen over a bottle of merlot. I know they fight, thrive on it in some ways, but the ice always thaws quickly. Like rising ocean level thaw-out rates.

Dad exhales through his nostrils. "Too late to skip out, I guess."

Skip out? My thoughts want to untether, but this isn't my first rodeo, and I won't let my bucking bronco brain win.

He offers a small smile that doesn't reach his eyes before following behind her. I inhale a sharp breath, pushing it out with extra force. I've been handling my anxiety for years. I refuse to be weird at brunch no matter what sensations are happening in my brain and body.

No matter how unhinged my parents are acting.

Breezy as a motherfucking summer day, baby.

~

They didn't respond to my correction of the reservation with even a sideways glance. Mom was on her phone, typing like mad and ignoring the world. Dad was glaring straight at her like his stare could light her hair on fire.

We're seated at one of the Polo Lounge's iconic booths. The cushions are covered in deco-inspired lime-green palms, tucked into a pink stucco alcove that overlooks the lush patio. I take my seat on one end of the curved bench, and Mom and Dad slide into the other side, keeping a notable distance from each other.

The empty water glasses wink, taunting me. Panic makes me parched. Like a killer hangover or the end of a cardio blast.

I distract myself by perusing the menu, even if we always start with the same thing. Pink sangria and ceviche for Dad and me, and farmers market seasonal fruit for the vegetarian Mom. Our waiter arrives to pour the waters—bless his soul! I gulp down the whole glass. The cold liquid cuts through the heat spreading across my chest cavity like a wildfire.

"You need a second to look over the menu?" our waiter, Gary—per his name tag—asks. "Or are you ready to get this party started?"

"Any special apps we should know about?" Mom asks, leaning forward to beam up at Gary from what I'm sure she thinks is an optimal angle. Dad's mouth twitches. He covers the move with the rim of his glass, gulping deep.

Five years we've been doing this birthday brunch. Five years and the only thing that has changed has been my plus-one.

"Sick of your old standby?" Dad says through a loud crunch of ice between his teeth. Dad never crunches ice. Teeth are his livelihood, and he's a stickler for healthy dental practices of all varieties.

"I could recommend the artisanal bread and butter, a new butter flavor every week," Gary replies. "Something we're trying out on the menu this fall."

"That would be scrummy," Mom says, closing her menu. *Scrummy?* Jesus Christ, is she about to have a stroke? I have never heard her use the word *scrummy* in my whole life.

"Ceviche and a pitcher of pink sangria," Dad adds. He leaves Mom's fruit off, and she doesn't correct him. And with that, Gary is gone.

Mom exhales, leaning back against the booth. Only now, for the first time since arriving, do I see her eyes trail to either side of me in search of my plus-one.

"David couldn't make it, Kitten?" She pouts, reaching for my hand and squeezing. "Next time."

Just rip the Band-Aid, baby.

"There won't be a next time." Both of their gazes fix on mine. "We broke up a couple days ago. I moved out of his place." *Took my two suitcases, Himalayan salt lamp, and bounced.* "I need to crash in the pool house if that's oka—"

"Oh for fuck's sake," Dad exclaims. "I can't take this anymore. Tell her or I will."

Mom's face stiffens. "We agreed to wait until after everything was finalized." Her lips are tight as she replies, and not just from the fillers.

"Fine," Dad says, nostrils flaring. He turns back to me, yanking his wire rims off dramatically. "Your mother is leaving me for a thirty-two-year-old British chippie she met coaching!"

My heart rate skyrockets.

Scrummy makes a hell of a lot more sense now.

My hands ball into tiny fists, which I shove into the fabric of the booth cushion.

"Chippie?" The word is the only question I can muster.

"She's incredible," Mom says. "So ambitious, so driven."

She???

Mom pulls out her phone and starts trying to show me the picture of her hot, barely-older-than-me girlfriend by swiping through an album on her phone titled "Lover."

I need a bag to barf into.

She's got wavy brown hair, tan skin, deep brown eyes, and a crooked but cute smile. I don't know what is more shocking, the fact that this album has hundreds of photos in it—some of which feature Mom and this woman kissing, snuggling, generally canoodling—or the fact that Mom is acting like this over a woman when I had no idea she was into women at all.

My brain immediately glitches and I see *her* face. Ten years ago, cheekbones already sharp, aquamarine eyes bright, lips pink and swollen from kissing.

No, not a chance. I will *not* think about her right now.

"Her name is Willa, and her Libra Moon really brings me so much balance," she says. *Swipe.* "She works at Erewhon as a health and wellness guide," she continues, "but her real passion is Pilates." This gets an eye waggle. "She wants to open gyms in Brentwood. She has investors—"

"Jesus Christ, Camille, I'm sitting right here," Dad exclaims, just as Gary returns with the pitcher of pink sangria and our appetizer. He makes quick work of dropping off the food and drinks as I watch Dad count down to an explosion.

Mom reaches for a glass, pouring her own sangria since Gary doesn't stick around for that part. Dad's brows twitch. His nostrils flare. She shakes the ice cubes into the glass and pours in a little more of the soft rose-colored liquid. Dad's hand curls around the hilt of his butter knife. She lifts the glass up to drink. He smacks the table and the dishes and silverware all clack in a metallic screech.

"Order your own pitcher," Dad says, yanking the glass from her hands. "This one is ours." He turns his eyes to me and then to my empty glass.

"I don't see why you're acting so immature about this. You're the one who ruined our plan, you're the one who spilled the beans right here," Mom says, yanking the glass right back and chugging it down. She hiccups, shrugging dramatically and swiping her thick, blond-laced-through-with-gray hair over one shoulder. "We were going to sell the house and get the details all sorted before we told her—"

"That plan is out." He looks at me. "I'm afraid you can't stay in the pool house, cupcake, because that's my current squat."

Mom reaches over the ceviche growing warm on the center of the table and cups my chin. "We can help get you a short-term rental, Kitten."

They had a plan.

I pull away from her grip. My chest grows tight. The steadily simmering embers in my belly ignite into flames that travel up my esophagus and into my throat. They lick the length of my neck and consume my eyeballs with their heat.

They had a plan to keep me in the dark while they packed up my childhood home and sold it to a stranger.

"Katherine." Dad says my full name. Mom immediately stills.

My throat is closing up and the only thing I can do is breathe in, out, in, out through my nostrils.

I push against the booth with my fists and stand, smacking my thigh on the underside of the table. I shake my head. I need a small, confined space where I can ride this out.

~

I burst into an empty bathroom stall and slam it shut.

My eyes are frozen open. As much as I want to conjure my safe space from hypnotherapy, once I'm this far gone I can't risk dropping my focus to get there. That means finding something to visually hold the weight of my spiral. I pick the small spot of chipped paint on the back of the door, press my fingers to my pulse in my throat, and breathe.

It's been years since a panic attack took me by surprise in a public place. Hypnotherapy sounds very LA, I know, but I swear it's on doctor's orders. My *actual* therapist suggested it as a supplement to our sessions, a way to get off meds and reframe my triggers through my subconscious. It's been a game changer. But as my adrenaline begins to drop back down, a wave of sadness and shame sweeps over me, hard on impact, cracking through all my resolve.

And I have to give in.

Her brown hair fell across shoulders that were sun-kissed from spending all summer by the pool. I watched her walk away, her kiss still lingering on my lips, but my heart was already racing, running back over the promises I'd made as I fell asleep beside her.

I close my eyes and breathe into the feeling.

Let's go on a date. A real one. Like at a restaurant with fabric napkins, she'd said.

I'd said yes, and I had wanted to mean it.

In the sunlight, I knew that I couldn't.

I try to swallow the emotion down, down, down.

Still it bubbles up.

Hurting her almost destroyed me.

The one time I came close to dating a girl, it turned into a disaster tailspin of emotional confusion. Feelings got all jumbled and what I believed about myself—my *ideal* of myself—came into question. Sure, it all settled eventually, and I tried to write it off, move on without looking too closely at what the whole thing actually meant.

But the yearning never did go away.

In college there was Maia. She sat next to me in Western Civ. She smelled like citrus, saffron, and rose petals, and her hair was long, dark, shiny. When we weren't in class side by side, she occupied the space in my head between asleep and awake. Moments when my mind was vulnerable enough to wonder how the curves of her hips in her skintight jeans would feel cupped in my hands, or how her plump lips would taste, or what it would be like to make her laugh and then moan in the very next breath.

Midway through the semester I did the unthinkable and moved seats, causing a disruption to the implied structure of our auditorium classroom. I couldn't take her passing in front of me to get to her chair anymore. She'd brush against me; she'd whisper responses and critiques of the lecture, her necklace would taunt me from the dip in her clavicle, the pendant dropping down to disappear between the mounds of her breasts, and my eyes would drift, my pulse threatening to give me away.

My TA called me out on the move. Maia took it personally, and not for the right reasons. I almost flunked out of the class rather than attend in a cloud of embarrassment. Another massive mess, only that time I didn't even let myself kiss her.

I blink, squeezing the bridge of my nose, exhaling a sharp puff through my nostrils.

I've had oodles of crushes on women, but I'm still not brave enough to take my yearning outside the safety of my daydreams.

I'm not straight—not even close. But, wow, the undeniable existence of my queerness doesn't make it any easier to *be*. How do you take a secret you've kept hidden away for all of forever and make it public? How do you say it out loud and have it not become the only thing anyone ever sees again?

Acceptance doesn't mean it's comfortable.

Or easy.

It doesn't make you ready to process other people knowing; it doesn't make you willing to change your life—because it does change your life. There's no way it doesn't. Maybe for the better, but then, I cite my previous experience and Exhibit *Mom's B-Day Brunch* as evidence to the contrary.

So . . .

I daydream. I yearn.

But my reality stays the same.

Why the hell does Mom have to shake everything up?

The Ideal Rom-Com Life Path is just fine. It's a path Mom and Dad always made look iconic. It's a path that was supposed to ensure that all-important Happily Ever After. Hugh Grant in a ruffled button-down, Tom Hanks at the top of the Empire State Building, *insert your favorite rom-com hero here*, that's what we're going for.

That's the path.

Your mother is leaving me for a thirty-two-year-old British chippie. Dad's words ring again in my head. They land, a lead weight in my gut. The perfect Nancy Meyers couple is splitting up.

Maybe the path is fucked.

Chapter Two

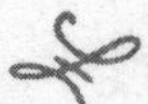

Julia

There's a spot on the collar of my button-down. Dark, like a bit of ink, and it's dotted right where the swoop meets my collarbone. A small detail that's not quite right, but the exact kind that I fixate on without any discrimination. I also prepare for such a time as this as if it's an inevitability and not an inconvenience. My therapist—the most recent one—called it a trauma response. When she tried to schedule a follow-up appointment, I left her on read for weeks until finally I replied with my go-to excuse.

Busy.

Always busy. Never available even for myself.

I open my desk drawer and pull out the Tide to go pen standing upright in the tray. Easy access for me, or any one of my brides, in a pinch. I carry a few of these in my Wedding Day belt bag at all times. Along with a travel-sized hair spray, mouthwash, and touch-up mascara to make the bride feel blissfully at ease on her special day.

The pen does its work, and I breathe out a sigh of relief. I swear to God, watching stains disappear is an unmatched catharsis. My previous therapist wanted me to unpack that further. I ghosted him without any remorse.

Don't you want to relinquish control? Well-meaning friends always ask this, always as if they are the first to inquire and this question will be the catalyst to my emotional rebirth. It's sweet, and I usually humor them because, despite all the thorns on my skin, I crave connection and community like the only child and formerly motherless, desperately lonely woman that I am.

But that never changes the truth.

Relinquish is a synonym for *lose*. I only lose when I let go.

A quick rap of knuckles on my door pulls me back to the moment. Zoe Hayes, my assistant, peeks through the opening. Big brown eyes, tan skin, more hair than she knows what to do with. Mostly she braids it or wears it in a black mass on top of her head.

"Ten-minute warning," Zoe says.

I cap the Tide to go pen and set it back in its place, shutting the drawer.

"Let's go over the high points, just so I'm refreshed," I say. Her smile is a bit dramatic, wide with very straight, white teeth. Dramatic, but lovely. Just like Zoe. She pushes into the room and closes the door behind her. She's clutching an iPad to her chest like it's priceless.

And I suppose it is, in a way. A priceless tool of the Morgan-Hayden wedding. A boho-chic, spiritually infused California dream set against the whimsical desertscape of Joshua Tree. Not only is Millie Morgan, the bride, a high-profile client with her two-million-plus social media following as a lifestyle influencer (yeah, that's a thing), but this wedding is a first for me in more ways than one.

Zoe sits across from me, waking up the iPad, which is linked to my desktop computer through Bluetooth.

I used contacts I'd cultivated on my own over the last few years working at Love, Always Weddings and Events to build out the four-night, three-day wedding experience the bride wanted. I've coordinated not only with the resort, Celestial Sands, a luxe boutique experience in a rustic setting at the edge of Joshua Tree National Park, but also with multiple other venues, glamping sites, and excursion providers, to ensure that the whole wedding party and fifty-plus guests are immersed, leave the place rejuvenated, and give me a fucking five-star review to take into my next gig.

Launching my own wedding and event agency.

A dream I've been building toward for years.

A secret dream, as of now, but not for much longer. This wedding is the last one I'm planning as a Love, Always employee. As soon as I return from the desert, I'm handing in my resignation. The first move in my carefully calculated plan. Essential, since I won't be able to work any weddings for six months per the noncompete in my contract.

Zoe pulls up the bullet point list we created for the final walkthrough meeting with the bride and groom before we leave for Joshua Tree on Friday. It's a comprehensive look at all the major moments we have planned for her fairy tale come to life.

I know I seem like a cynic, and I am in almost every area *besides* this one.

To me, a wedding is more than a party. More than a show of commitment or an excuse to get drunk and dance the night away. Weddings take two individual human beings and set them on a new, integrated path. Weddings turn two people into a family unit.

I lean forward, using my mouse to click through the presentation.

Friday night is the Goddess Awakening, at Desert Skies Glamp-Out. The bride was in charge of booking her own energy healers and psychics for the evening since she "had a direct line through her socials."

The bachelor events are as polar opposite as possible and were one hundred percent the handiwork of me. Somehow I didn't think that frat-boy-turned-financier Sean would be into anything too woo-woo. (His words.)

Saturday is chock-full with a picnic brunch, spa treatments, and, of course, the rehearsal dinner.

Sunday evening is the wedding, at sunset, and the reception under the stars.

I scroll through the aesthetic mock-ups of the decorations, and the itinerary that will be handed out to all the main players and followed to the letter no matter what catastrophes attempt to arise.

"Any word on the bride's bachelorette party entertainment?" I ask Zoe, leaning back in my chair. We're not responsible for the success of that event, but I still want it to be a dream come true. One misstep in a wedding weekend can lead to a stumbling, tripping, snowballing mess that lands us in the hot seat no matter who made the first mistake.

"I'll make sure to ask her at the meeting," Zoe replies, jotting it down in her presentation notes. She looks up; her eyes flick behind me to the clock hanging on my wall, right between the two massive picture windows looking out on Rodeo Drive. Love, Always is situated in a swank locale, caters to a swank LA-based clientele, and was founded by a woman who *might* (talking about it is forbidden) have been featured on *Real Housewives of Beverly Hills* as a main character. For a girl who grew up in Pasadena, and not in one of the beautifully restored historic homes the city is known for, working this location has always felt a little like playing a role in a life that isn't quite mine.

I look the part. Polished, well-educated, sharp, clean-cut, designer style—now. But I'm still an awkward emo punk kid who was once all about a '90s flannel, ripped jeans, Doc Martens look in my heart, even if my heart doesn't ever get to run the wardrobe selection.

That flew out the window a couple years ago and hasn't ever come back.

"I'll meet you in the conference room in three," Zoe says, standing.

"Remember, Millie works with that posh sparkling tea brand, so set out a few of those in case she wants to promote."

"Roger that," Zoe says, handing over the iPad. I like to run the meetings, even if normally that would be the assistant's job. She gave up trying to relinquish that task from my steel grip after a few failed attempts and at least one bathroom crying session. I felt like shit, tried to give her the day off, which backfired. Zoe is spurred by ambition, a trait I respect without any irony. She didn't want the day off, she wanted me to let her prove herself.

I look down at the title page featuring the bride and groom. Two white, wealthy hotties on the surface, but in the time I've spent with them I've come to see that they both have hidden depth worthy of respect. I can't always get there with the Love, Always clientele, no matter how much I want to believe that all the weddings I've worked have created families that will sustain the couple's lifetime.

My eyes trail from their perfect faces to the single personal item in my office. A minimalist silver frame featuring a family photo from last Christmas. Dad, tall, dark, and lanky; me, a shorter, curvier version of him, right down to my thick brown hair and bright ocean eyes; and my stepmom, Ana, snuggled near me, wearing her signature bright smile. Before they got married it was just Dad and me, two lonely grumps without anyone to force out joy. But when he and Ana said "I do," she made sure I knew her commitment was to both of us.

They say those who can't do, teach. Change *teach* to *plan* and you have me. I've never come close to the altar. None of the women or men I've dated in my twenties have even come within orbit of the mark, or made me feel that feeling. That *safe to do anything, be anything* feeling I get when I think about family. I had one ex—the last ex—who I almost thought would. But she wasn't ready to come out to her snooty family. I loved her enough to go back in the closet for a while, but eventually that closed door made me feel trapped.

And that feeling, it wore me down.

Wore away the love I felt because I was treated like some sort of dirty little secret, and not the fun kind. Wore away the hope I had that we could one day stand together and make that commitment I desperately wanted. And then when that love had eroded completely, I realized she'd done more than shove me into the closet again. All the heat fizzled into hate; her nitpicking went deep, slicing away anything that made me *me*; and escape became my only option. I'd been hurt before by someone who couldn't love me out loud, but now I had been molded and shaped by someone like that as well. I didn't recognize myself.

The only thing to do was leave.

The alarm on my phone chimes, and then the front desk receptionist, Paige, buzzes through the office line to let me know my clients have arrived.

"I'll be right there," I call back, blinking away the cloud of emotion.

Those who can't do, teach.

I may not *do*, but I can *plan*.

~

Millie's clap is a gentle flip of her wrists to bring her long, trim, perfectly manicured hands together with a soft puff. I always expect to impress, but this is new. My cheeks feel warm from the praise.

"We really just took your beautiful vision and brought it to life," I say, proud that I manage to conceal the faint wobble of emotion in my voice. It's a compliment to myself and my team as much as it is to her, and the tiny crinkle in her lightly freckled, perfectly poreless nose is the only indication she gives me that she noticed.

Millie is a dream client. Smart, focused, passionate. She knows what she wants and stays true to it, even when bright shiny new trends come her way. I hate when clients want to "pivot" because some hotter concept has captured their attention. It helps that she's genuinely into all the mystical elements we've incorporated into the ceremony.

She didn't just pick "spiritual, modern desert oasis" as a theme; she lives and breathes the idea that the Universe is working on your behalf. Millie broke out as a spiritual wellness influencer on Instagram, leveraging brand partnerships, highlighting practical (and luxury) ways to bring the mystical into every day.

Sean—who looks like a Hollywood Chris and acts like a

himbo even though he went to Princeton—seems to go along with everything Millie wants, says, and thinks. Which is good, since everything from the location to the wedding officiant is metaphysical magic of the most California variety.

When Zoe asked about Millie's Goddess Awakening party—Millie's name for the bachelorette fete—Sean let out a small guffaw of amusement at the title.

"Sound Healer Suni is locked in—she's worked at the Glamp-Out before, so it was easy," Millie replied, smacking Sean in the stomach. "I've reached out to a fellow influencer who does tarot, so, fingers crossed." She did the motion and Zoe followed suit. "She's a little flaky, known for last-minute confirmation. But one hundred percent worth the risk."

My stomach does a little flip at her nonchalance. I telepathically will Zoe to make a note to check on that first thing in the morning. Tarot, of all the spiritual practices featured in this wedding weekend, is the one I know the most about. I once was peer pressured into visiting a medium at the Haunt O' Ween fair in Old Pasadena—a reading that was hard to forget.

I have tried. Believe me.

"All right then," I say. Millie has finished clapping; now she just beams. "Ready to sign on the dotted line?"

We have all of our clients sign off on the final presentation before the wedding events get underway. Insurance against anyone getting a wild idea at the last minute and wanting a change, and, of course, protection if they "forget" they agreed to anything and try to get their money back.

Millie flicks her eyes to Sean, who doesn't look up from his phone. "Babe," she says, pressing her hand gently over the screen. "Good to go?"

His eyes drift up to Millie, then me and Zoe sitting across from him. He's playing catch-up as he flicks his eyes over the iPad with the checklist ready, and then furrows his brow.

"Let's get it!" It feels like something he just says. Like "Go Lakers" or "Doing great" in response to the question "How are you?" even if his arm is being chewed off by a wild hyena.

"Promise me something, Julia," Millie says, turning her attention away from her fiancé.

I feel a tremor of nerves through my center. As a rule, I don't promise. My assurances come with the asterisk that I will do all within my power, but promises are a contract, and the only contract I adhere to is the one she's about to sign with all the final and approved details.

I pause too long, and Millie's hand shoots forward, gripping mine with a friendly squeeze. "It's a party," Millie says, finishing up her signature on the wedding checklist. "Cut loose a little." She stands, pushing the iPad over to Sean. I must look ill at her suggestion—I certainly feel ill—because she chuckles and makes a tiny *aww* sound before adding, "All I'm saying is, just, feel free to enjoy yourself, too. The magic in the desert is for everyone."

I want to protest. I should protest. Nothing comes out.

"Right, babe?" she adds, touching the nape of her fiancé's neck.

"Millie knows best," he says, but it's another one of those autoreplies he seems to excel at delivering.

Sean launches up and stretches. The move shows a sliver of tan, sculpted abs and we all take a moment to stare. He looks between us and his face contorts with confusion.

Millie snorts.

"You did that on purpose, dumbass."

Zoe stifles a laugh and I stand, extending my hand for them to shake, but Millie snaps her fingers. The crack hits me with a jolt of surprise.

"Oh! I almost forgot, Bridesmaid Ellen—the one who chose that dusty pink dress, off the shoulder?" I nod, affirmative. "Well, she broke her leg in three places skiing in Switzerland, so she's trapped at a recovery resort near the accident site." *Sounds nice.* "My sorority sister, Piper, is the same dress size, similar coloring, so she's stepping in to fill her spot."

Piper.

Similar dress size, similar coloring to Ellen, a tall, fit redhead with a peaches-and-cream complexion.

Piper. The name of my ex-girlfriend who fits that exact description.

"She's been so incredible since I announced the engagement, offering to help in any way she can even though she wasn't in the wedding party," Millie continues. "And when Ellen had to bow out, she immediately stepped up."

This sounds like Piper. Not just the appearance, but the behavior. A trademark manipulation tactic was to gently offer up helpful advice, unsolicited gifts, anything she had at her disposal that she thought someone would want. And it wasn't until she had her hooks firmly planted that it became clear just how deep her control had breached.

Pro it up, Julia. You could be psyching yourself out for nothing.

"Oh, um, we need to switch out her info in the dossier folder for check-in." Smooth as butter. *Not.*

"Of course," Millie says, yanking her phone out to pull up Piper's contact profile. The pic attached is a tiny circle, but it's still clear enough that I can see her face.

“Piper Cunningham,” Millie says. “I’ll airdrop this to you, Zoe.”

Piper Cunningham.

Loving her nearly maimed me. We tore each other apart at the end, said things we didn’t mean, and a lot we really fucking did, until finally, I said nothing at all. But I wasn’t lying when I told her I’d rather eat glass than ever see her again.

And that sentiment definitely hasn’t changed in the year since I lost her number.

None of them notice the jumble of feelings I’m trying to tamp down with a mallet of reason and self-control. Zoe confirms receipt of Piper’s contact info, offering to walk the couple out. Millie reaches in for an air-kiss and Sean hoots something about “go time,” but I’m not sure I really respond to any of it.

I drop down in my chair and grab one of the cans of sparkling tea and crack the aluminum lip, taking a long sip. I’m going to need something stronger—much stronger. I cannot let this throw me off. I will not let it. I’m a pro; this is manageable.

I will not freak. I cannot back out. There is too much riding on the success of this wedding.

I have to nail this even if it means I have to breathe the same air as my ex.

Chapter Three

Kit

Nina delivers a heavy pour of chardonnay to me as I sit cross-legged with a pillow over my thighs, my phone propped on top, swiping through profiles on Hinge.

"Hey bish, he was cute," Nina chimes in, pointing her purple coffin-shaped nail at the screen where the cute guy no longer stares back. I slump against the velvet cushion of her vintage couch and let out a guttural groan.

"He was, but he also looked like a flavor I've already tried," I say, gulping wine and making meaningful eye contact with my best friend. "You know. Vanilla with strawberries on top. That's his vibe."

"You like vanilla. You like strawberries," Nina lists. Her dark brown skin is kissed with this golden apricot blush from Benefit, and she's a got a dramatic neon swoop lining both of her dark, hazel brown eyes. Nina's style is effortlessly artistic and utterly cool. She looks like she just stepped out of a Nike ad, but like, for the expensive kicks, not sportswear.

"And both get boring after a few big bites," I reply. She cackles.

I don't tell her the deeper reason for my meltdown. I can't. Nina has been my best friend since sophomore year of college, when she transferred to Berkeley from some tiny liberal arts college in North Carolina where she grew up. She knows my bra size and my favorite book, has helped me through countless breakups—I introduced her to her talent agent, she introduced me to cheesy bacon grits. But she doesn't know everything there is to know about me, even if she knows more than any of my boyfriends ever have. My heart does a flutter from my nerves, and I decide that's enough of a sign not to push it.

"Vanilla with strawberries on top is not what I need right now."

"You thinking more of a Rocky Road situation?" She gives me a devious smile. I grab my phone off the pillow, tossing the soft, fringy puff in her face.

If Rocky Road is what it takes.

I do like guys. I like abs and strong pecs. Arms that fold around me, making me feel small, feel safe, feel like the ideal. That is also an *undeniable fact*. I need to run my fingers over a chiseled jawline and feel stubble scrape my neck while he plows me until I forget my name and birth date—

Her fingernails scrape the cold metal clasp of my jean shorts, flicking them open. I feel the memory scamper through me with a shiver up my spine.

Fuck me. What I need is a solid distraction. Something that will push everything else out of my mind.

"Hey lovely," Nina says, her tone gentle but commanding. I look over at her, gulping more wine. "You wanna talk about it?" She means the mom and dad divorce debacle.

"I really don't," I reply.

"You know that means you probably should."

I know—and hate—that she is right. But thinking about the situation with Mom and Dad treads close to territory I am terrified to enter right now. Any question I would have about why Mom did what she did, or how she could, can also be turned back on me. *Shut up, brain.* Unraveling the notion that I can keep this thing to myself and still live my best life to the fullest is not in the cards—I'd know if it was. Right?

I settle on the one part of this that I feel safe to focus on.

Dad.

"You should have seen his face, Nina. Crushed. The happy, bashful dwarf Dad usually is was replaced by a Gremlin who got fed after midnight," I say, twisting the stem of my wineglass in my fingers. They're handblown, brightly colored glass. Nina got them at the Jackalope Artisan Fair last Christmas, and she only brings them out for special occasions. "He was seething. Smoke-out-his-ears-level pissed off."

"Yeah, but behind that rage is so much hurt and fear," she says thoughtfully. Nina has been in therapy since she lost her brother in a car crash at sixteen. Survivor's remorse, she said, with anxiety and depression like a yoke around her neck. Her ability to psychoanalyze may be armchair, but it's still pretty spot-on.

"He deserves to feel hurt," I reply. And I totally believe that he does, even if the moment I say it out loud my earlobes and chest feel warm with anger. Mom is at fault here, not Dad.

"And your mom still deserves to find her way to her most authentic life," Nina adds, eyebrows rising. "You know I'm right, even if you don't want to admit it yet."

I let out another guttural groan, scrubbing my hands over my face.

"Goddammit, okay, maybe you have a point, but I'm not there yet, not even close." I won't get there sitting here swiping dudes on Hinge or fucking someone hot enough to make me forget. "I need to clear my energy. I need space. I need—"

"To get the fuck out of LA," she finishes. "Didn't you say Millie Morgan inquired about a gig this weekend?"

I perk up. I forgot about the inquiry in all the breakup mess. And, okay, I also like to play hard to get until I make up my mind and am ready to commit. In relationships as well as in professional circumstances. But really, this time I didn't follow up mostly because I was moving out and freaking out, and forgot to check back in on my DMs.

I swipe my phone open again, clicking away from Hinge into Instagram.

Millie and I have crossed paths a few times since she started pushing her brand in a more spirit-centric direction, and I started getting hired to work the most recent crop of beach yoga retreats and Brentwood baby showers of the rich and semifamous.

Once on her profile page, I click on the picture of her and her bridesmaids. They're all influencers, but among them is Coco Mulligan, CEO of the popular lingerie brand Coco's Intimates. Not an A-list celebrity, but her social media draw, plus Millie's budding presence in the lifestyle influencer space, could open me up to a higher-end clientele.

After my breakup, this could be exactly what I need for more than one reason.

I slide into Millie's DMs.

Hey Mills! Happy to take you up on the gig. Can you send me the deets to make sure it aligns with my schedule?

I sound like a fake, but I swear LA influencers have a tone. I have to follow suit. Aloof Valley Girl with a baby-high, light bringer but a little bored—you'd know it if you heard it. I'm born and raised in LA; I speak these words in love.

Millie is quick to reply. Not playing hardball or hard to get, and I have to respect her for it. She lays out the schedule for the weekend and asks what kinds of services I usually offer for events like hers. I've never done a three-day event like this one, but since the audience will change over the course of the weekend—from just bridesmaids and Millie's mom to the rehearsal dinner guests and finally the wedding attendees—I think sticking to tarot for the whole weekend will still be interesting.

She's typing back when Nina returns with the bottle of wine in hand to refresh both our glasses.

"What's the verdict?" she asks.

"I think it's affirmative." Since I'm confirming last minute, and she's a fellow influencer, I decide to give her a discount for one of her events or offer her a free private reading at a future date.

When Millie replies, it's enthusiastic and effusive, so I drop my prices and the discount options and wait. "We should order food," I say to Nina, but my eyes are still on the screen.

"I'll Postmates it." She backbends to grab her phone off the side table behind her. "Thai or pizza?"

As soon as Millie agrees to my terms, I feel the heavy weight on my chest lift. Breathing space in the desert, at a resort with a healing spa, no less. This is exactly what I need to get over this hiccup and get back on track.

"Pizza," I say, dropping my phone to the couch cushion. I'll email her the contract after sustenance. "And probably more wine."

"You land the gig?" Nina asks.

"Three nights and four days in the desert . . ." I offer my wineglass for her to clink. "Here I come."

Chapter Four

Julia

I'm aware that Zoe has already arrived at the venue ahead of me and confirmed (multiple times) that everything is under control and running like clockwork. I'm aware she encouraged me to get an extra hour of sleep since the next few days will be hectic and unpredictable despite our attention to every single detail.

But Piper is going to be there. This curveball is enough to set me on edge.

I'm pulling off the freeway when Zoe FaceTimes me. I've ignored her last few texts, something I never do, which immediately signals suspicious behavior.

"You're in the car." She squints into her camera to get a better look at me. The phone is on the dash in my hands-free holder, so she can easily see the scenery behind me. "I recognize that hill of sand and scrub. You're almost to Joshua Tree. Oh!" she exclaims. "That was a Joshua tree you just passed. You're basically here."

"Did you confirm that Millie secured entertainment for this evening?" I don't have a roster of tarot readers to draw from, but I do have Google and I will use it in a pinch.

"If you had looked at my texts . . ." she begins, her tone playful despite the annoyance flaring up her nostrils and making her already massive eyes bug out a little.

"I was driving," I say. "That's illegal."

"Ha, wow, you text and drive all the time, Julia," she says with a grunt of amusement. "The other day you texted while driving with your eyes slightly dilated." I don't need glasses, but sometimes stress makes me think I do, which leads to an eye exam that is largely unwarranted.

"You're straying from topic," I counter. She huffs.

"Yes, Millie confirmed Mystic Maven last night."

I cough, choking on a laugh that catches in my throat. "What a name."

"She's really good," Zoe says coyly.

"I didn't know you were into that stuff." I have one eye on the road, but the other is focused on her and the way she's squirming at being found out.

"This is LA." She shrugs. "Everyone is looking for answers in the stars." Or the cards, if you're consulting tarot. When my face screws up again, she rolls her eyes. "Anyway, what I'm getting at here is that you did not have to leave until at least noon. I am holding down Homebase just fine."

Homebase is what we call the central meeting point at any wedding venue, on location for a whole weekend or just for a single day at a single site. For the Morgan-Hayden wedding, it's my hotel room. I feel a pang of remorse in my gut that Zoe thinks I'm coming in early because I don't trust her. "It's not about whether you can handle it or not. This wedding has a lot riding on it for me. I just need to personally make sure all goes well."

Zoe's face softens and she nods. "See you soon."

In the time I've been talking to her, the number of Joshua trees sprouting from the sand has multiplied exponentially. I can almost see the outline of Celestial Sands in the distance. I'm not a person with a sixth sense. My five normal ones work great, but trying to stretch beyond those is like trying to dig up concrete with a shovel. I wish I could reach out now and sense whether Piper has arrived yet, how she is feeling, if she knows I'm the wedding planner. When we split I said I'd rather eat glass than ever see her again, but Piper promised worse. *Vindictive* is a word I'd use to describe her. *Cutthroat*, too. And scorned, carrying a grudge, she might be lethal.

It's nothing I can't handle. I just wish I could make a plan of attack ahead of time.

I pull off the road to a more rugged dirt path. I rented an all-terrain vehicle for this weekend, used my per diem for the expense. My Jag would not be able to handle this rustically magical setting.

Celestial Sands was built from an existing estate once owned by a TV medium from the late '80s. The home was designed with spiritual flow in mind. Drawing on Asian and Moroccan influences in its sculptures, carved trim, stained glass windows, organic contours, log-beamed ceilings, and colored tilework, the original main house was a five-bedroom oasis of tranquil energy and artistic embellishment. It was turned into a hotel in the early 2000s, at which point they added multiple guesthouses, a yurt, and even a few luxe-designed Airstream trailers.

The gate into the property opens, and I pull through onto the winding road that leads to the entrance. The green canopy feels like a jungle oasis in the middle of this desertscape, unfolding into a succulent garden planted around an ornate fountain pluming from the center. I then take a curve in the drive that directs me through a grove of date trees, which clears to reveal the white stucco cutout design of the Celestial Sands entrance.

Two strapping males wave me forward, both wearing loose, heavily patterned pants and thin tank tops. One has a septum piercing, the other a smattering of tattoos. Both have buff pecs and biceps. They wear woven raffia sun hats to stave off the heat, and sunglasses to protect their eyes. As soon as I stop the car, they shoot into action. Opening my door, welcoming me in, asking if these are all my bags.

"Julia Kelley, arriving for the Morgan-Hayden wedding," I say, unhooking my phone from the charger and climbing out. I'm dressed in jeans and a crisp pin-striped button-down—my go-to *dressed down but still on duty* look. The jeans ride up my ass and I adjust them. This guy, the driver's side greeter, notices.

"Just the bag in the trunk, plus the garment bag hanging," I say, ignoring his interest. "I can take this monstrosity." I yank out my catch-all purse. It's vegan leather, covered in pockets, and still manages to look sleek, sophisticated but practical. I hate it, and not just because I bought it with careful guidance from my ex-girlfriend. It's form and function on all points. It's also boring as fuck.

"We were told you'd be arriving soon." The driver's side greeter extends a small envelope that is clearly made from that compostable paper you can plant to sprout wildflowers. *Nice.* Millie's guests will love this detail. "Room information and key inside. We'll make sure your bags arrive shortly."

I feel a small smile creep up. There's nothing like pro greeters at an on-location wedding venue. When the staff is well trained, our events always run more smoothly. They are easier to coordinate with and are usually willing to work with us to problem solve while also not getting in our way when we can handle it on our own.

I hoist my purse over my shoulder and walk through the double door entrance into the lobby. My eyes take a second to adjust to the new dimness of this room. Furnishings sit low and sexy—it's the only way I know how to describe them. Mixed textures, velvets, burlap, funky glass sculptures, candles. A grouping of Reiki singing bowls are situated on a round table at the entrance with a sign that says UNLEASH YOUR SONG. The interior designer is famous for his mixed-media approach to décor, utilizing sculpture, glass, antiques, and modern one-of-a-kind pieces.

My eyes search the room while I walk. There's a sunflower-yellow-painted fireplace decorated with brightly colored lanterns hanging in a staggered pattern in front of it. On the wall is a towering piece of colorful artwork. To the left are double doors covered in velvet and studded with iron buttons. They lead to Oasis, the main bar and lounge on the property. I peek inside as I pass, curious.

Sleek dark countertops. Low light. Candles.

And Piper Cunningham, a ray of sun in the atmospheric, dreamy space.

She looks *good*. Her long red hair is up in a tight pony, cascading over her bare left shoulder. She wears a light green strapless jumpsuit that makes her creamy, freckled skin glow. Her breasts mound, full and soft, showing tasteful cleavage beneath the strands of gold chains around her neck.

Her lips are the perfect red.

She's still stunning. I still feel heat between my thighs when I see her, but I would never, ever go there again.

Her eyes flick up from the bar, where she is clearly fine-tuning the offerings on the charcuterie board that was just delivered. Picking it apart just like she does everything else in life.

Like she did me.

Her eyes trail up and stop right on my face. Something flickers in them. Not hate, not love, probably not any human emotion since she's practically soulless.

"You're here," she says. Her voice is bright and bell-like, a perfect match to her flawless Connecticut socialite persona. The Cunninghams are one of those families with ties that go way back to the first settlers off the Mayflower, and they are so out of touch with popular culture that they still brag about it at dinner parties.

"Of course I'm here. I'm the wedding planner," I say, dry, matter-of-fact. "You're the one making a surprise appearance."

"I was coming anyway, even if Ellen hadn't shattered her leg."

"Being here as a guest is different from attending as a bridesmaid."

She's unreadable, and I immediately feel paranoid. When a person breaks your trust over and over, it's easy to see them as a villain, to believe the worst. I have a hard time believing that Piper didn't know I was Millie's wedding planner, and that this knowledge didn't influence her behavior.

I'm not saying she somehow sabotaged Ellen in a plot to get her bridesmaid spot.

But I'm not *not* saying it either.

She doesn't look away from me as the bar attendant delivers an ice bucket with a bottle of champagne and four flutes. "Thanks so much. All looks great. Can you please have this waiting in the bride's room for her two p.m. arrival?"

I have to pull it together. Piper sucks, but she didn't brutally injure someone just so she could spend the whole weekend here with me.

The bar attendant nods, walking away with the offerings.

"Wasting no time making sure you have Millie under your thumb," I say. My tongue is a sword slicing her open to expose her true nature. Bomb people with love, then squash their spirit. Piper gets what she wants, and she gets it no matter the cost.

"I don't know what you mean by that, Julia. I'm just giving the bride a welcome present. It's proper etiquette." Etiquette, of course. She had an honest-to-God coming out party—the debutante kind, not the closet kind. She's still in that second one as far as I know.

"Right, and etiquette is important to you." Socially, she's a saint. Her reputation as an opportunistic, *whatever it takes* journalist is a better indicator of her true personality. Her face twitches. A little tremor of hurt passing over it. I don't have to stand here and be emotionally manipulated, either. I turn to go, and she rushes up behind me.

Her fingers graze my wrist but don't hold on. "Wait." One word, a plea in her voice. I stutter to a stop as if her desire still has a hold on me. I twist around so I can glare in her face. "I've wanted to text you so many times over the last year, but this is better. This way we can really talk."

"I don't have anything to say to you." I step away from her. I feel words bubbling up in my throat, threatening to spew like acid. There are a lot of things I've wanted to say to her over the last year, but none of them are kind or professional.

And I'm here to work. Not be vindicated.

"Oh thank God, Julia, there you are." Zoe's voice comes from the Oasis entrance. "We have an emergency."

I let my molten stare cut through Piper one more time before walking away. Zoe's eyebrows dance, and then her eyes flick back and forth between us. She has the presence of mind not to ask the details.

"What's the emergency?" I ask as we walk.

"Geometric altar drama," she says. And then she adds with a squeak, "Guess it's good you arrived early."

"If I hadn't, then you would have handled it." Her posture immediately grows with pride. "I need to drop my bag at Homebase and then you can take me to the ceremony site."

Shake it off, Julia. Just shake. Her. Off.

Chapter Five

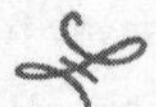

Kit

A sunburst right overhead is the perfect Universe-delivered final touch to this selfie photoshoot at Cabazon Dinosaurs, a kitschy roadside attraction on the way to Joshua Tree. The giant green and white T-Rex with the red heart inscribed with "Be Mine" on his chest looms just off-center in the shot. I do a quick "natural" edit and post it on Instagram with the caption, Just a little me time in the desert. #loveyourself #breakingupishardtodo

That will keep fans and foes alike busy for hours. Most of my followers are supportive, light-centered, love-driven humans on a genuine quest for spiritual growth. Some of them are dudes who can't get past Instagram's safety features to send me dick pics but do leave comments on my photos. And a small percentage are people who can't wait to shit on anything I do, no matter how magical or mundane. They like to fight it out in comments or share my posts in stories with derisive asides, but my blue check means I basically never see anything unless it's from people I follow.

Unfortunately, my verified status doesn't protect me from

Mom seeing my post, immediately liking it, and sending me a DM to ask why I'm heading into the desert.

> Are you trying to get away from me, Kitten?
> Is this because I'm bisexual?

Yeah, she spells out the whole word. *Bisexual.* And then she sends three hearts, the colors of the bi flag, and I wish I could bury my phone in the sand right beneath the giant pink brontosaurus on the other side of my white Jeep Wrangler.

My phone then starts buzzing with an incoming call. Dad. A FaceTime.

I message him that I'm driving and I'll text him later.

He hates texting because he's a stickler for grammar and punctuation, can't get past it to send a quick message.

> We still haven't talked about brunch. I know
> you're upset, and you have every right to be.
> This is not ideal, is it, cupcake?

I yank my car door open and throw my phone in the passenger seat.

Ideal.

If I had a nickel for every time my dad has used that word to describe me, Mom, our roles in the rom-com movie of the life he's writing, I'd have a vacation home to escape to and wouldn't have to work this wedding. The word burrowed beneath my skin and tattooed itself on my bones, fusing with my own identity. Dad's definition of the ideal rom-com ingenue is more Meg or Drew than Sandra or Kate. She's dreamy, funny, quirky, cute; she has a creative job and carefree attitude, and girls and guys both adore her.

I snort at the last one.

Closer to home than he thought.

I release a deep breath and wring out the tightness in my upper body, twisting around to the backseat to grab my tarot deck from the inside of my purse. I hold the cards in my hand, closing my eyes and inhaling a few quick breaths. My eyes open and land on the top of the cards. This deck is personal, not one I use with clients or in my "Choose Your Own Tarot Adventure" readings. It was the first deck I ever got, a birthday gift to myself when I was nineteen. Some people believe you should be gifted your first deck, but when tarot came into my life, I needed help understanding my emotional world more than I needed to listen to superstition.

I chose this deck because of its botanical design. A Cali girl through and through, I'm aesthetically inspired by nature in all her wild forms. Even in LA we love a run through a canyon, or a mountainscape at sunset.

The back of the cards is black matte with a winding white vine running over it.

Each card is uniquely designed, though it follows the Rider–Waite structure of traditional decks. I shuffle, *swish swish swish*, and place the deck on my bare thighs. The cards feel warm and heavy, alive with energy. I cut the deck with my left hand and hold my palm over the two top cards. The one that radiates extra warmth is it, always, even when my soul doesn't understand why. I reincorporate the deck with that one on top. Breathe. Turn it over.

The Two of Cups, upright.

A beautiful card featuring two serpents entwining their tails. In the center is an orange poppy. This card doesn't have to mean romance, but it almost always comes to you when there is or will be attraction, partnership, unity.

Romance vibes are so not what I'm sending out, Universe. Please take my hint and act accordingly.

I shake myself out one more time, listening to the chimes of my bracelets rattling together over my wrists, and shuffle the deck again. A single card sticks out askew from the others. I flip it out, turning it over in my right hand.

The Wheel of Fortune, upright.

My heart does a nosedive into my stomach. Spikes of heat shoot over my chest, down the length of my arms, to my fingertips.

I've seen this card combination one other time in my life.

Just one time.

The Haunt O' Ween festival in Old Pasadena is a suburban kid's playground in the week leading up to Halloween. My friends and I had been attending it since we were tiny tots, and the year I pulled those cards, my new, cool best friend had joined us. Julia Kelley had transferred into Forrest Chapel Private Academy the fall of seventh grade. A scholarship kid, a wild card even if she was mostly just sarcastic. Everyone had immediately been fascinated by her.

Fresh meat in middle school always draws a crowd. But while the other girls had mostly lost interest after Julia refused to play any of their mind games, I'd gotten attached.

She was more than fresh. All her dark, sharp edges made my bright, pretty curves feel safe. So when Karen MacMillan, the resident queen bee, dared Julia to visit Madame Moira—psychic reader and neighborhood legend—I couldn't let Julia go it alone.

Madame Moira's tent was set up beside the South Pasadena Historical Museum, a wood-frame building that looked like it was dragged from a ghost town out West. Purple velvet curtains draped over the entrance to her den. Julia and I clutched hands, whispering promises not to abandon each other no matter what Madame Moira's reading revealed.

Madame Moira was not a crone, not even close. She was a pretty woman with raven-black hair, long fingers, nails painted midnight black, and a face that appeared ageless. And not LA ageless. Legit *untouched by the hands of time* ageless. Julia handed over her five dollars, which got her a three-card spread, and Madame Moira got started without much preamble.

Her shuffle was fast. The cards almost looked like they were flying; Julia noted that they seemed to float in the air for a second, and it totally spooked her out.

But I was mesmerized. By the cards *and* the woman who didn't fit in any sort of box. Unmarried, unconventional, and absolutely un-fuck-with-able. She had both of us cut the deck with our left hands, which surprised me since the reading was supposed to be for Julia alone. Julia had been dared; she was the one who paid.

The cards drifted out of the deck, balanced perfectly in Madame Moira's long, trim fingers.

First, the Fool. *The spark of a new beginning.* She looked back and forth between us.

You two, each, both. This. She motioned at our hands, still clasped, dangling unseen at our sides.

Then, the Two of Cups. The art in her deck featured two girls holding their cups up toward each other, smiling, laughing. Full of love. I knew, even without Madame Moira saying it. I knew they were Julia and me.

This bond is special. Unique. The flame of her candle flickered and her eyes sparked with interest. She flipped over the last card.

The Wheel of Fortune.

Twin Flames, two halves of the same soul. Her candle flame sparked and expanded. She smiled, then frowned. *No matter what you do, you will break apart one day. Lose each other, believe it's forever, brokenhearted. But Twin Flames are rare and they can't be extinguished. They always find their way back to each other.*

I flip the Wheel of Fortune card over now, blinking away the memory.

How long has it been since I thought about that night? Easily, the day comes back to me. I was eighteen. August heat enveloped me as I packed up the back of my car—a Bronco my dad had gotten cheap for me when I got my license. I was leaving for Berkeley, putting space between myself and everything that had happened between Julia and me that summer. I had kissed my parents goodbye, gotten the directions ready to go; the only lingering, unfinished thing was her.

Julia.

She had texted me and called a couple times since that fateful night together. I had avoided her in person, kept the conversation light, noncommittal. She got the drift, and she was angry. *Seething.* That much I knew. Her anger was easier for me to deal with than telling her I wasn't ready would have been. That I couldn't do it. That I had never felt more lost or confused in my life, that I didn't feel like myself anymore and couldn't start college like that.

I just had to put it aside. Push it down.

I had plans; so did she. She'd forget about me eventually.

Twin Flames always find their way back to each other. I heard Madame Moira's words in my head and I ignored them.

What did she know about us?

I reshuffle the cards, my heart doing a dance in my chest. My breathing uncomfortable, unsteady.

Fuck off, I think, directed at the Universe herself.

And I yank my car into gear.

~

I walk inside the Celestial Sands lobby sweaty, my jean shorts riding up my crotch, my silk camisole drenched at my cleavage.

"Hi there," the manager, a sexy Black man with an Afro and a winning smile says as I approach.

"Hey," I say, and I sound grouchy even if I don't mean to. His bright grin falters. I try again. "This place is gorgeous." I adjust. No need to be a bitch to him; he didn't give me that horribly nostalgic reading. That was all me, myself, and I. "Kit Larson, checking in for the Morgan-Hayden wedding."

His smile is back. "Wedding party or Love, Always staff?"

"Neither. I'm the tarot reader."

"Ah! Then you're staff. Report to Bungalow Ten. It's the *Homebase*" —he places air quotes around the word—"of the operation. They have your room assignment."

He directs me on how to get there by exiting the main house and taking the path toward the bungalows. I snap some shots of the interiors to post in my stories when I leave the hotel next week. As a rule, I never share my location until after I'm well on my way home. One stalker at the Mercer in Soho was enough to teach me that lesson.

I push through the back doors into the breezy garden space, following the winding path toward the bungalow. November in Joshua Tree is my idea of the perfect weather. Warm during the day, chilly at night. You can still sunbathe, and then don a sweater and sit by the fire roasting marshmallows and telling ghost stories, blanketed by starlight.

Bungalow Ten is a small cube with a hammock slung right outside. The door is open, and out of it comes a twentysomething woman with gorgeous black hair and a harried expression on her face.

She nearly bowls me over, barely sideswiping me before stopping short.

"Mystic Maven," she says, her voice a little misty with awe. "Oh my God."

"Oh, yeah, I'm Kit," I reply, and my cheeks feel warm.

"Sorry, that was unprofessional. I'm Zoe. Assistant to the wedding planner—let me know if you need anything." She steps aside. "Room key, et cetera, is inside." She motions back to Bungalow Ten before hurrying along to whatever mission awaits her.

I step up to the entrance and give the open door a courtesy knock. When no one responds, I walk inside. The room is brightly lit by every lamp and overhead light in the place. They've shoved couches and other comfy furniture to the walls and pulled together the tables to form a maze of solid surfaces throughout the room.

A woman—I'm assuming the wedding planner—stands with her back to the door. She looks like she's on the phone, but her voice is low, not audible. Her dark brown hair is swept up in a half-up-half-down do, wavy and thick. She's short, with shapely hips and a tiny waist. She stands like she's got a rod running the length of her body, perfect posture and pretty golden skin.

Jesus Christ. Stop cataloging her body features with such engrossed interest.

She ends her call and spins around.

For the second time today my heart makes a beeline for my stomach. My breath catches in my throat like a jagged pill. My brain short-circuits.

"Julia."

Her name in my mouth is the most decadent forbidden fruit.

Chapter Six

Julia

I gave up on believing the wisdom of psychics years ago.

Then I gave up on the hope that Kit Larson would ever sashay back into my life.

For a second I almost convince myself that she's nothing more than a mirage. Her platinum hair is kissed dusty rose at the tips like it's fading out from hot pink. Edgier than the muted beach sand color it was the last time I saw her. She's all curvy lines. Ample hips, perky breasts, soft pink full lips. Her skin is creamy sun-kissed tan, her eyes are cool fresh-mown-grass green.

"Julia." She says only my name again.

Oh, she's real. And just as beautiful as she was in high school.

Objectively attractive beyond the face, the body, the effortless style. Not a *cool girl*, per se, but definitely in the same sphere. More dreamy, all curves and secret sweetness; Kit Larson was the girl even straight girls crushed on.

I swallow, dry mouthed. Dry throat. All moisture rushing elsewhere.

I feel a tug toward her. A raw instinct—the kind I've trained myself to interrogate for flaws. The kind of primitive, illogical draw that would start a war or incite a duel if I were a man.

Then I get a handle on it, because I'm not a man, and Kit Larson is not to be trusted.

Kit Larson was off-limits and then all mine. We were playing with fire and then we were consumed by the flames. Kissing wasn't enough, and before that weekend was over, we went all the way.

Kit Larson was everything.

And then she broke my heart.

"One of us has to say something," she says, as if that contribution gets her off the hook for more. "Hello." Her eyes trip to mine, crinkling up with her tentative smile.

My backbone stiffens and I look down at my paperwork. It's the flower order, a list of every single arrangement, flower type with all the prices itemized. It swims in my vision like an eye exam I've convinced myself I'll fail, and so I do. I squeeze my lids closed, raking my eyeballs around behind them, then I press the tips of my fingers to the rims of my lashes and hold them in place.

When I open my eyes, she'll be gone.

She'll realize she's in the wrong place, realize whatever she's here for isn't worth it and turn tail and run. That probably won't happen. Despite this horrible coincidence, she drove all the way out to the desert for a reason, one she is unlikely to abandon just because I'm here.

I can't expect her to leave, but I can control my own behavior in her presence. When I open my eyes, I will be a cool-as-a-cucumber, pro wedding planner capable of handling any adversity that comes my way. I will be Julia Kelley, entrepreneur in the making. Not Julia Kelley, girl whose bones turn to putty at the sight of her high school crush.

"I'm still here," she says. "Just, FYI."

My eyes shoot open. "Of course you are."

"You were hoping I'd run." She cocks her hip out in a challenge. The motion ruffles her camisole so that it reveals a sliver of golden-kissed skin above her waistband. I ignore the magnetic tug to look closer.

"Wouldn't be the first time."

She grits her teeth, probably to hold in her own venomous response.

"Why are you here, Katherine?" Her face twitches at the name, and that gloriously curved hip uncocks in retreat. The sliver of skin mercifully vanishes.

Katherine is an old queen name, I can still hear her say, nose scrunched like an accordion, while we ate gelato outside the library that late-summer day before we turned fourteen. *If I were a queen, I'd only ever want to be a young one.*

"There's a wedding," Kit replies.

"I'm the wedding planner." There is no way she's a guest—none of the general attendees are arriving until Sunday. She can't be a bridesmaid, because I have dossiers on all of them, including headshots and social media profiles. She's not family. She's not Love, Always staff. That leaves only one thing.

"You've got to be kidding—"

The rest of my exasperated guess is cut off by Zoe entering in a whirlwind of long, lean limbs, smelling faintly of patchouli and panic. She abruptly manifests a deer-in-the-headlights freeze before widening her massive brown doe eyes in SOS alarm.

"Geometric altar crisis averted, but Healer Arynne would like a word."

A curl of smoke wafts through the open door to collect around Kit like a fog machine at a rave. She lifts her fingers to her nose to delicately block out the scent.

"This energy will not land on me," comes a syrupy voice.

Zoe nudges Kit heroically out of the way, just as Healer Arynne and her entourage of burly, barely clothed men enter Homebase. They aren't carrying her on a pillow, waving fronds and feeding her grapes, but that's the aesthetic they bring. Shirtless, pecs oiled, booty shorts leaving nothing to the imagination, they flank her.

She's shaped like a ripe plum, with a fuzzy spray of multicolored, predominately silver-streaked hair, and a plethora of crystal-covered jewelry. She turns heavily lined, hooded, huge eyes on me.

"The entire vibe is off out there and I'm told you're responsible for fixing it," she says, waving her smudge stick at me like it's a dagger. She begins to circle, plucking invisible grime from my aura as she talks. "The crystals in the centerpiece arrangements are a complete disaster, your florist is a sadistic monster—three tourmalines broken, do you even comprehend how apocalyptic of an omen that is?"

I twist away, trying to get clear of her plucking, desperate to bat her hands back but conscious of my responsibility to remain professional, to defuse.

Healer Arynne is both the provider of the crystals for the ceremony—which are featured everywhere from around the altar to the head table for both rehearsal dinner and wedding reception—and the officiant of the ceremony. She's TikTok famous for her interfaith marriage ceremonies and crystal healing rituals, all of which can be purchased for a hefty price on her website.

When I don't reply right away, she snaps, "I can't possibly allow this ceremony to go on," head shaking in angst, seconds from dropping to the ground in a heap.

This can't be happening.

The bride hasn't even arrived yet and the officiant is already objecting to the nuptials.

It is too goddamn early for this huge of a red flag to be flying high.

"Healer Arynne?" Kit's voice is wispy. Nothing like the tone she was using with me before chaos arrived at my doorstep. She takes a graceful step forward, stretching out her hand toward Healer Arynne. A stack of delicate bracelets made of gold and natural stones circles her wrist. She tosses her hair over her shoulder just as her hand comes to rest lightly on the older woman's forearm, stilling her. "Millie hired me to read tarot for the weekend's events." Her smile is coy, accented with a scrunch of her perfect turned-up nose. "Maybe the cards can show us the way forward. What do you think?"

Healer Arynne's shoulders immediately drop out of high alert stance.

"I don't know why, but I *instantly* trust you," she breathes, the anguish leaking out of her voice. Her hand falls to rest over Kit's. Her eyes flash and she squeezes. "Why, yes, of course, we were canaries together in a past life." She releases what can only be described as a chirp.

Kit's smile broadens. "Naturally." She gives a teeny shoulder shrug and releases her own cheerful chirping reply. Healer Arynne lets her smudge stick drop to her side.

"Thank Spirit you're here." The sigh of relief is *sizable*.

"Just in time," Kit replies.

She can't be serious. Her eyes flick to mine. A momentary connection or an invitation to play along, I'm not sure, and I'm not engaging. She's not luring me in—that is not how this is going to play out.

Kit reaches into the pink monochromatic Louis Vuitton satchel slung over her shoulder, tugging out a rectangle of hunter green velvet. She quickly unfolds it to reveal a set of tarot cards, the iridescent pastel of their design catching the light, making the tops of the cards practically glow.

A memory flashes in my mind, lightning fast. Three cards laid out on a black lace tablecloth. Our hands clutched, her breath in my ear, *are you scared?* I was, more than ever before, and that rush never left me when I was beside her.

Now, Kit shuffles the cards deftly with both hands. Her fingers curling over the edges, sliding them into each other, sliding them out and back in.

"Our intention here is to bring Millie and Sean together." Kit says, her voice mellow. Zoe edges closer, transfixed, just like everyone else at Homebase.

Just like me.

I blink, cross my arms, glare at my watch, but my eyes unwillingly travel back to Kit's hands. The shuffle. The surety of her movements. The way she does it all without ever pulling her focus from her subject.

"Tourmalines breaking, that's not the vibe we want, so we just need a nudge from Spirit to uncover where we've gotten off track so we can get back on." She makes it sound so obvious, simple even, and Healer Arynne and Zoe both nod, taken in, mouths parted. It's only then that I realize my mouth hangs open, too, the inside dried out. I clamp my teeth closed, wishing for water to quench the desert on my tongue.

"Now," Kit says. The sound of the shuffle ends, and I shift my eyes back up. Hers drift to mine; her brow hooks up. "Cut the deck once." She lifts the cards toward Healer Arynne.

We all watch as she curls her hands around the cards, breathing out before breaking them into two uneven stacks. Kit raises her left hand over the two, hovering, before nodding.

"This is the one," she says, tapping the top card on the section of cards in Healer Arynne's hands. She nods for her to turn it over.

From this angle it's hard to see at first, but the noise of relief and understanding that bursts from Healer Arynne's lips immediately lets me know she's appeased.

"Temperance," Kit says, taking the card between two of her fingers and lifting it toward her face to examine it. "The card depicts an angel whose gender is not immediately obvious, expressing a balance between the masculine and feminine energies. She is firmly footed between the spiritual world and the material." Kit takes the rest of her deck back from Healer Arynne, leaving the Temperance card face up on top. "You are someone who has mastered the art of not letting little things get to you."

I have to stifle a snort. Zoe and Kit both glare at me in warning. This fire is so close to being stamped out; I do not need to be the reason it reignites. Especially since the reason it's dying down is thanks to Kit Larson.

"With balance and flow you can find a compromise to this stumbling block with the florist," Kit goes on, her voice easy, almost hypnotic. "Let go of control, accommodate all perspectives for the best possible solution."

"I know you're right, you're right," Healer Arynne says, sounding resigned. She raises both hands to Kit's shoulders, squeezing them tight. "An angel."

I can't tell if she means the reader or the card. Kit blushes, clearly certain it's the former.

Healer Arynne snaps her fingers. "Come along, we have some balancing to do."

Attention, march! And with that she and her band of merry shirtless men leave, taking the scent of sweet smoke and sharp earth with them.

"Follow them," I say to Zoe. She's staring at Kit, awestruck.

"Wow," Zoe says. She's a cartoon character with stars in her eyes, my God.

I clap. "Zoe." She jolts, her eyes flick to me, and she nods, but then looks once more back to Kit.

"Just. Wow." She offers applause and Kit curtsies.

And then, just like that, we're alone at Homebase. Just the two of us. Just the girl who broke my heart and grew up to be a goddamn masterminding magical goddess.

"A professional," I say, my voice raw.

"It's a calling." She shrugs. "It pays the bills and I love it for that."

Our eyes connect; years stretch out between us, mysterious and magnetic. I have to be the one to pull away first, to look down at the table where all the staff hotel keys are laid out, room assignment information printed. I scan the stack, and sure enough, there's her card.

"Mystic Maven," I read aloud.

"That's me," she replies.

My fingers brush the soft pads of her palm as I lay the key in her hand. She closes her fingers over it, the very tips grazing my skin. It's a real metal key with a quaint piece of plantable paper dangling from a string, containing instructions to her accommodations.

"It's an Airstream trailer," I say, glancing down at my dossier notes. "Millie wants it to be Instagrammable." I cringe.

"Wow, good job not puking."

"Thanks for that," I say, glancing over her shoulder in the direction Healer Arynne scurried off to.

We give each other another loaded look. I hate every second of it. Every twinge of feeling in the dark, deep crevices I'm desperate to keep out of the light. The messy places inside me that no one needs to ever see. This is not the Julia Kelley I am supposed to be.

My walkie-talkie scratches with an incoming signal.

"Bride and groom have landed," Zoe's voice screeches through the speaker.

Duty calls.

Chapter Seven

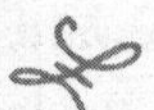

Kit

We both shoot out into the late afternoon heat, going our separate ways. Was it this warm earlier? I'm suddenly sweating, and I'm not deluded enough to think the damp film over my skin has anything to do with the desert heat. That credit goes to the sudden reappearance of Julia Kelley in the narrative of my life.

Not exactly a meet-cute, Universe. Since, despite my goal to be the ingenue of my own life, this is not a romantic comedy.

This is not on the Ideal Rom-Com Life Path.

I have to focus on something that isn't the way she's grown out her hair, or how her ass looked in those fitted high-waist jeans, or the fact that she still wears that single gold chain with the tiny red heart around her neck that dips into her clavicle just like it did when we were eighteen.

I decide to fix my attention on the tiny printed instructions typed out on the back of this piece of seed paper.

Take the path toward the sculpture of the moon

I flick my eyes up, searching. This sidewalk leads back toward the main building, which I am guessing is normally the starting point for these directions. So I wind over that way until I see a fork in the path. One path leads toward an arm of the main property, while the other trails away. I decide the latter is probably a better bet since an Airstream trailer wouldn't be located right up against the main facility.

Sure enough, as I pass a crop of giant organ pipe cacti, their spiky, slim bodies stretching up toward the sun, I see it. A cement moon, set in a sandy bed, like it's in space.

Veer west

Left. Thank you, nearly setting sun. I follow that path until I reach a courtyard that acts like a walking roundabout.

Take the path toward the fences

I guess that means I go in the direction of the hills, since upon arrival I noticed the perimeter of the property faced the crop of hills on the right. I know I'm correct when I see a collection of trailers spaced out with little adobe fences separating them.

Mine is number 555, and damn, Millie Morgan really leaves no detail to chance. Or this could be the Universe signaling to me that I am on the brink of a massive shift.

Julia's sharp aqua eyes flash in my mind like a siren.

Nope, this message is part of Millie's mission to make my digs as Instagram-worthy as possible. That's it.

The gate to my Airstream trailer is made of copper, great for keeping energy clear and channeling connection to the spiritual world. Also, downright photogenic. I film my opening of the gate, my light-pink-painted toenails peeking from my sandals as I walk the gravel path toward the trailer. Pan up, up, and capture the whole shiny silver bullet against the hills. Joshua trees create visual interest, their craggy, crooked arms twisting toward the sky. Desert sands, shaded by cloud cover slowly edging across the azure sky, roll out in front of me for miles.

I'll prep videos for social media and a vlog for YouTube, all to publish after I'm far away from Celestial Sands. These videos always get oodles of hits, and often get me offers of free weekend getaways from similar properties in exchange for a few posts.

I drop my phone to my side, surveying the space, focusing on the details and not my building internal dilemma over *she who won't be named*.

The Airstream trailer is small and round, set at the far right corner of this rectangular fenced-off space. Outside is a soaking tub positioned close against the metal fencing that makes up the back perimeter and offers privacy from the other units. I walk over to see it's got a shelf fixed with some spa amenities, plus this gorgeous industrial-designed copper faucet to fill the tub. It's not for bathing but for stargazing.

Good thing I brought a bikini.

There's also an outdoor shower with a rain head, an outdoor bed set on an elevated platform, and lounge chairs facing the hills for optimal sunset views.

I step inside the Airstream and glance in either direction. It has been fully refurbished in a deliberate vintage boho style. Creams, dusty pinks, soft grays, and muted purples. On one end are the bedroom and bath tucked together like a puzzle, on the other a tiny living/dining nook with a bench sofa and a bar. The kitchen is a galley that runs down either side of the trailer's center, with pastel pink cabinets, rich green glass tile backsplash, and soft maple butcher block counters. There's even a cute teal fridge tucked up beneath the countertop at the end of the kitchen.

There are hanging air plants strung up in crochet, bouquets of dried flowers and herbs, mismatched wineglasses set out on an exposed beam above the sink, leading me to think there is a bottle of something chilling inside that fridge.

I crouch, yanking the handle to reveal a bottle of rosé from a winery in Temecula, plus some simple snacks and bottles of water. I consider going straight for the wine—maybe it would help calm my nerves. I opt for water instead.

I drop to the couch, curling my legs underneath me.

Julia is *here*. The reality crashes over me.

Our lips crushed together, our swimsuits there and then gone. Fumbled questions of consent, muffled giggles as we explored each other's bodies.

It hits me in waves. The desire, the yearning, the prickle of fear mixed with that giddy, almost drunk, heady feeling of want.

I had never had sex with a girl, but I was pretty sure that our fingers counted as *all the way*. She seemed to think so, too, because later on—as we sat on the couch together watching *When Harry Met Sally* for the thousandth time, her fingers tracing symbols over the skin on my thigh—she told me. I was her first, and she loved me.

I said it back—it didn't even occur to me not to.

I remember watching the movie and thinking how silly it was that after they hooked up, Harry bolted. Ghosted on his soulmate—*what a tool*. And sure, he eventually gets her back, but what would have happened if she had moved on? Why risk losing the love of your life, just because you're scared?

My eyes prick with tears. "So silly." I breathe in and out, fast, through my nose.

What a tool I was, too.

What I understand now—which was impossible to comprehend when I first saw those cards spread out on Madame Moira's table—is that the reading she gave us told a very specific kind of love story. One that would start way too early, one that was reciprocated, one that may always be out of sync.

It's why the Wheel of Fortune holds so much meaning.

And why, even though I have tried hard to forget her, Julia showing back up in my life smacks like a slap from destiny. Sharp and sure, with painful inevitability. Just like the turn of that goddamn wheel.

I huff and shake my body loose. I gotta get my head in the game and out of the past. She's here, and so am I, but we're both professionals. We can handle this. I won't play the Universe's little game, no matter how tempting it tries to make it.

I pull my phone out to FaceTime Nina. It rings a few times before connecting. I can tell immediately that Nina is working at one of her temporary gigs she takes in between acting jobs. She's been a dog walker, a plant waterer, a brow specialist at a pop-up makeup kiosk in The Grove mall, and currently, a candle au pair at the Farmers Market for her friend Cara's witchy brand.

"You're working," I say. "I can call you back."

"There's a lull," she replies, flopping onto the stool behind her. The purple fabric of the tent mixed with the sunlight makes her glow aubergine. Her eyes travel to look past me in the camera.

"You've arrived at . . . an Airstream trailer?" She both looks and sounds confused.

"Celestial Sands has a wide selection of lodging options outside the main facility," I say, spinning the phone around to show her the digs. "I think they even have a dome."

"Like for viewing stars and/or aliens?"

"Max Evans is not here, but I'll keep my eyes peeled," I snort. Nina and I discovered the original WB masterpiece *Roswell* at the last remaining DVD rental store in downtown Berkeley. We binged it the weekend after midterms sophomore year, solidifying it as one of our comfort shows for the rest of our college careers.

"You know good and well that there isn't a single alien on that show I would kick outta my bed," she says. The casual mention of Nina's queerness sets my own secrecy in stark contrast. She's been out since she was in high school, and I know it wasn't always easy—especially when she was still living in North Carolina. A Black queer teen was scandalous to say the least. "Well, except for that teensy blond bitch who tried to split Liz and Max apart. You can't separate soulmates."

Soulmates. The word sends a shiver down my spine.

As far as fated love types go, Twin Flames and soulmates aren't exactly the same thing. One is complicated in a way that feels combustible. The other is what they make movies and write sonnets about. It's not a sure thing that Twin Flames ever get on the same page long enough for a Happily Ever After.

It's not that I really believe in the concept, anyway. Just because a psychic used those words to describe the relationship between Julia and me doesn't make it true. It also doesn't make it romantic. There are plenty of Twin Flames—and even soulmates—who don't fall in love romantically.

I take a swig of water and let out a groan.

"Whoa, that was guttural," she says. "More mom shenanigans?"

"She's not taking my unsubtle hints that I need space from her in particular, but no, that's not what the exasperation is about."

I should tell her about Julia. The whole story, even the parts I'm scared to look right at.

Oh, by the way, I'm into guys and girls, and a girl I once gave my heart and soul—and almost everything else to—is at this wedding looking like a snack.

Nina wouldn't blink. No matter how surprising the information was, she'd roll with it, offer support, encourage, send thirst traps, whatever I needed to get used to the truth being out there.

"Do you remember that friend I told you about—the one I had a falling-out with the summer before college?"

I'm a coward who can't even come out to her best friend. Can't even come clean about what happened and how I was the one to blame.

"How could I forget? You made me work extra hard at friendship thanks to that chick."

An unearned fear. *Such a tool.*

"I had a lot of walls up," I say. *Tool, tool, tool.*

Nina gives me an exaggerated raise of her eyebrows. "You were totally bricked in."

"She's here."

Her eyes widen and she stands up on instinct. Fight or flight, I can't be sure.

"*Here* as in, at the wedding venue?" she asks, and I nod. Now it's her turn to take a hefty gulp from her rainbow-colored reusable water bottle. "What's the fucking chance?"

Pretty high considering I pulled the same tarot cards as we pulled on a fateful Halloween night back when we were twelve, right after we shared a churro and went through the hall of mirrors holding hands, the same cards that the psychic told us meant we were Twin Flames, cards that almost always accompany the start of a fated romance.

"She's the wedding planner," is the detail I decide to share instead.

"Name," Nina says, clicking away from the FaceTime screen.

"Do not google her."

"I most certainly am," she says. The screen is paused because she's typing. "It was Julia something . . . ?" My jaw clenches. "You can tell me or I can look at Millie Morgan's Instagram and find the info through sleuthing. Your choice."

She's a bulldog when it comes to getting what she wants. I'm in a losing standoff.

"Julia Kelley," I say through tight lips.

Seconds skip past while she googles and I rethink my decision not to open the bottle of wine in the fridge.

Her face rematerializes on my screen. "She's a stone-cold hottie in a very *all of my shirts are dry-clean only, I need to be fucked into oblivion* sort of way." Her eyes flick off to somewhere that isn't my face in her phone and she grins, toothy and broad. "No, ma'am, you are not the one who needs to be fucked into oblivion." Ah, a customer. "Have a magical day." I snort. Nina looks back at the camera. "I don't know what a beige banana like that was even doing in the Heathen Hearth booth, anyway."

"Maybe she's corporate in the streets, pagan in the sheets." I try to sound lighthearted, but it comes off more as *swallowed a bug*.

"You're totally freaking out," she replies.

"It's been over ten years since I saw her." Gulp. Water. Wish it was wine.

"You never looked her up or anything? Not once, not even when you were drunk or PMSing?" She sounds skeptical, but she's wrong. The pain of our falling-out plus the yearning for her closeness was an equation for inaction. I never gave in to the urge, even when it did fleetingly flutter through my brain. I was petrified of what I might find—or feel—if I did.

I shake my head.

"Wow, look at the universe," she says.

"My karma can't possibly be this bad."

"Doesn't sound bad to me, babe," she replies, her voice thoughtful. "These sorts of fractures need repairing. Ya know, maybe this is all for your healing."

"Julia was a lot of things, but capable of healing me isn't one of them."

"Your life is in chaos. Your mom and dad are splitting up, with Momma coming out and proud, Daddy-o unraveling at the teddy bear seams. You broke up with a hottie who was definitely marriage material without so much as a tear shed. Then this gig dropped into your lap like *fate*." She says the word like it's a gift, but I feel it like a gut punch instead.

The Wheel of Fortune card is most intrinsically, most authentically, linked to the hands of fate. That turn of the wheel can't be stopped, but where it does finally land is most certainly right where it should.

"You're Mystic Maven," she continues. "What does your intuition say?"

"I think my compass is broken." The words are almost a whisper.

Broken. Or used to being forced to trek toward a false true north.

I could let it spin out, caught in the force of this seemingly fated magnetic field. I could see where it lands when it finally does. I could follow fate rather than the Ideal Rom-Com Life Path.

I could just try it, just for a second, just to see.

"You got any candles for getting rid of an ex?" A stranger's voice through my phone speakers jolts me back to reality. Nina gets two mischievous lines like the number eleven between her brows. "By violent or nonviolent means?" I can't see the customer, but I can imagine the horror on their face. Nina grins back at me. "Gotta jet, but—" She pulls the phone close to her face. "Take the dare, babe. What's the worst that could happen?"

Twin Flames always find their way back to each other.

This journey with Julia started because of a dare from a twelve-year-old girl who had just gotten her period. I could end it with a dare from an ageless universe determined to fuck with my status quo.

Nina ends the call, leaving me alone to survive in the storm of my thoughts. I exhale sharply, glare at the water that isn't cutting it, and decide rather than get tipsy t-minus two hours before the bachelorette party events—of which I am an important spiritual attraction—that a walk to clear my head and work out some of these jitters is just what I need.

When I see another text from Mom, I nearly throw my phone across the Airstream trailer.

It's just three question marks in a row followed by a photo of her holding up my graduation gown from Berkeley, and standing in the background, right at the edge of the frame, wearing a cherry red Alo Yoga matching set, is her girlfriend, Willa.

> Keep or toss, Kitten?

I glare at the phone, zooming in tight with the spread of my fingers to try to get a better look at Willa. I have so many questions bouncing around in my head for my mom.

When did she know she was bi? Why did she keep it from me?

How does it feel to be out now, after being married to a man for so long?

How does it feel to be out when everything she ever showed me about love made it seem like the only way to have it for real was to have it with a man?

But I have this willful resolve to keep her dangling and in the dark—to give her a taste of how confused I feel right now—so I don't ask them.

Do not get rid of any of my stuff, I text back, before putting my phone on Do Not Disturb and shoving it in the back pocket of my jean shorts and heading outside in a flurry. I follow the paths around toward the main building and purposefully avoid the one that leads to Homebase. Fate or whatever the hell is happening can just be patient—we've waited ten years, what's a few more hours?

I round the corner, right into a pillar of soft human flesh smelling intensely of expensive perfume.

"Shit, sorry," I sputter, jumping back. She's taller than me by at least a head. Pilates body, lithe and lean, hair bouncy red waves.

"Let me guess." Her eyes trail up and down. Sharp green with shimmery apricot powder swept across the lid. "Sound healer?"

I'm immediately aware of how my flowy camisole under a bohemian-printed gauzy jacket probably looks to someone like her. This chick is dressed in head-to-toe Chanel, her earrings are Prada, and her heels are undoubtedly Louboutins, but I can't see the red sole from where I'm standing. My gem jewelry and messy blond hair tipped in fading pink couldn't possibly be a more opposite vibe.

"Unqualified," I reply. "Tarot mystic." I try to come off as cool and detached, but with a Pisces Sun and Moon, and the most chaotic air sign as my Rising, I never quite nail that.

Her microbladed copper eyebrow hooks up. "Millie didn't used to be into all this stuff." *This stuff*, meaning me. Like I am just a walking tarot deck or something.

Which . . . okay, sort of fair. But I don't care for her tone.

"When was the last time you saw her? She's made *this stuff* her brand for a while now." Millie doesn't read her own cards, as far as I know, but she's created a presence for herself right at the intersection of spiritual enlightenment and lifestyle aspiration.

And it's totally working for her.

"Infrequently," she says, her peachy cheeks darkening. "I was her sorority president, she's a couple years younger than me. I split my time between New York and LA, for work." She doesn't offer up information about her work, but my guess is that it's something high paying with a boys' club. She feels like a woman who would smoke a cigar and drink a Scotch while shooting the shit in a room with a lot of dark wood paneling.

Her eyes trail over my head in the direction of the main building.

"Sorry, you were on your way somewhere," I say, stepping out of her path. Clearly, I'm boring her. She blinks rapidly a couple of times.

"No—well, yes. I'm trying to decide if I should go back to the main lobby and wait for the bride and groom, or wait until Millie settles in and meet her in her room."

She has an aesthetic of smart, tall, immaculate tycoon, which doesn't track with the indecision I hear in her voice. She's calculating her moves like there's more at stake here than just how she occupies her time for the next half hour.

"I don't have my cards with me to help discern the right path for you," I say, smiling, which she nearly returns before skepticism scrunches her nose. Okay, not a believer. *Noted.* I press on. "But, when I was checking in, I overheard that the bride and groom had arrived." My information doesn't seem to assuage any of her concerns. "If it helps, the wedding planner went over to meet them, so I think you wouldn't be out of line to show up, too."

"The wedding planner," she says with a flare of her nostrils. "Perfect." The word has sting.

"She's a challenge." I try to read her body language, but she's closed off.

"To say the least," she replies, still with that sharp edge to her tone. I shake out the knot forming in my stomach this gives me. Her eyes lock on me. "Shall we go face the scorpion's stinger together?"

Electricity zips up my spine in a warning.

Julia is a Virgo Sun and Aquarius Rising—perfectionism and individuality personified—with her Moon in Scorpio. I always look up people's birth chart when I first meet them, but this woman doesn't seem like the type to do that. And Julia isn't the type to offer that information up—she may not even know it herself.

The words *scorpion's stinger* could be a coincidence. It could be a dig and nothing more.

But as my eyes trail after her walking up the path that leads toward Julia Kelley, the spinning compass needle in my soul halts in that same direction.

I know I'm supposed to follow.

Chapter Eight

Julia

The bride and groom are dressed in matching denim and mustard yellow. A flowy dress for her, a t-shirt for him, ripped jeans hugging his thighs, plus a fitted jacket accentuating her trim torso. They are all smiles, glorious blond hair tousled from a drive out in a windows-down all-terrain vehicle. Their arrival has gone off without a single dramatic hitch, though I did have to turn down my walkie-talkie and pray that Zoe could handle any disaster that might come our way in the interim. On the way over to meet them her voice scratched over the speaker to tell me that florist Francine was going rogue on the bride and groom's "Blessings Table" centerpiece, claiming it wasn't "grounded in love," whatever the fuck that meant.

"Tell her we can't follow our bliss," I walkied back through gritted teeth. "We have to stick to the approved designs."

There was a pause. Zoe had her finger on the call button and I could hear Healer Arynne egging Francine on: *"Listen to your soul, what does Spirit say will most serve Millie and Sean?"* as if ten minutes prior she hadn't been ready to cancel the wedding because of a trifecta of broken tourmalines.

"Yeah, I'll figure it out," Zoe said, before going silent.

Fortunately, no further dramatics have interfered with the bride and groom's arrival.

"It's going to be such a vibe," Millie exclaims now, spinning around in a circle to take in the lobby entrance. Sean is on his phone, texting like mad—his usual way.

"Tucker says they're just around the bend," Sean says in an unexpected outburst. He lets out a *woot* and fist pumps into the air before running back toward the main entrance.

"He had a beer at the bar while I was checking in." Millie shrugs.

My pulse shoots into overdrive. "You should not have had to check in."

They should have been handed champagne flutes and wildflower seed recycled-paper envelopes with their names written in calligraphy on the front, containing their room keys, lodging information, and itinerary. That's standard for all Love, Always wedding venues, and even though this is our first time partnering with Celestial Sands, I was assured everything had been assembled and sat ready at the front desk.

"Oh no worries, Armand"—the day manager for the property—"and I went to a yoga retreat in Morocco together once." Her eyes are misty with memory. "A whole lifetime ago."

She's barely twenty-seven. By most standards, that's relatively early on the lifeline. It's hard to believe she's acquired long-ago memories to pine over dreamily and delay checking into her bridal suite. My face twitches, wanting to give my judgmental thoughts away, but I'm a neutral-faced pro, skilled in the art of faking the soft smile and interested gaze of someone who just *gets it*, while in reality my brain is on fire.

"We were catching up," she says, her voice still wistful.

"But you received the envelopes containing your room assignments, itineraries—"

She gives me a bighearted hug to cut my impending spiral off, causing me to immediately stiffen. Arms, legs, everything goes rigid. "Remember, it's a party." She presses me back, hands squeezing my shoulders lightly. Her face is a sunbeam of happiness.

I decide to drop the envelope inquiry for now, which is perfect timing since the entirety of the groom's party has arrived in a cloud of CK One and designer muscle shirts. I clock them, cataloging each one by one as they tumble through the doors into the sunlit lobby.

Banks Bartlett, son of a real estate tycoon. Blond, tan, rocking a short king energy that he probably doesn't deserve. He's wearing an iridescent hat featuring a decal of a fist flipping the bird, shades hooked to his ears backward, and a watch that probably costs more than my whole year's rent.

Next is Tucker Hawthorne, son of an oil baron (yes, those still exist), who is currently working in venture capital as his day job. He's tall and slim and the only one wearing real pants, but the snakeskin cowboy boots and nipple piercing outline beneath the paper-thin fabric of his shirt make up for that modicum of class.

Cash Kim (not his real name) comes in hot. He's Korean American and a rising star at a major record label. He looks like a Gucci store threw up on him. When he waggles his tongue in greeting to Sean, I notice a glint of metal from a piercing, then immediately loathe myself for liking it a little.

They call themselves the Final Four, a nickname they coined at Princeton (where they all, inexplicably, graduated with honors), though I'm guessing they've also lost heaps in March Madness betting schemes.

"Did you see the fucking desert out there, bro!" Banks practically spits, slamming down a hard high-five-fist-bump combo. "Miles of dirt and dunes—who wants to sand surf?"

A nervous young woman dressed in the orange and navy uniform of the resort approaches the crowd of males, carrying a tray of ice-cold beers. Not champagne. Beer. A request that must have been made by the groom. The murder of men flocks, splashing piss-colored liquid onto the silver tray as they yank the glasses up in a toast to the groom.

"To Seanypoo, the first of us to lock one down," Cash says with cheer.

"To Seanypoo," the other men—including Seanypoo himself—salute.

"They're fucking idiots," Millie says, but she's grinning with admiration as she watches the display of male bonding.

I'm scrutinizing the scene for all possible logistical nightmares that could (probably will) arise from the equation of this scenic, secluded desert setting plus this wild buffalo stampede of men, when Sean turns his attention squarely on me.

"You"—he points a meaty finger my way—"planned the bachelor night festivities."

I see the knowledge ripple through the men like a tsunami-level wave. I step forward, putting on my best *bro in control* energy, which is mostly just me puffing out my chest like a baboon in a dominance dance.

"Gentlemen"—I use this term *so* loosely—"Bachelor Town will not disappoint."

Pioneer Town, which—for the purposes of the itinerary—has been renamed Bachelor Town, is a local favorite for men and boys alike. Not sure which category these guys fall into, but we're running with it.

"It's got paintball. It's got skeet shooting. It's got s'mores and a bonfire pit." The crescendo of affirming excitement is a symphony to my ears.

"Beer?" Tucker chimes in. I nod in an affirmative.

"And, for when you're tired of running around and full on the buffet of brats, burgers, and twice-baked potatoes, there's also first-person shooter video game . . . stuff"—*Jesus take the wheel*—"to play to your hearts' content."

Basically, shooting, shooting, and oh, yeah, more shooting, with a little wholesome campfire fun thrown in for variety.

The males are pleased. And with a kiss to Millie, the Final Four flop off in the direction of the bachelor's wing of the building.

"I owe you big-time," Millie says under her breath. "If it was up to Sean, they would have gone to that casino in Palm Springs and come back smelling of cigarettes, hungover from cheap booze."

"All part of the Julia Kelley experience," I reply, before catching myself. "Love, Always experience, I mean." I'm giving myself away. Millie nods, not noticing the glitch.

"I'll be singing your praises to all my newly engaged girlfriends. You can count on it."

Joy ripples through me. Now all I need is the rest of the bridal party to arrive—and the women from my past to miraculously disappear—which is what I'm thinking when the tiny hairs on the back of my neck rise in high alert. My sense of smell is obstructed by the haze of *male* and puddles of spilled beer, but even so, Chanel No. 5 and sunscreen tinge my nostrils.

Piper Cunningham has never stepped foot outside without both.

I inhale through my nose, not to take in the scent, but to fortify against it. I'm going to see her all weekend, and if I'm truly honest with myself, seeing her isn't the worst of my problems. That credit goes to the girl who broke my heart into so many pieces that I'm uncertain if it ever mended. Millie's eyes brighten as she looks over my shoulder, raising her hand to Muppet wave in that direction. Her lips barely move when she whispers, "*The Odd Couple*, anyone?" and then, loud enough for everyone to hear, "Ladies!"

Someone. Kill me. Now.

I spin to see the two women I once loved standing side by side.

Kit is a good three inches shorter, curvy where Piper is lean, and looking at me like I'm a jigsaw puzzle she is trying to solve without having all of the pieces in hand. Piper looks like she has one of Healer Arynne's crystals shoved up her asshole—and not in a fun way. Her eyes dart from me, to Millie, peripherally to Kit, and then land in a neutral spot over my shoulder.

Kit is the first one to move.

Glide, actually.

She's at ease with her body in the most annoyingly admirable way. But she always was, even when we were teenagers and no one was comfortable in their own skin.

My palm absently goes to the buttons on the front of my shirt and I smooth them down, then adjust the hem to make sure it's firmly tucked in, and touch the cold metal of my belt buckle. These aren't nervous tics—they're just tics . . . generalized. Good old-fashioned distractions from uncomfortable *feelings*.

Kit smacks two air-kisses to each one of Millie's cheeks. "You are glowing—my God, *your skin*," she says, touching her own flawless skin with a grimace, as if hers isn't creamy smooth, but instead prickly sandpaper. "No filter necessary, for real."

"Please, I'm an elephant hide. I'll need to do a hyaluronic sheet mask or ten before tomorrow." My mind is truly baffled by this exchange. "We are so thrilled you were able to come for the whole weekend."

"Meant to be," Kit replies, flicking her eyes to me for a fraction of a second. "Clearly."

That didn't happen. I made it up.

Even if making it up is ridiculous. I'm not trying to care about where her eyes are glancing, or what said glances may or may not mean. Neutrality and professionalism is the name of my game.

Millie turns to Piper, grabbing her by the hand and tugging her in for a warm hug. Millie seems to only ever offer one kind of hug, even to frosty recipients.

"Kappa Kappa," Millie says, gleeful.

"Alpha Alpha," Piper replies, her face a mask complete with a signature glimmery polished smile. She straightens, not yet pulling away from Millie.

"Theta Theta Theta—" they chant together, gripping each other's biceps and bouncing. "We're the best, hell yes!"

Kit's eyes widen. There's a brief twitch of her mouth before it clamps closed, firm, like she's keeping a chuckle hostage behind her teeth. It's an expression shift so subtle there's no way Millie or Piper would notice it—I shouldn't either. But she must feel me looking, because she glances over at me (again) and then her cheeks flush deep pink beneath whatever balmy blush she's dabbed over the high, plump apples.

I distract myself by turning my walkie-talkie back on and stepping away to radio Zoe.

"Any word on the bridesmaids?" I ask, soothed by the crinkle of static coming over the receiver.

"They stopped to do a photoshoot at Cabazon," Zoe says, her eye roll implied in her tone.

Every influencer who comes in the direction of Joshua Tree National Park does a photoshoot at Cabazon. With the exception of Piper – the unexpected fill-in bridesmaid – the rest of the party are varying levels and styles of fun, fit, fab content creators. Kit probably falls into the same category, though I haven't looked her up online. (*Will not* look her up online.)

"ETA?" I ask Zoe.

"Your guess is as good as mine," she replies. "Within the next hour."

"Thanks," I reply, turning the radio back down. Millie should be getting settled into her room, enjoying a soak in the saltwater hot tub, getting an in-room massage, before her evening off-site at the Glamp-Out's facilities. I need to move this along, check back in at Homebase to see who's still due to report for work and room assignments today, do any other necessary chasing and fire extinguishing, before I close up for the evening.

I cannot freak the fuck out that my ex-girlfriend is hanging out with the girl who ghosted me the summer before college, for an entire weekend in the desert, and I have to watch it go down.

"I can wait here for the rest of your bridal party to arrive,

Millie," I say, trying to keep my voice even as I near them. "If you would like to head over to your room."

"Ah! Thank you," Millie exclaims. "Piper was just telling me she prepped a whole charcuterie and champagne situation for us." Wow, Piper dropped that love bomb in record time. "Pre- and post-massage sustenance."

I'm pretty sure water is the ideal beverage for that, but I'm not a doctor.

"Perfect," is what I say.

Millie squeezes me into one more warm hug and says, "I know you're technically on duty all weekend long, but you should really come with us tonight." She pauses, raising her brows and smirking. "You can even pretend you're working, if you want." I exhale, but say nothing in response. She squeezes my shoulder. "Think about it." She's not moving on until I comply.

"I'll think about it." But I know the answer already.

Kit and Piper are supposed to follow the bride. It's clear from their expressions they both know that's expected. I'm hoping for it and dreading it. Wishing for a second alone with Kit and wanting to never be alone with her ever again. Frustrated at the instinct to reach out to her, even after all this time and space and pain. She edges forward, like she's about to say something that will allow her to stay behind without raising suspicion, like she read my mind and made the decision for me, but Piper steps in her way, squashing her opportunity with the red sole of her Louboutin.

"I just have a few minor details to work out with Julia," Piper says. "Bridesmaid questions." She flashes her teeth at Millie, who buys the smile as more than a dismissal, and absorbs Kit into her sashay toward the double doors out to the courtyard. Kit's gaze lingers; my heart somersaults.

"She's the one." Piper's voice is double-edged. *The one* is an arrow hitting its mark.

She knows.

I force myself to make eye contact. Hers are molten hazel and laser focused. I straighten to my full height for intimidation, but even then I have to angle my face up to look at her.

"The one?" I fire her words back.

"The first," Piper replies. She edges closer. "You haven't forgotten how you talked about her for hours, have you?"

No. I clench my jaw. I remember every word.

I just didn't think Piper would recognize her that easily. It's been almost three years since I made the endorphin-induced mistake of telling her about my first love.

"I'd just fingered you until your knees buckled." Piper's voice reminds me of a serpent's hiss. "In the comedown, you couldn't stop talking about her."

"You asked about my exes." I fight the instinct to retreat. "It was weird-ass timing, but it was yours." Heat licks its way across my cheeks. She's desperately close now, leaning over, fingers unfurling to brush the hair off my ear.

"Mystic Maven." Her fingers graze earlobe skin. The nearness isn't tantalizing; it's a taunt from a bully. "She's got quite the following, the little manic pixie dream cunt."

How has she already had time to look her up? They just met as far as I know.

"Can't wait to see her in action tonight." Her breath down my neck makes my skin crawl.

I step back, untuck my hair from behind my ear, and grit my

teeth. She's going to make this miserable for me every step of the way. Piper Cunningham's actions are difficult to anticipate. She'll strategize, playing this like a chess game, because she wants to get me to join her on the board. But I can't give her a chance to get ahead of me.

The only option is to take Millie up on her offer to join in the fun.

Chapter Nine

Kit

No matter how many times I tried to get away this afternoon, once the bridesmaids arrived I was held hostage as the circus performer in their ringside seats to spiritual enlightenment. We're three *hydrating* champagne bottles into the afternoon and less than half an hour away from the party bus's arrival to take us to the Glamp-Out location for tonight's festivities, but I already know more than I should about these women to give them truly intuitive, unobstructed readings.

"We're doing shots tonight—not of cacao, Millie, Jesus Christ—don't even!" Coco Mulligan, my prime target for an on-camera reading, said within three minutes of her arrival.

"We most definitely will be drinking a heart-opening cacao mixture at the sound bath," Millie replied, as she poured herself more champagne. "Tonight is about more than partying." This was received with a dramatic performance of Coco pretend-vomiting in disgust.

Coco was named after the designer, so it was fate that she became one herself. "Lingerie isn't Chanel," she said between sips of champagne, a heavy side-eye directed to the Chanel-clad Piper. "And that suits me just fine."

She and Millie met through their manager—just like how all truly iconic Hollywood relationships begin. They bonded over being rich bitches trying to make it on their own, which I assume means they don't live off trust funds or employ nepotism to get ahead.

She reminds me of a raccoon foraging trash cans and I adore her. In another world, I would be picking her brain for stories. Without even touching my cards I can tell she has oodles of secrets hidden in the strands of her blond pixie cut.

Natalie Geffin is the maid of honor and Millie's oldest friend in the world. She's vixen-level gorgeous and *expensive*—even her phone cover drips money.

"It's Dolce," she said, thumbs tapping away at the screen, eyes firmly on my face. "Dolce and Gabbana, you know?"

She's a lawyer and foodie, but her real passion is "the intersection of design and cuisine," which she plans to showcase in her new restaurant opening in Malibu this coming spring.

"There's a restaurant in the Arts District that serves grasshoppers, but you simply must request hot sauce to enjoy them with or you might as well be eating ants." She gripped my wrist. "I wouldn't steer you wrong." I don't know how to talk to her in a normal way, but also can't stop ogling her.

Fuck. The champagne is talking. My ears feel hot at the thought.

Piper Cunningham, the redhead from before, is the one I know the least about, and that seems intentional. She's a bit standoffish, only engaging in polite, tempered ways.

Everything about her screams that she isn't here to make more friends.

In fact, I get the distinct impression that not only is she a last-minute replacement for a much closer friend, but she may even be an unwelcome addition. There are vibes for days coursing back and forth between Coco and Natalie. Sideways glances at Piper. Incognito whispers as they refill their champagne flutes. They either hate her fundamentally, or just hate her presence in the bridal party, but either way, it's borderline tense.

I learned from Google—while I was using the bathroom earlier—that she's a journalist with bylines in all the major newspapers in the US. Her social media footprint is impeccably professional, but reporters always have second or third accounts they use to shitpost, or like, post pictures of their kids. Still, even with her air of mystery and the potential bridesmaids drama brewing, to me the most interesting curiosity about her is the nature of her history with Julia.

I can tell they know each other; I just can't discern how.

"I must get my cards, ladies." *And a quick shot of espresso.* "Or the tarot portion of this evening will not happen." I stand to leave.

Millie checks her watch. "Meet us at the entrance in twenty minutes—the rest of the bachelorette crew will be here by then, too." She looks at the others. "I invited Heather, Maddie, and the twins."

Coco waggles her brows. "Ooooh, the twins." She makes a vomit motion. "Pretty sure Jenni has me on mute, but whatever."

"Pretty sure you cheated on her with your SoulCycle instructor." More casual mention of sexual fluidity and me over here prickling up beneath the honesty.

"Potato tomato." Coco downs the rest of her champagne and then pouts. Natalie snorts, rolls her eyes, but follows it up by cradling Coco with affection.

"I'm freshening up and you all should, too," Millie continues. "The photographer is arriving to begin shooting our festivities before we board the bus."

The women scramble to attention at the mention of a photog, and I use the mayhem as an opportunity to make my exit. As soon as I step outside, I shiver against the dropping desert temps. Millie's bridal suite looks out over a tiled courtyard that features a bubbling fountain, some funky outdoor beanbags in varying bright patterns, and a perfect view of Homebase.

The curtain is pulled back, the window hanging slightly ajar. Framed inside like a portrait stands Julia, looking down over the array of tables, shuffling papers into a folder. One hand absently goes to her temple, pressing some tension away, and then runs back to where a hairband holds her thick dark locks in place. She tugs it, releasing her hair to cascade in kinky chestnut waves that brush her angular cheekbones.

My breath hitches, catching between my ribs as my heart pounds. Thump thump thump. *Her hands in her hair, pulling it off her shoulder.* Thumpthumpthumpthumpthump. *My hands white with sunscreen, placed on her sizzling skin. Heat licks between my legs as I rub slick lotion into her skin.* I squeeze my thighs together, clenching my hand into a fist, curling my toes in my sandals and rooting my feet to the earth.

In three seconds, I'm going to move.

I'm going to breathe in and out.

I'm going to stop the feelings erupting like firecrackers all across my skin.

One. *I brushed my fingertips along the hem of her bikini top.*

Two. *She exhaled a sharp sound of desire.*

Three. *Move.*

I shoot out in the opposite direction of Homebase, back toward my Airstream. Faintly, from behind me, I can hear the clack of high heels on the courtyard entrance as the other bachelorette partiers arrive.

I need a costume change, to hold the cards in my hands and breathe. Fortunately, the one thing I no longer need is a coffee. Every bubbly, wobbly sensation has sharpened and sobered into one thing.

The command order: Do not fantasize about kissing Julia Kelley.

~

When I step outside the main lobby doors to meet up with the bridesmaids, I try to embody the Mystic Maven persona with absolute commitment. I changed into a white spaghetti strap dress with a sweetheart neck, added a patterned wool shawl, and secured it with a vegan leather belt. On my feet are distressed gray vegan suede booties; in my hair I have quickly threaded thin gold ribbon into a few carefully placed mini braids. I carry a small beaded bag with my cards and the cleansing spray I use to protect the spaces I work in.

Despite all the elements being perfectly in place, I can't get the vibes quite right. I yank out the tiny brown bottle of spirit cleanse aid and spritz myself from head to toe for good measure, breathing in the mist containing mugwort, lavender, and California poppy. Its earthy smell is bright, fresh, with gentle floral notes, and it's not doing its goddamn job.

It's not the work that worries me. If I can read a room full of Kardashians without breaking a sweat, a few bridesmaids should be a breeze. What worries me are all the questions I have swimming around in my head and all the feelings bubbling to the surface. Tarot readers work with energy and intuition, which means keeping mine clear is a top priority when I'm on the job.

I'm the furthest thing from clear, and can only hope the sound bath Millie has scheduled ahead of my readings will move the rest of this pent-up energy far, far away from me.

When I first stumbled into tarot reading as a self-care method during college, I didn't work with herbs or crystals, had never had a Reiki session or been to a sound bath. Now that world is my second home, somewhere I reside almost as much as my day-to-day. There, the Universe has everything we need to heal, which is so different from my LA life, where Peloton is God, psychodermatology is all the rage, and everyone is either in therapy or talking about it over mimosas at brunch.

I live in both, but I don't fully fit in either.

Story of my life.

I shove the currently useless mist back in my bag and suck air through my nostrils. *Cleansing breaths, focused thoughts.* This is all manageable. This is all fine. Julia isn't coming tonight. She passed on Millie's offer, she's all work and no play—which isn't how she once was, but okay. I should take her lead and buckle down, but the other racing thought in my head is Piper Cunningham shaped.

A very distracting shape.

It shouldn't matter to me who Piper is to Julia. It's none of my business, really. I'm not trying to wash the last ten years—all the pain of those few smoldering weeks that one August, or the turmoil that tormented me for months afterward—under the bridge. I'm not trying to feel that rush of adrenaline from brushing skin on skin, or taking in the scent of her hair as I nuzzled in close before we kissed. I'm not trying to be in love with a girl again, not when I still can't say the word for what that means out loud.

"Impeccable vibes," comes Millie's sunny voice from behind me. I take a calculated pause to get my smile painted on before turning to see the bridal party—including the new *bachelorettes only* arrivals—dressed in varying shades of cream, blush, and ecru, skin glowing in the golden hour light.

The twins are easy to spot. Glam, leggy, East Asian, and equally stunning. One of them—likely Jenni—is staring daggers at Coco, popping bubble gum in a fit of barely contained rage.

The other women look like influencers: camera ready, all flawless, all branded.

Even though they are dressed to match Millie's boho spiritual goddess color scheme, their true styles still shine through. One of them is clearly a full-figured vintage-Disney model, who likely goes to cons and talks about Star Wars on podcasts. She's wearing a cream corset dress with a subtle Minnie Mouse etched into the boning. The other is probably a fitness influencer, because she's wearing Alo Yoga pants and a sports bra beneath a fluffy white oversized jacket she's left unzipped to show off her rock-hard abs.

Beside them hovers a woman holding a Fujifilm camera, newer than the model I use to shoot YouTube content, and carrying a bulky gray bag that's likely full of camera equipment.

We close the gap, and Millie does some soft finger claps for my ensemble as if we're at a poetry jam and I just read out some especially poignant iambic pentameter.

"We should get some shots in front of the entrance," Millie says, going into influencer mode.

"Lighting's good here," Coco—who is doing a fantastic job ignoring Jenni—says.

She's wearing a cream romper and white (probably not vegan) leather jacket. She chases the sunlight for a selfie but comes to a standstill beneath a wash of amber light a few feet in front of the doors. I'm watching her smirk into the camera when I feel a body move up behind me, and I turn with a jolt to see Piper practically leering, covered head to toe in—you guessed it—Chanel.

"I see you didn't get the all-white memo," she says, but her eyes trip over the lines of my patterned wool shawl.

"Call me a rebel," I reply. "I'm not a bridesmaid, so I don't think the dress code exactly applies."

"She'll want you in the photos."

"She said it was an impeccable vibe." My palms are sweating.

"It's not the same thing as being the aesthetic."

Jesus, okay. Claws out. It's probably a waste of energy to argue, but I won't let that stop me. "My style is a brand staple. Millie hired Mystic Maven for *my* vibes."

Piper's lips dance into an almost sneer. "I only said something so you wouldn't feel embarrassed that you stick out." She winks. "Just looking out for you."

I get a twinge in my stomach and the knee-jerk desire to say thank you. What the hell is that about? I should want to trip her on her way into the party bus—which has just pulled up—but there's something about Piper that disarms normal survival instincts. She pounces, digging in her claws, and then I feel the need to apologize for getting blood in her fur.

Millie motions me over to take a photo with her crew, pointing to the inviting space between Coco and Natalie, but now I'm second-guessing if my aesthetic will *actually* ruin the vibe, and rather than make a decision or run back to change with my tail between my legs, I pretend to be checking a text and make my way hastily onto the bus.

The party bus is one of those sleek Mercedes sprinter vans, complete with a single pole for dancing. There are leather bench seats running the length, breaking only for the neon-lit bar in the center. It's fully stocked with booze, plus those bougie sparkling teas that Millie is a brand ambassador for. I grab one, taking a seat at the far end of the bench. I hear them moving toward the bus and I instinctively brace. I don't know why I'm on the edge of a meltdown. I've taken complicated jobs before, been on major TV shows, read cards for stars, had a fucking stalker even. Being in the proximity of a girl I once knew should not be throwing me for such a goddamn loop. But it is. It's not Piper's viper gaze or the way she's picking at my loose threads. It's not stage fright.

It's Julia.

Just knowing she's nearby makes my heart race and brain go foggy-fuzzy.

I close my eyes, picturing my hypnotherapy safe space. Thank Spirit, it comes to me quickly this time.

The sound of birds, the gentle lap of water from the lake, are almost real.

For most of my childhood and adolescence, my parents had a timeshare near Big Bear Lake. We'd go for the summer just to hang out near the water, hike the trails, and canoe. But there was a spot under heavy tree growth where the shore of the lake curved around and my parents couldn't see me from the house. I used to hide there to get a few minutes of alone time.

It was just the three of us, and that meant I was the center of every single activity, pitted against each parent in their competition of who could love me—or the other—more. It sounds shitty to complain, but love can smother just as easily as neglect can make you wither. It felt like if I had any emotion besides *totally content*, I would crush their souls. To satisfy their expectations, I played a role, a performance I got supergood at giving over the years. It wasn't like they *ever* requested it out loud, or got angry if I wasn't perfect, but they never really had a chance, either. I never disappointed.

Still, it made me want to bolt, so I would sometimes. They'd be cooking dinner, or drinking wine on the deck, and I'd peace out just long enough that they didn't get worried.

On that little curve of rocky beach, under the cover of fir trees, they couldn't see me, so I didn't have to pretend. I see it now—can almost smell the musk of those fir trees. In this safe space, my mind can go quiet, my subconscious can take over. I let out a sigh as calm settles on my skin like dew, feeling reassured, capable, slipping into a sense of—

A ruckus of voices breaks through the birds chirping, lapping of water, motherfucking calm of my safe space. And then her voice—"Where should I sit?"—crashes my lakeside retreat into a million tiny pieces.

My eyes fly open, defenses pricked, senses on overdrive.

Julia stands at the entrance to the bus, wild tendrils of hair wisping around her head like she ran here, lips tinted berry red, cheeks flushed, wearing a structured bomber jacket over the pinstriped shirt from earlier.

And staring right at me.

Chapter Ten

Julia

The ride is tense. Every muscle, *tense*, every breath, *tense*.

I've never worked this hard to keep the side of my thigh from brushing against another person's body, *ever*. I've never tried to ignore the scent of someone's perfume, shampoo, or skin *harder*. And none of my efforts are actually working.

Not because I can't control my attention. I am a master of self-restraint. I could teach lessons on compartmentalization, especially in stressful work scenarios where getting thrown for a loop simply can't happen.

It's not my self-control that's in question.

It's the driver's ability to navigate a rocky road without sudden, sharp corrections. The bus takes a turn down a new, lonely road, and in the distance I see the glow of the Glamp-Out. But only for a second, because his overcorrection of the wheel jostles me in Kit's direction. My hand drops to the seat between us as I try to maintain my balance, but the jostling goes both ways. Her hip rolls over the leather seat and right on top of my hand.

"Sorry," she gasps. We go over a bump and my hand slips farther beneath her.

"Sorry," I say, yanking it fast, forming and unforming a fist. She clutches the beaded bag she's holding until her knuckles go white.

"You could have sat literally anywhere else," she hisses through tight lips.

"In the fray of bridesmaids and bachelorette mayhem?" I reply, looking down the length of the bus to where two of them—Natalie and one of the twin influencers Millie invited for the kickoff of her marital bliss events, Lisa—twirl around the pole giving the bride-to-be a show. They somehow manage to stay upright and on beat to Rihanna's "Diamonds" despite the haphazard driving pattern of this journey.

Kit's eyes follow my gaze, fighting back a smile. She wants to agree. And I want to play along. The camaraderie we once shared as best friends flares between us like a freshly lit wick.

"You don't want to sit next to Piper?" The tenor of her voice raises a tad at the end of Piper's name. The sign of a person trying for casual and failing.

She's already figured out that there is some kind of connection between Piper and me. Somehow. And no, not because she's psychic. Kit Larson has exceptional people reading skills. Always has. A gift to her, a curse to everyone else.

And, anyway, I don't believe in psychics.

I look away from her, ignoring the draw I feel to rekindle our connection. It's just muscle memory, nothing else. It can't be more, not with how things ended between us that summer.

Kit texted me a goodbye before she left for college. It had only been a week since we were making plans to go on a date. It had only been a week since I told her I loved her after we hooked up. It had only been a week since she stood me up.

She said she was sorry. She said she hoped I would be happy at NYU.

She said she would miss me.

It shouldn't be this easy to talk to her now. I shouldn't want to know everything that's happened since she walked away from us. I shouldn't care about her at all.

But somehow, I still do.

Millie rises, calling all of us to attention as Rihanna belts out the final "shine bright like a diamond" through the speakers and the engine shuts off. The pink, purple, and blue neon lights beam over the backdrop of Millie's white dress and fair skin, turning her into the bi flag.

"Before we get swept up in the magic, I wanted to make sure to thank each one of you for being here." Her eyes drift over the bodies of her bridesmaids and friends, even dropping briefly to land on me and Kit. I feel weird about being here, trespassing on her meaningful moment with the women she calls her friends, just because I want to keep Piper and Kit away from each other. A feat I still do not know how I'll actually manage since Kit will be giving tarot readings to every member of the bachelorette party, and Piper is a panther on the prowl, impossible to trap.

"Marriage is a wild adventure, and you all know Sean is expecting me to take the wheel and steer us on the road," she says, chuckling. Her friends snort and hoot, and Heather, the full-figured fandom model, makes a swift reference to Captain America's ass, which seems to be some kind of inside joke I don't even *want* to understand.

Sean may be the consummate bro, but where his frat boy exterior and lucrative job should make him a chauvinistic dick, he never fails to pivot in surprising directions. In our first meeting, as Millie passionately laid out her vision for the wedding of her dreams, Sean quietly dipped her tea bag in hot water and nodded in agreement with every word she said. "Millie knows best" feels like more than a platitude. It's a mantra he happily lives by.

"It's just fate we're all here together," Millie says, blinking back tears.

Goose bumps rise on my skin at the sound of the f-word. My eyes reflexively slide to glance at Kit.

And I mentally kick myself for it.

~

"The sky is trippy," Coco says, her massive brown eyes searching the expanse above her.

The sun set while we were driving over, turning everything outside an inky black. The stars blanket the sky as far as we can see. Vast, tiny, twinkling diamonds, just like that Rihanna song. Somehow, the black isn't solid, but infused with a wash of deep purple and indigo, glowing silver around the full moon.

The Glamp-Out is designed for parties of ten to twenty guests max. There's the ceremonial yurt at the center, the focal point which everything else is designed around. The smaller sleeping tents spiral out from it, so that from above it looks like a shell in the sandy desert. They light the paths with electric lanterns that look like old-fashioned gas lamps, but that aren't a fire hazard to the groves of Joshua trees surrounding the area. A little way off from the main campground is a firepit area that sits low in the earth and is surrounded by a basin of water for safety.

I trail behind the bachelorette group and Kit as we make our way toward the center yurt. The canvas tents are all prepared with name plaques for each guest who is spending the night on the grounds. Neither Kit nor I have a spot, so at the end of the festivities we will have to take the bus back together.

Alone.

A reality I did not consider when I made this fairly rash decision to crash Millie's party. I shove the thought away and focus my attention toward the main event. I don't have to deal with that problem yet. I won't let it derail me.

The yurt is a circular, tent-walled building with a painted-wood front door. In the center of the door is a window where some golden light seeps out from inside. Moonlight hits the side of the tent, cutting sharp lines against the desert backdrop.

Piper hangs back to walk near me.

"I'm glad you came," she says, her voice low. She smiles. "I mean, I know you have ulterior motives." She pointedly looks in Kit's direction. I keep a neutral face even though my heart rate just skyrocketed and my pulse is loud in my ears. "I don't mind, if it also means I get to spend extra time with you."

My cheeks heat, but not because she's trying to flatter me. Holding her attention was never an issue. When we were together, she had a way of making me forget everything else in my life while also feeling like the only thing that mattered in hers. My standards were replaced with hers, my goals were compared and then weighed against her own. What I needed was easy to lay down when she convinced me she had a better way.

I promise. You'll like it, she always used to say. And I did, always, until one day I looked at myself in the mirror and Julia had disappeared. I was at her parents' vacation home on Cape Cod for the

Fourth of July, hiding in the bathroom in a hideous seersucker ensemble she convinced me to wear, while I played pretend "friend and roommate" in the fictional story of her life.

"I like what you've done with your hair," she tries again. "I always wanted you to grow it out."

"I didn't do it for you," I say. When we were dating, I had a much more "butch" haircut. Her dad's words. He was suspicious that I was queer; he liked to poke me to see if I'd snap and reveal the truth.

"I know, but I was right," she says. "It suits you."

Thankfully we've caught up with the rest of the party, so I can't respond to her assertion with any more venom than my clenched jaw. Somehow, I find myself standing between Kit and Piper like some sick joke of that f-word Millie mentioned earlier.

The door to the yurt swings open, nearly pummeling a couple of the other women, who scramble out of the way and into each other. One of the twins—Jenni—collides with Coco, hands to breasts, face contorting in rage. She shoves her away in the same motion, but Coco's smirk is a challenge, and Jenni doesn't seem to want to back down.

A woman with salt-and-pepper hair, dressed in multiple layers of draping fabric in muted colors that resemble desert sands, steps into the golden light of the overhead lamp. I recognize her as the owner, Freya Dan, former supermodel turned spiritual influencer, author, and *healer.* She founded the Glamp-Out to create a safe space for spiritual exploration and celebration.

Or so her website copy claims.

Millie booked the Glamp-Out all by herself, planning every element, but I still had Zoe put together an information dossier so that if anything went awry, we wouldn't be in the dark. She followed up with Millie to make sure she got all the necessary paperwork that protected her deposits and laid out the details of the evening and what the location was required to provide. You'd be surprised how often these places don't deliver what they promise.

And how few clients are prepared to take action when it happens.

Freya Dan lives on-site in a yurt that sits near the main campground where she upsells exclusive packages promising all sorts of healing that not even medical professionals can provide.

I know I sound like a skeptic about all this stuff.

Because I am.

When my mom died, I went through your basic existential crisis . . . at nine years old. Looking at her body in the open-casket ceremony, she didn't seem much like the lady who had once held me when I cried, or like, made me pancakes for breakfast on my birthday. But I didn't understand *why*, so I decided to do some research on afterlife beliefs.

Nail down some facts.

But there weren't any—at least not any that seemed universally accepted to be true. And nine-year-old Julia wouldn't settle for less than that. And ever since that brush with the universal unknown, spiritual practices of any kind became synonymous in my mind with people trying to make sense of a thing that no one can make sense of—that maybe we aren't supposed to make sense of at all. And it stuck.

Despite what happened in that psychic's tent on Halloween or how—for a few brief years—it actually made me believe there was more to the universe than matter and energy.

"I recognize your aura immediately," Freya Dan says, eyes pinned to Millie. More likely she recognizes her from Instagram.

I know both the Glamp-Out and Freya Dan Official accounts follow Millie's. Call me a petty bitch, but I looked it up one night while scrolling my phone in bed in the dark.

"Welcome, welcome, welcome." Freya Dan presses her hands to heart center and bows.

Most of the partygoers are into it. Kit bows in return, and the other women follow her lead. I fumble to keep up, not wanting to stand out, and even worse, not wanting to mirror Piper, who remains a pillar in the sand. I let out an involuntary huff of annoyance and Kit shoots me a big-eyed glare.

"Stop that," she whisper-scolds.

I make sure to roll my eyes dramatically enough that she can see them beneath the shadow of my hair. Her nose scrunches, creating tiny, wavy lines of skin and faint freckles. Such a familiar expression to see on her face that it makes my stomach twist.

We rise in unison, or competition, I can't be sure. She's smirking like it could be the latter, and I have to fight back my own smile so I don't let on that I might be enjoying it.

"Inside this yurt is a safe space to realign with your heart center," Freya Dan continues. "Healer Suni has already arrived."

"Do you think she's friends with Healer Arynne?" I lean over to whisper in Kit's ear. My lips almost brush the loose hair that lifts in the light breeze, kicking up the smell of her shampoo. Earthy and sharp, with the faintest hint of something floral. It could almost be the smell of the desert itself, if it weren't for the fact that I just noticed it for the first time *right now*.

She covers a chuckle with a cough, and then pats her chest. "Excuse me." She cringes. "Inhaled some sand."

Freya Dan's face remains serene. "Blessed," is what she says in response.

She turns her attention away from us to give further instructions to the group, and Kit leans over to elbow me in the ribs. "Do *not* get me in trouble," she warns.

"This isn't high school," I reply, not thinking. Her face glitches at the words, the soft green color of her eyes sharpening with a shock of pain. Her features pinch, closing, and she turns her attention back to Freya Dan.

But I can't tear mine away from her face.

Chapter Eleven

Kit

I swear I can feel Piper's eyes boring into my head. She was standing right next to Julia, and that momentary rapport we shared seems to have put me on her radar. The last thing I need at this wedding where everyone is a social media darling is a pissed off bridesmaid making my job more complicated.

I have to keep my head in the game.

I decide to focus my attention on getting into the vibes. The domed ceiling of the yurt has wooden planks that extend out from the center, where a broad circle skylight reveals a snatch of the nightscape. On the wood floors are mismatched rugs of varying sizes and patterns, some with fringe, some without, some fluffy cream like an Abominable Snowman's hide, and others of the dark luxe faux fur variety. In the center of the room, on her own fluffy Abominable hide, stands the sound bath healer, surrounded by an array of frosty white bowls.

Suni is well-known on the wellness/spiritual entertainment circuit—I don't know if she knows Healer Arynne, but she does know *me*. We've been booked for a handful of events together, and

I have always been impressed with the presence and composure she brings to her work. Her dark eyes catch mine as I make my way to a purple crocheted puff. I wink a hello and she returns the sentiment. She's Native American and Aztec, born in San Diego and now based out of Culver City.

It's a small community that I work in—it helps to know who the competition is so you can decide who will make the best ally. Suni and I often refer each other for gigs looking for a roster of spiritual entertainment.

I drop down to my cushion, just as another woman comes around with a bamboo tray holding small silver cups. She bends, offering me one.

"Cacao," she says. "For heart opening." I take it, gratefully, even if I'm not sure if I'm actually supposed to participate in the sound bath, since I'm here to work, not play.

"Cacao, Coco," Coco says from beside Millie, who cuts her a look laced with warning. "This is my first sound bath. I'm a little nervous."

"Oh, wow," Suni says, her voice a warm, low rasp, deep like a cavern hidden well within a mountain. "How many here are the same? First timers?"

Coco raises her hand unnecessarily, as does the fitness model—whose name I have learned is Maddie—and in a great non-plot twist, both Piper and Julia lift and then lower their arms at lightning speed from the opposite side of the room.

"I love virgins," Suni says, and the seductive tone sends a shiver up my spine.

Julia's eyes bulge out in surprise and I have to pinch off a snort.

Piper and Julia aren't sitting next to each other. Natalie took the plush velvet cushion in between, but Piper is edging her body language toward Julia with precision. She's positioned herself on a paisley patchwork pillow chair, her long legs stretched out in front of her and crossed at the ankle. Her shoulders angle in Julia's direction, not toward the center of the room, where Suni stands ready to start.

Julia literally looks anywhere else *but* at Piper.

Well, Piper or *me*. She's looking from Suni, to the contents of her silver cup, to Millie, and back around. Stiff and serious. The *determined to look anywhere else* bit helps with my incognito investigation of her.

Julia holds her body in a state of tension at all times. Her posture is rigid, strong, with core control like I've only seen in dancers, but I know she isn't one. The pinch of her jawline and sharpening of her cheekbones, the swift twist of the ends of her hair as she untucks it from behind her ears. The slight lift to her shoulders, and the way she breathes efficient, shallow breaths, or speaks with a shortness that seeks maximum efficacy.

Tense, precise, focused. And so different from the girl I knew when we were young.

She dresses with style, designer brands, clean lines, classic colors, but the flair of rebel that once caused her to shave off a section of her hair, or wear midriff-bearing tank tops in winter without a bra, is gone. Julia was edgy and cool in high school. Somehow she always found a way to subvert the snooty dress code at our private school, adding a strip of leather around her wrist or a stud in her nose; wearing her polo collar up and cutting the hems of her khakis, then rolling them to a cuff so the teachers technically couldn't fault her.

She was apathetic about other people's opinions of her.

Except mine.

Whatever happened in the last ten years has replaced *devil may care* with *dot every i, cross every t.*

She's beautiful with all her sharp, straight lines running into the curves of her full hips, the pinch of her tiny waist, and the sneaky dip in her collarbone where her tiny heart necklace rests, but the nose ring is missing; her hair is all silky waves and gentle balayage highlights; gone is the emo punk girl with the secret soft side.

At least, on the surface.

This isn't high school. She knew what she'd said as soon as the words tripped off her tongue. High school is a trigger. *Bang bang, here's a whole lotta pain.* I don't have a right to be upset when I was the one who walked away, but I ache with the memory.

Maybe *because* I was the one to walk away when I should have stayed.

Me and Harry, both fucking tools.

But not just because of what happened that summer after senior year. The pain slips in just as easily when I think about every bright moment, transparent whisper, shared truth that lived and breathed between us, and how I've never been as close to another person, longed for anyone's attention, desired another's approval, like I did hers.

The warm, sunny sound of Suni's flute calls everyone to attention. She plays a few bars of something that sounds an awful lot like the chorus to John Lennon's "Imagine" before she sets the flute aside in favor of the metal cup containing her cacao. She holds her cup close to her heart, and after a few seconds everyone in the yurt follows her lead. Including all the sound bath virgins.

"The ceremonial cacao in these cups is ethically sourced from a small collective of female growers in Southern California. In

Aztec culture, cacao beans were more sacred than gold, as we believed they were given to us by the gods. Ancient Mayans believed cacao could open the heart chakra, helping us to release past traumas and heartbreaks that still live in our hearts."

My eyes drift back to Julia, but hers are already fixed on the spot where I hold this cup close to my chest. The jolt of heat that shoots through my core drags an exhale through my lips. Caught, she yanks her attention away, focusing those unearthly aquamarine blues back up on Suni.

"Science backs up the notion because cacao contains theobromine—a cardiac stimulant that both relaxes the blood vessels and stimulates the heart muscle." Julia looks inside the cup with suspicion. "Each cup was prepared with the loving intention that whatever you came here burdened by will fall away, and the space left behind will come alive with possibility." Suni takes a pause as her eyes search across the faces of the bachelorette party, touching on Julia, drifting over me. "Everyone close your eyes," she says.

It should be easy to let mine drift closed—taking part in spiritual practice isn't new to me. Trusting a guide with Suni's experience level should feel natural, simple. But as soon as my eyelids drop, it's not meditative, focused darkness that I see.

It's Julia.

"Drink as slow or as fast as you like and let the heart chakra open as you listen." Suni's raspy voice falls away, replaced by the lilting, dancing song of her flute.

Let go of the burden. I take a long drink from my cup.

Julia, then. Hair shoulder-length and messy, holding a buzzer to her head as she shaves a section of her dark locks away.

I sip.

Julia, now. White buttons up the front of her blouse, face tight with focus.

Sip.

Julia, then. Her face close to mine, the sun beating down as we swing back and forth together in a hammock.

Gulp the rest down.

Julia, now. Face washed in moonlight, hair wild, fingers pinching the thick strands that brush back and forth over the small rise of her breasts beneath her pin-striped shirt.

My eyes fly open; she's right there, looking straight at me, remnants of cacao rimming the curves of her mouth.

Faintly, I hear Suni instruct everyone to feel free to move about, let the natural rhythm of their bodies act according to the sounds. She takes a seat, readying herself at the bowls, but only faintly do I even realize she's started.

My heartbeat pounds in my ears, drowning out the singing of her bowls.

My skin is too small and tight around my bones.

My mind races, running from Julia, chasing after every single memory of her face.

I stand up from my cushion, and I'm not moving with the rhythm of my soul, I'm trying to get the hell away.

I burst through the door to the yurt and into the chilly dark of the desert night. The low light of the lanterns and the soft silver of the moon should be soothing, but still my heart sprints laps around my chest. I close my eyes, try to get a grip, picture the curve of the lakeshore, the sway of those giant fir trees, but my closed eyes aren't safe.

Behind them I see nothing but Julia's face.

"Fuck fuck fuck," I say to the sky. "The timing of this is the fucking worst that could ever fucking exist." I start to pace like a man in the '50s in a hospital waiting room anticipating the birth of his baby, except I'm not wearing a three-piece suit or smoking a cigar, so I just look manic. And not the cute kind John Green wrote all those books about.

Not the kind Kit Larson is so good at playing in her own life.

I was doing just *fine* in my little bubble of self-denial until Mom popped it by bringing her secret truth out into the sharp light of the midday sun. I was doing *fine* dating guys, falling in lust that almost felt like love—it was good enough, sometimes great. It was eventually, for sure, going to lead me to Mr. Goddamn Right.

I was *fine* with fine. I have been busy, anyway, building my channel, branding myself, living a goddamn lie that wasn't hurting anybody.

Sure, lying is exhausting, and the truth about my attraction to women felt so natural—like knowing which side of the bed I like to sleep on, like deciding how to part my hair. But the lie was safe, it was proven, there was no reason at all to change that now.

"You're kicking up a sand cloud," Julia says from behind me. I whirl, defenses raised, eyes eating up the sight. She's standing beneath a lantern, arms crossed over her bomber jacket, eyes sharp with focus.

"Call me Pigpen," I say.

"You're definitely more of a Lucy van Pelt," she counters.

"And who are you? Peppermint Patty?" It's too harsh. I regret it immediately. I want to backtrack.

Julia's mouth twists.

"If we're going there, I prefer Amity Blight from *The Owl*

House," she replies. "At least she gets to dance under the moonlight with the girl she loves."

"I figured you'd go with Harley Quinn."

Her brow quirks. "Harley was way too into the Joker for my tastes." She smirks. "You know I—"

"—barely even like dudes." We finish the phrase in unison.

Her eyes spark, the irises bright, the pupils wide and dark. She tucks a hand in the pocket of her bomber jacket, pulling the zippered opening closed with the other. I track up the line of the zipper to the sharp V where her blouse buttons are fastened.

"Enjoying the view?" There's way too much satisfaction in her voice. My eyes lock with hers.

"We can't," I say.

"Can't what?"

"Talk about us." I can hardly get the words out.

"There is no us."

"You know what I mean."

"Refresh my memory."

"I'd rather forget."

Julia nods, takes a step closer. I should bolt. I can figure out how to level up my career without this opportunity. Nina would still let me crash on her couch, I'm sure of it. Millie would be pissed, probably bad-mouth me around town—that would be a problem, but I'd bounce back.

Eventually.

"You're *still* playing the girl next door looking for her perfect boy," she says, not a question, not waiting for an answer. "Or was it unattainable vixen?" She takes a step closer. "Mysterious, wounded flower?" *Closer.* "Manic pixie dream girl." I can almost feel her breath on my cheek.

"What happened to your nose ring?" I hold eye contact. Desperate not to flinch.

Her eyes trek over my face. Everywhere they touch is singed like the flame burning a matchstick down.

"What happened to you that morning?" She whispers the question. My cheeks heat with the warmth from her breath, the smell of it all minty and chocolate goodness. We're almost nose to nose, but I'm taller. This close, the dark cerulean, silver haze, sea green flecks of her eyes are like jewels refracting the stars.

The Universe doesn't owe me better karma but I wish it would try a little understanding. I was young and scared and I wish with everything I could take it back.

"Yours is easier," I say, swallowing my nerves. I didn't come here expecting to clean up this mess from our long-ago past, but that doesn't mean I shouldn't try.

"It got infected." I can't get my smile under control fast enough. She smirks. "I had a cold and the doctor said I should take it out. The snot caked over the back and I had to use saline spray to loosen it, but it was all inflamed and red, warm to the touch."

I cringe, she snorts, and we're still standing so close that every move threatens contact.

"Did you take it out then?"

"No, it's still in my nose," she quips. "Entombed." She twists so I can see the dark dot of her scar. "Hurt like a motherfucker to put it back in so I never got the nerve."

"When?"

"Freshman year of college."

Where did you go? What did you study? How many girls have you kissed since me? The questions flood my brain with curiosity. A dangerous temptation. I take a step away from the heat of her breath warming the curve of my cheek. Immediately, the chill of the night air sobers my thoughts.

"Kit." My name on her tongue; gods, let me crumble.

"I wasn't ready," I say, somehow with no waver in my voice. She lets out a sharp breath, the deepening cold turning it to smoke.

"So you just ghosted your best friend?" Her jaw clenches, moisture making her eyes shiny. "You just said *wish you well*, like I meant nothing to you."

I was falling apart, I want to say to her. But the way her features have sharpened makes me think there's no excuse she'll take. She's got daggers for eyes and razor-sharp teeth. "I didn't want to hurt you."

"Fail." Her voice is a searing hot sword.

The door to the yurt opens. Freya Dan pokes her head out, looking around the immediate area. Julia follows my attention, seeing the moment Freya's eyes lock on me and she waves, the floaty fabric of her sleeve resembling a flag.

Cease-fire, surrender, thank you, Universe.

"My cue," I say.

"Convenient."

I'm careful not to brush against her as I pass, and she doesn't move into my way to stop me, but I feel her eyes follow me all the way up to the yurt even though her body lingers behind.

She's with me, tugging at the chains around my heart, begging me to let it out of the cage.

Chapter Twelve

Julia

Every instinct says to reach out.

Every instinct is clearly wrong.

I look up, blinking back tears. This is stupid, unprofessional—everything about my behavior tonight, from getting on that bus to following her outside. I'm not thinking straight—*ba-dum-bum*—the irony of the turn of phrase almost makes me let out a desperate laugh.

Kit isn't my problem. She isn't someone for me to show concern, care, or tenderness to.

She is just a woman I once knew. Clearly, she's still perfectly fine with playing pretend. This weekend isn't about us reconnecting. I shouldn't be entertaining the idea even in the vaguest sense.

I'm *not* entertaining the idea.

I'm just trying to make sure the two women I used to know don't inadvertently ignite a fire in this high-profile wedding I'm trying to execute with perfection.

That's professional. That's the Julia Kelley way.

I'm still holding the cacao cup in my hand, the bottom coated with remnants of the creamy chocolate liquid. I don't know what "heart opening" is supposed to feel like, and yes, I'm dubious that there is more to this whole thing than the physiological response created by the theobromine, but my skin feels slick, pulse all quick, and even more frightening, I can't shake the urge to push, brush, taunt the edges of Kit's buttons until I find the one that unwinds an apology from her lips.

She wasn't ready. But I would have waited.

If that's my heart opening, then please shutter the windows, lock all the doors, and close for the season. The only solution is to ignore all of my desires, impulses, and instincts, go back inside and play pro. I am still in control here; that hasn't changed despite what my questionable behavior suggests.

I shake the last bit of cacao into my mouth like this is some kind of dare.

Kit isn't wrong in calling attention to the changes in my style, but I can tell the observation is more than just an aesthetic curiosity. She's prying at the lid on my life, trying to tug the edges up to see if I'm still as messy on the inside as my outside once appeared.

I can call her bluff like the cool cucumber I've become in the years since we fell apart.

I whirl on my heels, eating up the distance back to the yurt and tugging open the ornately painted wood door.

Inside, the sound bath has officially come to an end, leaving the women who embarked on this soul journey in a state of apparent bliss. Millie seems to be the most blissful of all. It's rare that a bride ever truly reaches serene in the days surrounding her wedding. No matter how well planned, or how much she trusts the Love, Always team to make her dream day a reality, most brides experience this time—the *happiest of their lives*—through a haze of mixed-up emotions. Millie's cheeks beam bright even in the candle-glowing, moonlit wash of the yurt. Anything but mixed-up. The joy on her face makes me almost want to release the death grip strangling out all semblance of enjoyment I might have from this experience.

Kit's taken her place at the center of the yurt where they have set up a small round table with a chair on either side, covering it with a deep purple crushed velvet cloth. She unpacks the contents of her beaded bag. The tarot cards, she sets face down in a stack on top of the table, uncapping a small brown bottle and lifting it to spritz the air a few times. She takes a deep inhale through her nose, closing her eyes and slowly exhaling. Her lips part and she wets them with the tip of her tongue before drawing the flesh in with her teeth, nibbling.

She's nervous. The realization hits me like a zap of static electricity.

The room has gone quiet as the attention of every reveler has turned to the center, watching, waiting, interested, and eager—like this is real entertainment and Kit is a real star. Her shoulders pitch back as she elongates her neck, and my eyes can't resist the temptation to trail the full length of exposed skin. A simple gold chain with a raw crystal dangling just above the curve of her cleavage twinkles. She inhales deeply and her breasts strain against the neckline of her dress. She brushes the tips of her fingers together, and I notice a tiny cluster of stars tattooed on her pinky finger before she flattens her hand to the table, palms down.

When her eyes open, the pupils contract and expand, adjusting to the light.

She was always a star. That hasn't changed.

She holds eye contact with me, unblinking. One more breath, then a smile, before her focus moves over the faces of her captive audience. It's showtime and it's clear any nervousness she felt when she first sat at that table has melted away.

"This group of women has gathered here to celebrate the one and only Millie Morgan. Not just because she's marrying the love of her life, but because she's an actual badass bitch that every single one of us here has reason to admire." Kit winks at Millie. Coco yanks her in for a smooch on the cheek. The other women clap and hoot, calling out pet names for the bride. "Choosing to explore your inner world in this safe space of friends before embarking on the next great adventure of your life is more than just entertainment"—Kit pauses, smirking—"it's also one hell of a show."

The glee level rises in the yurt until even I feel a smile tug at the corners of my mouth.

"Now! Who here has never had their tarot cards read?"

Piper, Heather, and the sulky Jenni raise their hands.

I can sit this poll out.

Kit's eyes slide to me as if she's checking for signs that I remember the history I have with the cards. I reply with a raised brow. *Of course.*

You don't forget a thing like that, even if it was a waste of time. We didn't get any answers—none that we wanted, at least. We didn't get insight into a future we'd actually get to live out in Technicolor.

What we got was a haunting instead.

"Cartomancy—the more accurate name for divining fortune through tarot—isn't a science. The messages that come through aren't chiseled into stone, set it and forget vibes. Tarot is more like a conversation between friends. The cards present possibilities, but still the choices we make determine the outcome."

Kit isn't a mind reader, no matter how skilled she is at reading people or that deck of cards. Still, this tarot explanation is pointed. Like she read my thoughts and wanted to drop a response to the whole room.

"Tarot can be used to dig deeper into what your own intuition already knows. Asking questions that will color in the lines of the life you are actively living is always a good place to start." She motions to Millie, closing her hands around the deck.

I take a seat on a cushion close enough to see the cards, but out of Kit's immediate eyeline. Unfortunately, this puts me in the direct line of sight of Piper, who has taken her same seat from the sound bath, probably hoping I would do as well.

I redirect my attention to the table, examining the deck. This one is different from the one she used earlier to calm Healer Arynne's crystal arrangement freak-out. This one is a matte black background, with watercolor flowers painted around the edges and a metallic gold border. In the center of each flower is a crescent moon, pressed in that same metallic gold leaf.

She begins to shuffle as Millie settles into the seat across from her.

"I usually do a simple, but supereffective, five-card spread for these kinds of readings." Kits cuts the deck, setting each stack down on the table to shuffle them like they're playing cards.

"You're the expert," Millie replies. "I trust you."

"Close your eyes," Kit says as she works the cards back together. Millie follows her instruction. "Get clear on what you want revealed. Questions or concerns. Desires, guidance."

"Hopefully, they won't tell me to run," Millie says, smiling, her eyes still closed. Kit's brows twitch as if she's surprised by the statement.

"They'll only tell you that if you intuitively know it's what you want."

Millie's whole energy shifts at that statement. She's taking this seriously. Her spine straightens, her expression pensive. Oh God—or whatever deity it is that handles tarot readings—please do not tell the bride to bail. Generally, if the bride runs, the wedding is considered a flop. Jesus Christ, I do not need that on my record when I'm trying to break out on my own.

Kit does one more loose shuffle before lifting the cards toward Millie.

"Open your eyes and cut the deck twice."

Millie cuts them unevenly, before flicking her gaze back up to Kit for next steps.

"You can pick which stack you feel most drawn to," Kit says, "or I can."

Millie considers her for a moment. Trust herself or trust the YouTube psychic. Mystic Maven is the only one we didn't get a dossier written up about before we left for Celestial Sands. Her late arrival to the roster made that impossible. I'm sure Zoe could shoot me a fact sheet on her that hits the high points, but it's not going to explain who this person has become in the years since she bailed on me outside her parents' pool house, or what it is about her that makes people want to trust her with answers about their future.

"That's like, your thing," Millie says. "You pick the cards and they never lie."

Kit holds her eye contact. I can tell she's weighing out an answer.

"This is your reading. It's not about me or my *thing*."

After another beat of strong eye contact deliberation, Millie points to the middle stack of cards. "This is it."

Kit reincorporates the cards into one stack, putting the middle one on top.

"The first card is your purpose in the near future," Kit explains, her hand hovering about the deck as she speaks. "It can represent you, or be an indicator of the area of emphasis that the rest of the cards will give detail to."

Millie exhales. "God, the vibes are intense." She shakes out her body. "Do you feel that or just me?"

"It's okay to be nervous." Kit's voice deepens, smooth and calming.

"My whole life is about to change," Millie says, and her aching vulnerability cuts through me. "Is it stupid to hope I get a road map?"

Kit smiles. "Even road maps can't always show us the way."

Damn. She's good.

She flips the card. Upright, the Empress. A watercolor-style rendition of a woman, crowned in flowers, seated on a velvet chair. She is dressed in a sleek robe with pomegranates painted in sharp, colorful detail. She's surrounded by pale yellow wheat. She appears pregnant, her face softly serene.

Natalie slides forward, snapping a photo. "Mills, are you with child?"

"You really shouldn't have consumed all that champagne before, then." This is from Coco.

I notice Piper bristle. When we were dating, like heavily in the throes of dreaming of future bliss, planning for a home and family—before everything went sour—the one thing we never could agree on was bringing kids into the world. Piper likes her independence. She likes booking last-minute tickets to Ibiza, sleeping till noon on the weekend. She refused to put the baby question on the table despite the fact that she knew I wanted one.

I know I don't seem maternal. But there are a lot of mom types, and I have always wanted my own family unit, even if that meant unpredictable, uncontrolled; the unconditional would be worth it.

I don't know if it's even possible.

"Fuck off, you guys, I've been on birth control since I was sixteen." Millie shoves Natalie into Coco, who gladly receives her onto her lap. "That's not what this card means. Right, Kit?"

Kit observes the growing chaos with a knowing smirk. "It can, but in this case, I'm guessing it's more about your nature and direction—the launch of this new phase, which will undoubtedly require steady, creative nurturing."

Millie gives her a full-toothed grin.

"Do you want to see what's next?"

Yes. The word surges through me.

She's a magnet, my eyes are metal, and when she glances my way, for a split second, neither of us can resist the pull.

Chapter Thirteen

Kit

Breathing a sigh of relief after a multitude of tarot readings finish without any major glitches is a luxury in this economy. When you make looking into people's inner world your business, maintaining five stars on Google is the opposite of easy. I never know for sure what the cards will reveal about the querent, or if the revelation is something they'll want another human being in on. When things go south, it's on me to spin it or get spun out.

This group, at least, came for the truth.

Coco asked *point-blank* if her lingerie brand would go global. I modified my five-card draw into a "path and obstacle" spread, with three influencing cards. Pulling the Sun, upright, was a good start, even if the obstacle was the Five of Pentacles, also upright, indicating financial struggle on her road to success.

"Forlorn much?" Coco said, batting Natalie away from snapping a clear shot. The woman on the card wore an exaggerated expression of grief, holding an empty bowl. The five pentacles—which in this deck are depicted with pomegranates—sit just out of reach.

I spun the negative into a ball of light, emphasizing the importance of inner work reflected in both of these cards.

“So, more sound baths and Reiki cleanses?” Coco grunted.

“Up to you,” I said with a smile. “It’s a call to action. To dig deeper.”

“*Ick*,” she replied, as if I just gave her a homework assignment on the first day of school. “Isn’t there a spell or something I can do?”

“Not my area of expertise,” I said, with a small chuckle. This got a smile of approval.

I didn’t broach the subject of filming a reading with her, but hopefully this whets her appetite for more. Coco would be perfect for something on camera, and something tells me she still has stuff on her mind.

Namely, Jenni, whose entire reading was about moving on from a past hurt—Coco, I suspect. At one point, she even said, out loud, through an open scowl, that “the cards can tell me to trust again all night long, but can they at least acknowledge my issues are earned?”

They did. When I laid out Justice, upright, I explained that this card usually indicates a wrongdoing by someone other than the querent, and can be a sign that vindication is coming, but Coco was flirting with Suni and missed the meaningful glare Jenni shot her way, so maybe not tonight.

Maddie will definitely be meeting a guy in the future, and it looks like a promising courtship, despite pulling the Moon, upright, which often indicates delusion or anxiety.

"That's it, I am totally firing my manager," Lisa exclaimed, thanks to the meaningful placement of the Tower, upright, in her reading about her career.

Heather and her boyfriend are going to do it—move to Anaheim to be closer to Disneyland, that is.

There are two people left in the room who haven't had their cards read, and I genuinely can't decide if I want them to accept or pass on my services.

Reading Julia's cards feels like a conflict of interest given our history and my jumbled-up feelings ever since I saw her face at Homebase. I could douse myself full-body in cleansing spray and still not clear my energy enough to not influence her reading somehow. But if the cards could reveal something meaningful—give me some kind of insight into the mystery of her buttoned-up transformation—then fuck my conscience.

Piper? I'm less concerned about my energy, and more that the reading will fail. Bad readings—ones where the querent doesn't believe in the intuitive power of the cards or isn't willing to open up and receive the answers waiting—go south fast.

Piper doesn't seem like the type to *let Spirit lead*.

And, sure, she also seems to low-key hate me for some reason I can't figure out.

I clear my throat, shuffle the cards, and decide to let them choose their own fate. It's not up to me, and as soon as their readings are over, I'm done, off duty. Back on the party bus to my temporary home, where I have a date with a bottle of rosé and the bathtub beneath the stars.

"Last call for readings, ladies," I say, *shuffle, shuffle, swoosh, swoosh*.

Piper stands directly across from me at the refreshment table. She's sipping gingerly on a cup of cucumber-infused ice water. Her eyes drift to Julia, who is on my left, and has been for the duration of the readings.

Not that I've been keeping track of her or anything.

Shuffle. Swoosh.

I let my gaze drop to Julia's face. She's pulled her hair up, this time in a high messy bun, probably in response to the warmth in the room. Her bomber jacket rests across the tops of her thighs. Her cheeks flush, a gentle kiss of pink on the apples.

Take me up on it. Come on. I dare you.

Julia lifts her eyes to mine, holding the contact, one, two, three seconds; the moment stretches out between us like a rubber band poised on the points of two fingers, ready to snap. The dare in my heart resonates through me, begging her to take me up on it, and even though I shouldn't care about her, or wonder why she barely resembles the girl I was madly, intensely into when we were young, it's all I care about, all I can think about—

"I'll give it a go." Piper's voice breaks in, yanking me out of my spiral. She moves from her place by the refreshment table, stiff and resigned, dropping with impeccable control into the seat across from me. Julia shifts, the tension that was between us sharpening into something hostile directed at Piper.

I force myself to focus on the querent. She's a guest, this is my job; so what if there is an elephant-sized history between them that keeps making a play for the center of attention? I paint a smile on. *Swoosh, swoosh, swoosh.* "We could go with a more general reading—"

"Love," Piper interrupts. "Tell me about my love life."

"Oooooh," Coco chimes. Giggles erupt in pockets around the group. Noticeably, Julia is stoic as a statue.

"This should be interesting," Lisa pipes up. Piper doesn't care about the audience. Her focus is laser.

"Three-card love spreads are pretty classic," I say, holding the cards still midshuffle. "For that kind of query." Her nostrils flare, she considers, and then she gives a swift nod.

One more shuffle and I hold out the deck for her to break. She does it once, pausing, considering. She's taking this a lot more seriously than I expected. In my experience, the Pipers of the world look down their noses at spiritual practices like this. She might not be a skeptic at her core after all.

"You can break it again," I say, watching her closely for a reaction.

"But I don't have to," she replies, eyes up to mine.

"No, you don't have to."

She crosses her arms, resting them on the table. I put the deck back together with her choice on top before drawing the first card toward her.

Three of Swords, upright. Iconic, recognizable with its three swords piercing a heart shape. In this deck, the heart is entwined in vines, the handles of the swords are embossed with a gold leaf foil. They catch the moonlight, making it bounce.

I brush the edges of the card with my fingertips. In larger spreads, the message of the Three of Swords can be tempered by the cards around it, influenced to have a less harsh inference or to be representative of something besides heartache if the position allows. But this is a three-card love spread—this heartache can only mean one thing.

"I can assume this long pause is you trying to find a spin so I don't feel embarrassed," Piper says. Generous assumption, but not totally off base. "It's fine. I had a breakup last year."

I find Millie standing nearby and try to get a gauge on how much she knows about this situation. Her clear and present surprise tells me the answer: Not a goddamn thing.

When I met her earlier, Piper did indicate that she and Millie hadn't seen each other in a minute, and she isn't really the type to offer up personal details without laborious excavation.

"This card represents a sharp and sudden pain or loss. It's not a nonchalant experience. Placed so early on the road of the Fool's Journey through the swords, it also signals the kind of foundationally disruptive pain that leads to transformation." I let the concept rest in the air between us.

Piper blinks. "It was a bad breakup." She deliberates, her copper brows tensing. "Yes."

I flip the second card toward her.

Death, upright.

Murmurs sweep through the yurt. Someone—my money is on Coco—whisper-screams "shitballs." Julia moves for the first time since I started my readings. She stands, yanking her jacket back on, moving through the group toward the table of refreshments. Piper's eyes trail up, following her, and then back to me. Their color is a saturated hazel brown, deep and warm, and the energy emanating from them carries unfettered intensity.

Julia pours a glass of cucumber water so fast that some splashes out over the rim of the cup; she gulps it down with just as much haste.

Something about this reading has her on the run.

Piper's eyes sheen. "Assuming this has a less literal translation."

"Death is one of the most misunderstood cards in the deck," I say.

Stay the course.

My compass keeps pointing me this way, and as much as I want to run the opposite direction, I can't. I can try to ignore Julia moving in the room, try to ignore the feeling of her eyes shifting to me, settling, roaming my face. I can compartmentalize knowing this query of Piper's is linked to her.

Every feeling just has to be shoved *down down down*.

"Sitting next to the Three of Swords, Death compels me to believe you've taken the lesson from your breakup and used it to begin a transformation."

In love, Death sometimes talks about a change in the kinds of people you are attracted to, or even your whole idea about what it means to love or be loved. I take in her guarded expression. She and Julia are serving up *somebody that I used to know* energy, and I don't think it's merely a friendship that went sour. If Piper wasn't out when they were together—or even isn't out now—that could have led to their relationship falling apart, and it could be what this card is referring to now.

Julia wouldn't be with someone who couldn't be with her all the way.

That's what she wanted for us. All those nights holding each other close, dancing at the cliff's edge until finally we toppled over. I told her I was ready, and I knew what she thought that meant.

It's a lot harder in the bright sun.

Being out means being truly seen.

I don't wait for Piper to fill in the blanks about her transformation. I flip the final card, my breath stuck in my throat.

Three of Cups, reversed. Another three.

"By nature the threes in tarot represent turning points. Those action moments when the querent can harness the energy of the cards for the progress of their journey."

This three is full of celebration, but in reverse it can mean that the querent isn't finding enjoyment in being in the moment; they need the reminder to be present, to be grateful. My few interactions with pinched-asshole Piper have already shown me that joy isn't a high priority.

"I'm hoping to reconnect with someone," Piper says, her focus fixed on my ghost of a smile.

"Three of Cups reversed is more of a *find joy in the moment* message." I pause, watching her expression shutter. *Not* what she was hoping to hear. "You may be fixating on something serious, when really you should be playing the field."

"Slut it up, baby!" Coco cheers. Natalie steps up to snap a photo of the spread and then eyes the result in her phone.

"Jesus, Piper, you look like you're about to shit your pants." I swear Natalie almost smirks, as if this look on Piper's face pleases her for some reason.

Piper ignores them both, leaning forward and tapping the Three of Cups card. "Dating around isn't my thing." She pushes the card away, as if she can dismiss the prompt through distance.

"Buzzkill," Jenni growls. She pops a gummy I can only assume is pot-infused into her mouth.

"I don't like to waste time." Piper stares me down.

"Enjoying your life isn't a waste." I don't flinch.

"I'll enjoy it when I have all the pieces back in order."

The door to the yurt smacks closed. A quick glance around

the room reveals Julia has left the building, and I don't need a tarot card to tell me why. Piper wants her back. This chance reconnection in the desert is kismet, exactly the forced proximity opportunity she needs. There's heat and hurt between them, just like us.

Just like us. The words ping around in my brain, uninvited and way too honest.

Piper shoves up from the table. "Thanks." But it sounds more like *fuck you*.

There's no way to reframe this reading into something she wants to hear. No *please recommend me to your friends and relatives.* Definitely not a five-star review. She's on a mission, and she wanted confirmation, not criticism.

Right now, her Fool's Journey is one of singular focus. Her happy ending impossible to acquire without Julia beside her. Which is fine—absolutely great. Good for them. I wish them all the best, happiness, oodles of luck, tarot spreads full of blissful omens.

I do. Really!

Fuck.

I yank the cards up from the table, my thoughts drowning out Freya Dan's food and libation instructions. It shouldn't matter to me what Julia decides to do about Piper. It shouldn't matter to me that Piper thinks she has a claim on her heart, when I had it first. Both of us clearly screwed that up—neither one of us has the right to assume she'd want us back.

Stop this right now! This is not happening!

I'm getting out of control. The off-the-charts, annoying spinning sensation in my gut is just a freak-out in response to all this stress. Just me cataloging old questions the events of this week in my life have dredged up. Just a classic Kit Larson moment of hyper self-awareness and an overflow of feels.

Julia isn't mine to claim dibs on. No matter what the OG tarot reading promised.

I hope *she's* happy. Really.

I do.

Chapter Fourteen

Julia

The groundskeeper is an older man with a silver beard named Han. His gentle stoking of the bonfire has turned it from a whimpering, spitting bit of embers to a roaring blaze in the time since I stormed out here to get some space. I take a sip of my beer, some local brew that's extra hoppy, as I watch the flame eat through a branch.

The word *love* coming out of Piper's mouth sent me reeling. *Love is a special occasion*, she always said. *Like a diamond necklace, like the best restaurant in town for Valentine's Day.* With Piper, love was something to bring out as a contrast to the mundane, not a normal, everyday thing. Those tarot cards may indicate our breakup was a turning point, but nothing could move the needle enough for me. She could be reborn as the girlfriend of the millennium, and I still wouldn't want to dip back into her shark-infested waters.

"Hey." Speak of the devil.

I take another swig. Piper sits down, near enough that I can smell her perfume even with the fire burning. There was a time when the scent of bergamot and clove drove me crazy in the very best way.

"Remember Big Sur?" she asks.

"I remember you threw up on the drive," I reply. The windy roads of PCH did a number on her motion sickness.

"You held my hair back."

"Because you refused to put it up." She didn't want a crease in her hair, so she needed me to stand behind her instead. I didn't mind doing the job of a scrunchie—I was in love with her. Tenderness and affection made me take care of her, but those are traits she managed to snuff out of me in the course of our relationship.

The tug-of-war for power in our relationship led me to hold on even tighter everywhere else in my life. I could never win with Piper, but I could win at work. I could micromanage weddings and staff and my own self until there was no wiggle room at all.

"That was our first vacation together." She gives her hair an aggressive toss over her shoulder. "You told me you loved me."

There's that word again. I said I loved her and she just smiled back.

"Sure, that happened," I say, turning to look her right in the eyes. "Then you called me your *friend* on the phone to your mom."

"You *were* my friend." Her cheeks flush pink, flaring up in her own defense. "I wasn't going to say girlfriend over the phone. I wasn't going to just drop it on her like that."

"Then when they visited, after I'd moved in with you, you made me stay in a hotel. Hid all my shit, asked me to make myself scarce."

"I said to act normal."

"You meant *act straight*."

Her lips pinch.

"I gave you two years," I say; now that I'm talking it's hard to stop. "You shoved me back in the closet every chance you got." I stand, she reaches for me. Piper gets this look when she's called out. All emotion drains from her face; the expression drops into a low gear, like the tank just emptied. She clasps her hands on her lap.

"That's an exaggeration." She barely inflects. "But I understand why you would feel that way."

There's no exaggeration. We could quietly be a couple in the few spaces she was out, but if I acted too gay, looked too much like a woman who didn't play by the misogynistic rules, she would clench up. Tighten her hand around my heart until I softened into a palatable shape.

"You don't get that it isn't an exaggeration at all—but how could you? That would require empathy."

She gives *stunned deer on dark road at night* better than anyone. "I understand what it's like to feel trapped, and I'm sorry I treated you the way that I did, but I wasn't ready—"

"As you said, all the time, and if it had just been that then maybe I could have stuck it out until you *were* ready, but you know that wasn't even the worst of it."

I want to drop it, but every word out of her mouth is like Han's poker stoking the bonfire. Only it's my anger flaming up instead. Also, I'm a little bit buzzed from the beer (possibly that cacao, who knows) so I keep unloading.

"You made me question the things I value—my own value, actually. You wanted me docile, malleable, so I became clay." I tap the now empty beer bottle against my thigh in frustration. "And you didn't flinch as you molded me." Tears prick in my eyes.

"You can't deny how much I helped you." Her jaw clenches.

She stands, getting in my path. "You can't deny the growth in your career, the acceptability of you as a person—"

"Do you hear yourself?" I snarl.

Too bad she's also not wrong.

Piper Cunningham's touch is Midas. She shaped me into a ladder-climber. I became sought-after, the best at my agency, with success written all over me. I became what everyone expected me to be. I became the obvious choice to make the most important day in a couple's life a dream-come-true event. I'm still rigidly adhering to the mold, only now I'm beginning to wonder if the success within my reach would still be here if I weren't stamped with Piper's seal of approval, if there were more Julia Kelley essence left on my skin.

"I don't want to do that anymore. I want you to be you and *I* want to be with you."

She's reaching for me like that's it. Like one sentence of affirming my worth makes up for years of pushing me to question it.

"Not. On. Your. Life."

I hear the sound of laughter from the bachelorette party roaring over the dusty expanse behind me, and I whirl away for another beer.

~

The bonfire warms the air; glowing orange embers jump into the darkness near the farm-style table. It's lit by shallow lamps, set with a woven cream runner, and decorated with bouquets of wildflowers. The crew has dwindled down to just the bachelorette party, and Kit and me—Millie's honorary working guests—and the Glamp-Out overnight staff. The chefs have created a light, fresh, inclusively vegan and gluten-free menu, and I almost feel guilty for taking Millie up on her offer to eat. This wasn't a cheap excursion; it wouldn't have been easy to coordinate. It really should have been handled by her bridal party, even if the cumulative energy of this group is more in the vein of *cacophony of wild birds* than *reliable team players*.

I'm now three crab cakes in, one more beer down, and too intimidated to ask Kit if she's ready to head back to Celestial Sands. In my head, there's no way to pose the question that doesn't immediately make it provocative.

Coco drops down in the empty space beside me. Cupped in her gloriously long fingers are two shots of clear liquor, one of which she hands to me.

"Oh, no—" I set it on the table. "I'm heading out soon."

She picks it back up. "Not."

She presses the shot back into my hand, closing my fingers around the glass before she releases. "We have a whole thing planned. You can't miss it."

"As her wedding planner, I'm glad to hear you've come through on the planning."

"Wow, you're kind of a judgy bitch," she says, but her tone is kindhearted. I sputter out the beginning of an argument—but she quickly brushes my offense away. "Oh, fuck off, I don't care—we've been discussing you in the group chat and we all agree."

That isn't a complete thought, but okay. "On?"

"You need to cut loose."

"I don't." I balk, unsure if I should feel offended or charmed by them discussing me in this way. "I'm working the wedding, not attending it."

"You need to get laid."

"That would be incredibly inappropriate while on the clock."

She cocks a brow. "Just a ballpark guess, it's been what, over a year—thirteen months?"

Her ballpark must be small, because she's practically on the field.

"That's none of your business." This is really getting away from me.

"So I'm close?" She grins, and I expel a sharp huff through my nostrils. "What's your flavor?"

"Do you mean like what kind of person am I attracted to?" I am too stunned to be offended. Coco has this way of disarming through shock that most people would get canceled for, but that she seems to exploit to her advantage.

"You're giving strong Cate Blanchett in *Ocean's 8* plus a little Alanis on that *Jagged Little Pill*."

"In what way?" I look down at my pin-striped / leather bomber combo in confusion.

"Energetically."

"So my soul is intimidatingly queer-shaped?"

"As is mine." She winks at me. "Look, half the chicks here are some kinda gay, and I know for a fact at least one of Sean's sisters is full-on butch, but she passes as lipstick for the 'rents if you're not into that vibe."

"Please stop talking."

"We like you—you've done a baller job on Millie's nuptials so far," she says, her voice softening to something almost gentle. She nudges me with her elbow.

"The wedding events don't begin until tomorrow." I counter her compliment with my skepticism.

"None of us will judge you if you let your freak flag fly." She lifts her shot glass toward me. "Bottoms up, bitch." When I don't comply, she pouts out her bottom lip, begging with giant storm-cloud-gray puppy dog eyes.

"Fine." *Clink*, we down them in unison. It's a lukewarm tequila shot in the middle of the desert, no chaser. Absolutely disgusting. I cough, to which she responds by smacking me on the back like she's burping a baby.

"Okay, so, Mission *Sexy Times*," she starts.

"We're not giving it a name. It's not a thing," I spit, eyes watering from the booze. "I didn't agree to this so it's not happening."

"Anyone in the group you're into? Not Jenni—I'm working a multistep plan to get her to forgive me."

"Do I even want to know?"

"Unlikely." She turns her attention back out, eyes roving.

Mine betray me, ever so briefly, without even trying, by landing on Kit. Thankfully, Coco doesn't let on that she notices.

There is a bright, clear sound of a fork tapping glass as Natalie stands in her spot near Millie. "Everybody, everybody."

"Everybawdy," Heather sings in her bright, clear soprano tones. The rest of the women follow with "Backstreet's back, all right" before crumbling into a fit of laughter as one of them stands up to mime the moves from the music video. The tequila shot Coco gave me has settled in my stomach like one of the fire embers. The alcohol now buzzes through my veins, a little worker bee in Coco's Sexy Times mission.

It's not safe to watch Kit, but it's all I want to do. Sitting across the table diagonally from me, she sips a glass of chardonnay. She's twisted her hair into a loose braid, the other smaller braids that were already woven through adding texture to the plaits. A few strands tipped in pink whip around her face in the gently moving gust of wind.

"Seriously, though, I'm trying to make an announcement." Natalie raises her voice, the pitch sharp with annoyance. She waves the half-full glass of champagne in the air. "Hello-o."

"Is it time for strip poker?" Jenni calls out.

"I brought pin the pee-pee on Timothée Chalamet," Maddie, the fitness influencer, says.

"You can call it a dick, Mads. Jesus Christ, are we twelve?" Lisa says, yanking Maddie to her side and planting a kiss on her cheek. She blushes, likely because of the kiss and the callout. Of the whole crew, Maddie seems to be the most vanilla, easily the quietest, both in appearance and career choice.

"Timothée Chalamet?" I question.

"Millie has a thing for gaunt guys."

"Sean is a triathlete."

"Variety is the spice of life." Coco shoots up. This announcement of Natalie's must be the *thing* they have planned. "Pipe down and let our babe speak."

My eyes drift again to Kit and I see that she's already looking at me. She blinks, flicking her gaze away, but her face twitches to indicate she's holding in a smile. It's hard to tell from the glow of the lamps if she's blushing or if it's just the light bouncing off the pink wildflowers reflecting on her skin. When her face changes to interest, I follow her gaze over to where Coco stands behind Natalie at the head of the table, lifting, as if from thin air, two Marc Jacobs tote bags in canvas and black.

"Mills forbade the giving of gifts," Natalie says, chagrined, which makes the presentation of these bags all the more confusing.

"What I said was *please donate to the women's center in DTLA instead of buying me sex toys and lingerie,*" Millie corrects. "Coco has already outfitted me with a custom number for the wedding night."

"Sean's more of a nude-and-crude lover anyway," Coco breaks in.

Millie rolls her eyes. "He's never mad at a crotchless pantie."

"We're straying off topic." Natalie redirects. "We all donated, *blah blah blah*, but this is a party and we came here to cut loose—even Mills—so Coco and I put our brains together—"

"And our unique brand connections," Coco jumps in again. Natalie death glares, clearly not enjoying Coco grandstanding alongside her.

"—to create a swag bag and a little healthy competition to kick off this wedding weekend," Natalie continues. Coco lifts the bag, parading it around the table. As a spokesmodel, she'd give young Vanna White a run for her money. "Inside is another custom Coco's Intimates design, which can fit and flatter most body types. Edible body paint from Chef Gal Doran, which tastes better than most Michelin-starred desserts. Some spa goodies from Calendula in Beverly Hills, and a little finger vibrator called Lila that works like a dream."

"Fab for on the go." Coco, again, coming in with a truly bonkers sidebar.

I know she means *on the go* in the sense of *fits easily and discreetly in a suitcase*, but I can't stop picturing someone throwing it in their purse to use while waiting in line at Starbucks, and it's really throwing me for a loop.

"Two swag bags worth a cool three K each." Chump change to someone like Natalie. "In order to win, we are challenging every reveler here—"

"Us included," Coco says.

"—to a game of flashlight hide-and-seek."

The table erupts with excitement. Even in a group of successful influencers who are used to pocketing thousands in free merch, a swag bag of goodies is an irresistible get.

Piper rolls her eyes, and I notice the moment Coco sees her do it. Her face turns slightly monstrous as if Coco would, maybe, separate Piper's head from her body given the chance. It passes quickly, gone in a flash as Millie jumps in to hug her hard around her neck.

Piper isn't winning friends with this group, and I can't help how that thought warms my heart, making me want to join them just to see how it might play out.

When I look across the table to where Kit was sitting just moments before, she's vanished.

"So . . . we're supposed to ride back together," Kit says from behind me. "Or we could stay."

"Is that a dare?" I fight the quaver in my voice.

"Aren't we too old for that?" Without turning to look at her, I can infer from her voice that she doesn't think so.

This is a dare in every way.

A game with countless variables that I can't control. A sexy prize package. Tasks outside my job requirements, totally out of character. It's testing my limits. It's seeing how close we can dance to the past version of us without stumbling back into each other.

This is a chance to cut loose, even if that isn't what I came here to do.

I shoot up from the table, grabbing the shot glasses Coco left behind and turning around. My eyes lock on Kit's. "Go ahead." I push past her toward the bar that's set up at the edge of this picnic area. "Ask me."

My skin prickles with electricity as the words come out. This is almost like flirting, something I haven't done since before Piper and I broke up. Something I shouldn't be doing with Kit Larson of all people.

"Two tequila shots," I say; this time there is a definite tremor in my voice. "And lime wedges." The bartender pours the shots before handing me the lime wedges folded in a napkin. Kit presses up against the bar.

"You want me to actually say the words?" She grabs the tequila shot near her. "I assume this is for me."

"One of us was always the . . . darer?" I can't be sure that's a word.

Her laugh is swift and breathy. "And one of us was always dragging the other along."

"I never dragged you." Not into anything. When Kit made up her mind, nothing could change it; she'd steamroll ahead, consequence be damned.

"Julia." Hearing her say my name in that breathless, urgent way makes my pulse pound rapidly, sending a bolt of heat through my center. "This whole thing—us, here—it's a Universe mindfuck." Her fingers tighten around the shot.

"It's a coincidence." I swallow because suddenly my throat has gone dry.

"There's no such thing," she almost whispers.

We hold our shots up, ready to clink. In the indigo desert light, her soft green irises are pale and a current of gray skates around the rim like a ring of polar ice. The pupils dilate the longer she looks at me. It could be an intoxicating tell of her attraction or simply a trick of the light. It could mean nothing or everything, but I can't walk away without finding out.

I cock my brow in question. Back to the subject of this discussion.

She nibbles her lip, and I wonder if they feel as good to kiss now as they did when we were eighteen.

"I triple-dog dare you to play hide-and-seek in the dark," she says.

I tap her glass with the edge of mine.

Here we go.

Chapter Fifteen

Kit

Natalie and Coco will be the team of seekers, with the rest of us pairing off to hide around the grounds, sharing a single flashlight. We'll have ten minutes to get into position, at which point someone from the Glamp-Out staff will ring a cowbell warning that the seekers have left homebase—the yurt. Winning is determined by two factors: not getting tagged by either Natalie or Coco *and* making it back to homebase before any of the other teams.

Both members of the team.

The second requirement prevents teams from hiding out the whole game and winning by default just because they don't get found, or splitting up to attack the base from multiple angles.

First team back to the yurt, untouched by the seekers, wins.

We've all gathered around Natalie now to draw straws. There was some suggestion of allowing teams to be chosen amicably, but all of us remember high school gym class, and no one wants to relive the humiliation of being chosen last.

"Mills, the honor is all yours," Natalie says, readjusting her hands around the straws to make sure their lengths remain incognito. Millie wiggles her fingers around above the straws before diving straight into the center.

She pulls out one of medium length, holding it up so it's easy to compare. We follow suit clockwise, until Lisa exclaims a whoop of cheer and runs over to grab Maddie by the forearm when she matches their straws. Jenni and Heather are next to match up, their excitement minimal to the point of nonexistent. When it's my turn to draw, the only straw currently in play and unclaimed is Millie's.

Coco lets out a chortle of glee as I tug my straw from the remaining ones hidden in Natalie's fist. My draw is easily the shortest in the bunch, and with just a quick glance at the still unattached Millie, I can see we aren't even close. Piper and Julia remain as the only two options left for us to team up with. One for Millie and one for me.

Spirit, help.

Being alone with Piper in the dark sounds like the beginning of a slasher movie that I don't walk away from. But being alone with Julia is somehow more terrifying.

Julia and Piper step up to Natalie in unison. Piper chooses first, not giving Julia a chance. Her agitated energy is probably a result of not being paired up with Julia. My eyes catch on Julia's as Natalie drops her hand away to reveal the lengths.

"Mystic Maven and the Wedding Planner!" Coco announces it as if we are a circus act. Natalie looks disgruntled at the way the partnering has played out. And I don't think it has anything to do with Julia and me teaming up.

"Piper and I were sorority sisters. Rush leaders," Millie says, sunny and sweet as always. "We are formidable."

"This game isn't that serious," Piper chides. Coco's lips dance into a snarl.

"Excuse me, what happened to *we're the best, hell yes*?" Millie says, and then for good measure, "Kappa Kappa, Alpha Alpha . . ."

Piper fights it. "Theta Theta Theta," she chants, unenthusiastically.

"We're the best, hell yes!" Millie finishes, a little anticlimactically.

I move up beside Julia as a guy from the Glamp-Out staff begins to pass out flashlights.

"You know what this reminds me of—"

"That party at Dev Laghari's dad's beach house," she breaks in, nodding. "There's not a boathouse to hide in here."

After an entire tray of Jell-O shots, Dev Laghari instigated a free-for-all game of hide-and-seek with no prize up for grabs besides bragging rights. It was enough for drunken high school partygoers to make a go of it, but Julia and I never intended to go it alone.

"We were close to base at Dev's," Julia recounts, sounding slightly confused. "I can't see that working here, because they'd find us fast."

"I'm suggesting we strategize from a different part of that plan."

That time, hiding turned into a discussion of *The Five-Year Engagement*—which we had seen with my dad at the ArcLight opening week—and then a lovefest over Alison Brie—whom neither one of us had ever seen before that movie, but we were both immediately obsessed with. We dabbled in shit-talking Karen MacMillan, who had *not* become less of a bitch in high school, and laughed until our sides were in stitches as we tried to quote all of *Clueless* from memory.

The booze made us sleepy; the hours of laughter wore out all our energy reserves. We woke up the next morning to discover they had called a search party overnight, and the totally terrified—then super pissed off—Dev and his very famous father were worried we'd gotten swept away in high tide.

"Falling asleep in the desert won't work for this. We have to be *first* back to the yurt," she replies. "Plus, aren't you, like, terrified of wildlife? I'd think you'd want to limit your time out there."

"Oh, yeah, that fear's alive and well," I reply with a nod. Julia snorts. The camaraderie of her almost-laugh makes it hard to resist the urge to grip her arm and tug her close to whisper my plan in her ear. "I'm thinking most of them won't want to venture into the dark, including Natalie and Coco. So if we go out to the edge of the playing area, we'll be well disguised by the shadows and we can use that to sneak back up until we get within running distance."

"And then make one big break for it?" she questions, getting the gist.

I wait for her approval. I always wanted her approval.

Her eyes search my face. "There are snakes in the desert."

"Then we'll have to watch each other's backs." I quiver at the thought, but try to play it cool. I can't tell if she's onto me. I take the flashlight in hand, flicking it on and off, just as Natalie screams, "*On your mark, get set—*"

Julia grabs my hand in a loose hold, but my fingers close willingly, brushing the tips over her knuckles, holding on.

"Go!"

We both run.

Chapter Sixteen

Julia

We're huddled together against the craggy body of a Joshua tree. Kit keeps turning on the flashlight, quickly checking the ground, turning it back off.

"I don't think it was a rattlesnake," I say, after she does the motion for the third time in as many minutes.

"It was a distinct *rattle hiss* sound." She is a mess of restless, nervous energy, and I can't tell if it's just her fear of desert wildlife, her proximity to me, or both that is the culprit.

"I think it was the wind moving through that hollow branch." I point above our heads to a dead limb of the Joshua tree protruding from the trunk. I check the clock on my phone. "We've been at this particular tree for almost five minutes and we haven't seen anyone."

"I think most of the other teams scattered to the opposite side of the camp – away from the mountains and all the creatures that live in them." The moon is high and bright, so I can easily see the outline of her features in the light.

We ran together, hands clasped, all the way to the last crop of

Joshua trees before the fence line of the Glamp-Out. When we reached it, I felt her fingers go slack and let go. But for a while, she had gripped my hand back.

I'm sure of it.

"It was the right call," she concedes, despite her visceral distaste for creatures she can't see coming. "But I want it on record that I heard a rattlesnake. Leaving that in the Yelp review."

"I'm sure if the Glamp-Out was concerned about mountain lion attacks or rattlesnake encounters, they would have had us sign a waiver," I say, grinning.

She gives me a playful shove that I'm not prepared for and it knocks me back into the tree. The momentum makes her lose her balance, her slick-soled boots skidding across some precarious sand. Her hands extend to break her fall against the tree and stop her from colliding bodily with me. Her lips brush the side of my cheek, breasts beneath jackets grazing, hair tickling the edge of my earlobe. My palms flatten against the tree trunk, fingers clenching.

Her small gasp becomes visible in the chilly night air.

I can smell food on her breath, wine and tequila, the sharp acid of that lime we chased the liquor with. Then I feel her holding her breath, like she knows I'm cataloging the scent for memory. She doesn't pull back right away.

"We should make our break for it," I say. She nods. Her full lower lip comes tantalizingly close to brushing the corner of my upper lip.

Finally, she pushes herself up, adjusting her braid over her left shoulder and straightening her coat. Her crystal necklace rolls into the light. When she looks up, she doesn't make eye contact.

Her eyes drift over my shoulder in the direction of the tents nearest to the yurt, focusing, and then squinting in a narrow, sly expression.

"One team down," she says, and I whirl to get eyes on the events.

Maddie and Lisa have been captured. They make a show of holding up their arms in surrender while Natalie edges up, tapping them both on the shoulders and finishing the action off with some finger guns. Coco does a happy dance that gets a dramatic display of middle fingers shooting out from both the captives.

It's a quick exchange, and then Coco seems to spot movement from the other side of a row of tents.

"Now," I say. "They're distracted."

Kit flicks on her flashlight, casting the beam over the expanse of sand that makes up our designated path toward the yurt. It ends at a large boulder formation just on the opposite side of the building. The light reveals a few small rocks working their way up onto the surface of the sand that we will need to avoid, but no sign of rattlesnakes or other creatures of the night.

"One, two," she says, turning off the light. "Three."

We launch out, guided only by the moonlight. The bouncing flashlight beam would definitely give our movements away. They'd see us, and instead of regrouping at the boulder before making our final run, we'd just have to break for the yurt and hope we're faster than they are. My lungs burn already from the exertion. I squint to make out the rocks in the way, sidestepping one just as Kit screeches, "I swear to God something just brushed by my calf—holy shit, was that a possum???"

I let out a howl laugh, and she growls profanity in reply. "A possum in the desert? That's a new one."

It's not like old times. Not even close. But still, it all feels achingly familiar.

I never had to drag her along in the past, despite her aversion to things like snakes, or heights, or humidity ("My hair cosplays as Ms. Frizzle in a swamp at the concept of moisture in the air"), she wanted the rush of adrenaline that came with taking risks as much as I did. Maybe even more. Whatever has changed since the last time we saw each other, that desire seems to remain in her, even if it's been mostly squashed out of me. She would leap headfirst, ask questions later, and almost always have a bunch of mini freak-outs along the way. Emotions like fear or pleasure were to be felt, not withheld.

That is, until the last time she leaped and she became terrified of falling.

We reach the boulder, chests heaving, blood pumping, resting our backs against the cool rock for support. The moonlight drenches her face. It's hard to tug my attention away from the damp sheen of sweat puckering along her exposed collarbone, but when she reels her lids open, I manage to, right in the nick of time.

"I don't think they saw us, do you?" she asks, breathless.

I hold my finger to my lips to signal for quiet and we both listen. In the distance I hear screeches of laughter, maybe the sound of someone being captured, but I can't make out the words or voices. The only other noises come from the desert itself. The wind in trees, moving branches, rustling up the sand into tiny tornadoes.

"I think we're good." I point toward the opposite edge of the boulder and we both move to peer around at the yurt. The bonfire area is partially in view beyond the white edges of the building, and I can see Lisa and Maddie sitting in chairs they've pulled up to its side, holding skewers fixed with marshmallows they are roasting in the fire. Clearly, not too broken up about their quick defeat. "This is it—the chance."

I'm standing beside her so that I can see beyond the boulder, since she's a couple inches taller than me. When she moves her arms to put the flashlight in her other hand, our elbows brush. It's not skin-on-skin contact because of our clothes, but it doesn't matter. I still get a surge down my spine that makes me wobble.

"We will be the winners of the Sexy Times bag," she says. Her use of those specific words hits a button in my brain, reminding me of Coco's encouragement that I let my freak flag fly, a totally out of the question proposition. Loosening up is so not in my job description, and yet here I am willingly playing a game of hide-and-seek for a "pleasure for one" bag of goodies.

"Jesus Christ," I snort. "I should probably donate mine."

"Not me," she replies. Her smile is sly; I hope the heat in my cheeks isn't noticeable. The urge to ask her more is a swishy, sea-sick feeling in my stomach.

When you're a queer girl and you come out in high school, you hope for acceptance from peers and family; you sigh with relief that you don't have to pretend to *only* notice boys, or to *just* want friendship from girls. But coming out doesn't make you magically equipped with a faultless gaydar; it doesn't make you any more certain that you will find love in the hopeless landscape of adolescence. Your own queerness doesn't automatically mean you know if someone else is also queer, any more than any person can ever be sure of another's attraction.

I wasn't ready. Her words outside the yurt before the tarot readings. But—

She kissed me first.

She kissed me back.

Just like every other adventure.

"I can't imagine you're satisfied in bed—sleeping just with men." As soon as the words leave my lips, I wish I could retract them.

This is why I don't cut loose. This is why I have firm boundaries, fixed rabbit trails. The only insurance against heartache is control.

I see the muscle in her jaw pulse as she clenches her teeth.

"I mean, maybe you are." *Shut the fuck up, Kelley.* "Since you're straight." The word is said in heavily implied air quotes. *Self-sabotage for one, please.*

Kit flicks the flashlight on. Then off. She turns, whirls actually, and now we're nose to nose. There's a spray of soft freckles showing through her matte finish makeup, too covered up for me to see if the pattern has changed since high school.

"It's shitty to make those kinds of assumptions about a person," she says, her voice newly sharp.

"It's not an assumption when the person once said it themselves." I double down because otherwise I will wither.

"A lot can change in ten years," she says, hooking her left eyebrow in a pointed expression.

"What, exactly, has *changed*?" I edge closer, the curves of my body taunting hers. Her eyes drop to my lips but don't linger. She flicks the flashlight back on, shifting to put distance between us, and turns her attention to the path ahead.

"Think we can make it? I hear voices getting closer." Her tone flattens, like she is deliberately trying to control her inflection.

I force myself to focus. Dickish behavior (mine) aside, we're in this thing together. She wants to win the Sexy Times bag, or she wants the glory, or she's just trying to distract herself (like me) from all these confusing, conflicting, consuming feelings and this is the current best plan of action to do so.

"We just have to touch the yurt, right? Not make it inside or anything?"

"That's the directive."

She flicks off the flashlight. "Now or never."

And it feels like she's talking about more than just running for the glory of that Sexy Times tote bag. My eyes find hers. Trepidation melts away with the look she's giving. These words are an answer, more than an olive branch.

"Now," I reply.

I want her to want me.

And maybe she wants the same thing.

We launch out in unison, our strides easily syncing as our feet scrape the rocky sand. We have a straight shot to the yurt, maybe twenty to thirty yards, when I hear a war cry come from the left—the direction the other players had scattered when the game commenced—and I look over my shoulder to see Coco breaking out into a sprint with Jenni and Heather behind her. They look defeated, which tells me it's down to the last two teams.

Piper and Millie vs. Kit and me.

"I'm surprised—Coco—didn't—hand it to . . . Jenni," Kit says, between gulps of air.

"This could be part of her plan," I add, and then gasp for oxygen.

"Plan?" She exhales the word.

"To win her back."

"I don't know if that's in her cards." She's breathing heavy from the run, but when she says it all nonchalant, basically a throwaway, I'm caught off guard. The idea that the cards could predict Coco's future for real without any reason to question them makes me wonder if she puts the same stock in that reading of ours from all those years ago.

But I don't get a chance to obsess over the thought.

Coco is closing in from the left, and straight ahead Piper and Millie shoot out from a space between two tents with Natalie close behind. Piper has broken out ahead of Millie, her long, athletic form eating up the ground toward the yurt. We're closer, but not as fast. And she knows it. Her eyes jolt around the scene as she's moving, assessing. Her smirk is an evil challenge.

The professional thing to do here is slow down. Let them take it home. The bride is on that team. She's the client, this is her show. But then I hear Kit's husky voice in my head, *I triple-dog dare you*, and my competitive streak flares up with renewed heat.

I reach for Kit's hand as the muscles in my calves fire to launch me the last few paces to the yurt. With one hand I hit the wall before I twist into her body and she holds me up against her.

Our breath mingles in the air between us.

Her hair has come out of her braid in wild tendrils to dance around her face.

She lets her cheek fall against my forehead, exhaling a long, winded sigh. After a few seconds heaving air into her lungs, her breasts rising and falling against my body, our hands still bound, fitting between us against our abs, she begins to laugh.

Bright, hearty, and intoxicating.

The reverberation vibrating everywhere her body touches mine. When I pull back to meet her eyes, there's no mistaking that the pupils are dilated, and just for a second I let myself believe it's because of me.

Chapter Seventeen

Kit

We left the bachelorette party to the rest of the night's festivities, taking our spoils and their congratulations with pleased grins of success. Most of them were good sports, at least, which made the whole thing heaps more fun. The only one noticeably grouchy was Piper, whose dagger glare and sharp *congrats* punctuated with an angry period was the picture of a sore fucking loser in more than one way.

It shouldn't have made me giddy, but it did.

We hugged our Sexy Times bags all the way back on the party bus like teenagers with contraband we were afraid would be confiscated by the teacher as soon as we got to school. Every couple of minutes one of us would chuckle, clutch the bag, sometimes even share why.

"Mission Sexy Times," I said. Side-eye. "What was Coco talking about?"

Julia got immediately shifty at the mention of Coco and her insinuation. "No idea."

"She winked at you when she said it."

"That's her knee-jerk expression."

I couldn't argue with that, even if I did think there was more to this than sheer innuendo.

"The panties are, in fact, crotchless," Julia said, as light cut across her face from the moon through the window.

"And red."

"Mine are burgundy."

"Like the wine." I had to work extra hard to keep the quaver in my voice from tripping a fault line as a visual of Julia materialized in my brain without permission. The slight olive hint in her skin tone from her mom's side of the family—Sicilian—would offset the color beautifully. Her tiny waist showing through the sheer flowing fabric of the slip; her sturdy, taut thighs strapped into the garter— I clenched my fingers around the corners of the bag and looked away.

I knew that feeling would eventually subside. It always, always did. The tweak to my nipples, the pressure between my thighs, so warm and aching—I've learned how to ignore it when I feel it for other women. That particular itch was too scary to scratch, but still my brain materialized the image of the finger vibrator in the Sexy Times tote bag and how it could help. How good it would feel to think about her when I used it, if I used it before I fell asleep— That stupid train of thought only made the ache expand.

I made it through the ride back to Celestial Sands without exploding, mostly by picturing my safe place and ignoring every *tap tap tap* from the image of Julia trying to invade it.

We're standing outside the lobby doors now, and it feels like we're the only two people awake in the world. The compound is quiet, probably most have fallen asleep by now; even the nocturnal animals seem to have muted their late-night hums, but neither

Julia nor I seem ready to make the first move away from each other.

She tugs her phone from her jacket pocket, illuminating the screen.

"I have to be up in four hours," she says. "The rest of the guests start arriving bright and goddamn early." I see an Instagram notification on the screen as she checks the time, so that confirms it. She's on Instagram and she receives at least some of her notifications. "I should be filled with regret right now." She pockets the phone again and looks up. The tip of her nose and her cheeks are pink tinted from the chilly air. "But I'm not."

Her words warm me all over and I don't want to push the feeling away. Knowing she doesn't regret the game we played, even if it's not because she played it with *me* specifically, makes me feel hopeful that maybe this chasm between us can be breached. I don't even know why I want that, but I don't question the feeling. It's there. It's undeniable.

"Your assistant—what's her name? Zoe?" I ask, refocusing.

"Zoe, yeah." Her brows shoot together like she's surprised that I remembered her assistant's name.

"She's sharp. I bet she could hold down the fort for an extra hour."

"She'd love the chance. She's always complaining—in the most respectful way possible, obviously—that she *in fact* doesn't need me to regurgitate her job at her like a mother bird feeding her young." The image of Julia standing open-mouthed over the wild-maned form of Zoe, holding a flower arrangement and table linen swatches, is a little too vivid.

"Okay." I blink, eyes tearing with exhaustion. "I just visualized that metaphor in graphic, Tim Burton–style detail. Time for me to call it a night."

She nods, stepping up to the lobby doors to swipe her key. She pulls one heavy side open, motioning for me to enter.

"Will it immediately age me if I skip skincare tonight?" I ask, yawning. The way she sways a little toward me as I pass by her and through the door could be intentional, could be exhaustion, or just my imagination. Fuck—I really have to stop reading into every single tremor of movement or look she tosses my way.

"It's morning, so maybe just go extra hard on your a.m. routine when you get up," she replies, also yawning, her tongue curling toward her teeth like a cat. My eyes fix on the move for an overlong moment—thankfully, she doesn't see the slip in my attention.

We walk through the dimly lit lobby, where the only person awake is the night clerk. She's sitting at the desk, engrossed in some game she's playing on her phone. She doesn't look up as we walk past.

"Candy Crush?" Julia asks when we're out of earshot. "Tetris, maybe?"

I snort, flicking my eyes behind me. "No, look at the swipe. That bitch is catching Pokémon for sure."

"Gotta catch 'em all," she singsongs, her voice raspy with exhaustion.

We're outside in the courtyard, which has brightly colored lanterns that light the way toward the paths leading off to the bungalows and my Airstream. It takes every ounce of courage I have to hold eye contact with her in this warm, low, romantic lighting.

My brain is screaming, *This is her! This is the only girl you've ever kissed. This is the girl you ran away from. This is Julia, she's right FUCKING HERE—FREAK OUT ABOUT THIS, PLEASE!*

"See you tomorrow"—my tongue trips but doesn't stutter—"Julia."

"Later today," she corrects, her nostrils flaring as her eyes drop to my lips for a blistering second.

I walk in the direction of my Airstream trailer before I lose my courage, or worse, say one of the ardent, rambling thoughts breaking out all over my brain like tiny wildfires. That didn't happen. We didn't just play hide-and-seek in the dark. We didn't just look at each other with so much yearning we can't possibly ever abate it. We didn't just exist in the same space for hours and not implode from the closeness.

Twin Flames always find their way back to each other.

Can that be what's actually happening right now?

Madame Moira can't have known we were both queer when neither one of us knew it ourselves, but maybe the cards somehow did. Saw into the deep, dark corners of the closets in our hearts and illuminated it for that split second we sat side by side at the tarot table.

The cards never lie, but neither do rom-coms.

Or, at least, that's what I've always wanted to believe.

Movies about blissful, unmarred Happily Ever Afters between men and women were selling fantasy instead of the truth. Romance is mostly messy. Love is dynamite, not a bouquet. My parents have proven as much.

I want to hold on to the ideal I've tried so hard to embody my whole life, but with every second I spend in this desert, it gets harder to pretend.

I shove through the gate and up the path to my Airstream trailer, fumbling in my bag for the keys. My hands are shaking with adrenaline, so I struggle to fit the key in the lock; when it finally goes in, I twist the handle, drop my bags onto the floor and my body onto the bed. My shoes slip off one by one; I unbuckle my belt and roll out of my coat. My eyes drift closed and she's right there in my imagination.

Long, tan neck, the gold chain winking at me as the heart dips into her clavicle.

Her eyes are bright oceans.

Her lips are small, with a deep *m* and plump pout. They would fit so well between mine. I could work my tongue inside for a taste. I could run my fingers over her jawline, touch the gold hoops, the diamond-studded cuff in her earlobe, before losing my grip in the soft, dark waves of her hair.

I roll over and grab my purse, yanking out the phone. I ignore the notifications from Mom. A few texts, a missed call. Nina also texted, probably to lovingly check in on my ongoing freak-out about being in Julia's presence. I open the Instagram app where notifications from other verified accounts that I follow pop up, and the message icon is lit with a bunch of DMs. I go to the search bar and type in Julia's name.

The top hit is @jak_lovealways, which features a headshot of Julia as the PFP. There's another one @foreverbyjak, but it doesn't have a photo or any details in the profile so I click the top hit instead, going in for a closer look. The profile picture is also one of her pinned posts, which is captioned with information about her agency acting as a static pitch. In the photos, she's dressed in a green power suit, her hair tucked up in a low chignon, her expression fierce. She looks every bit the pro she wants to be, but nothing like the actual Julia Kelley that I used to know. Or even got glimpses of tonight. It's as if all the personality that made her a target for Karen MacMillan, that later turned her into the person I never got tired of, who always surprised me, has been smoothed out. Combed back into that bun, wrinkles ironed out with dry-cleaning.

Her grid shows how good she is at her job. Perfect, pristine, unique, dynamic wedding scenes play out in little squares of glossy color, but what I don't see in the shots is *her*—her mark on the scene. Maybe I'm not supposed to. What she does for a living is so different from my job. I've had to play up the manic pixie dream girl, boho goddess energy that exists in much smaller doses within me just to land jobs and carve out my own little corner of the internet.

The rom-com ideal is more than my daydream for a happy ending, it's my living. A vivacious, appealingly quirky ingenue is what people want. Men and women alike. It's fuckable and fragile; it's how they know for sure that they are the main character and I'm just there to inspire their greater appreciation for life. Clients and boyfriends, subscribers and followers, everyone succumbs to the fever dream it offers. I guess we're both playing a game of pretend, and I wonder if it's as much with ourselves as with everyone else.

My finger hovers over the follow button for a split second before I let it tap. No turning back now. I like the pic of her in the green suit for good measure since I'm not sure which notifications she receives, and I want her to see this one when she wakes up.

I click out of Instagram and am about to let the phone go dark when it buzzes. A text, not a notification. Dad is burning the three a.m. oil per the usual. He has never been much of a sleeper, claiming his mind comes alive after midnight and he has to seize the opportunity to write when he can. I have always thought his orthodontic patients would probably prefer him to be well rested when he tightens their braces, but whatever. He's set in his ways.

I check the text. It's a photo of a stack of boxes labeled with his name, *Clint*. My heart twists with sadness. I click on the icon of his name and tap FaceTime. It chimes to connect, and when the image comes clear he's holding his phone up so I can see his face. He's sitting in the rocking chair on the pool house porch—I can see the windows reflecting the lit-up swimming pool.

"Hey, there, cupcake." His voice is tired with an edge of pensive. His teeth are stained dark from the tannins of red wine. He lifts a mostly empty glass to cheers at me. "To the demise of love."

To be fair to myself, both my parents have a flair for the dramatic. I come by it naturally.

I scoot up to lean against the pillows at the head of the bed.

"It's shit to see you like this."

"Your mother doesn't care. She walked through the backyard before midnight in a bikini, talking loudly on the phone about vacationing in Cabo to her girlfriend." The words *your mother* and *girlfriend* so close together send a spike of adrenaline through me.

"She cheated on you, Dad. Maybe you shouldn't be pining."

"It's not that simple." He looks into the camera, the magnification of his glasses making his teary eyes look massive. "She was my true north. You and Camille—but it all began and ended with her." His voice cracks and he silences the wobble with a gulp of wine. "She was the love of my life, but I wasn't that to her."

"Don't say that. You were married over thirty years. She loved you." I rethink the past tense. "She loves you, even if she's not in love anymore."

"I'm not enough." He whimpers into his glass.

The concept of a true north, a soul your compass leads you to, is a romantic notion my dad has made as much a part of the Rom-Com Ideal as public declarations of love and the affable, good-natured male lead. Too bad that—for me—a psychic promised mine was a girl I met in seventh grade.

"Did you know about Mom?"

"Cheating on me?" he asks.

"No, the other thing," I say, nibbling my lip with nerves. "The thing where she's bi."

"Oh," he says, waving me off. "Always, always. She was with a woman before she and I got together—it was the late '80s in Laurel Canyon. I didn't think anything of it."

"Mom was with a woman before?" My voice gets all high and weird. Awesome, I sound as shocked as I feel. "I can't believe I never knew that."

"Why would you need to know? She was married, it was in her past."

"But how could it be in her past? I mean, I get it, she married you, a man, and you two were monogamous—" He groans at the trigger word. "Sorry—but that doesn't make her any less of a queer woman."

"Oh, well, sure, cupcake, of course I see what you mean," he says, shaking his head. The dismissive tone of his voice makes me wonder if he really does. "But in the end, it wasn't real love."

"Because it was a woman?" My cheeks flare with unexpected heat at the idea he'd dismiss her feelings because they were about another woman.

"No, of course not. It wasn't real love because she told me. Not every affair measures up equally." He lets out a long sigh. "I just thought she chose me. Wanted me forever." He looks defeated. Shoulders slumping forward, head dropping back to rest against the rocker. I can't imagine what it's like to have invested so many years into a life with someone only to find out they weren't as happy, or as all in, as you thought.

Even with them playing Happily Ever After perfectly, I think there was always a part of me that was afraid of falling that in love with another person, needing them more than they need me.

"I'm sorry she fell for someone else," I say.

"Me too," he says, offering a sad smile.

When I say goodbye, it's with the caveat that he go get some sleep and stop drinking merlot on the porch. I drop the phone to my side, sliding down into the covers and turning off the lamp, too tired to get up to wash my face or brush my teeth. I never thought that being attracted to women was wrong on a global scale. It just wasn't the way I had expected to find romantic happiness.

I wanted the Nancy Meyers kitchen with the rumpled button-down, floppy-haired husband. I wanted the Nora Ephron kiss at New Year's with the guy who had once been nothing more than my best friend, but over time became the love of my life. I wanted what my parents had. And all along, my mom knew she was queer and never told me. All along, I didn't have the whole story about the life I believed was the epitome of ideal.

My eyes drift closed, just as I feel my phone buzz with a notification. I let myself daydream that it's Julia following me back on Instagram, and that she took it for what it was. Me offering her access. An invitation to slide into my DMs and back into my life.

CHAPTER EIGHTEEN

Julia

The mother of the bride—Evelyn, a Goldie Hawn–style iconic blond who seems to think it's her job to ensure my mental demise—and the mother of the groom—Blythe, a regal-looking Emily Gilmore type with the sourest look of disapproval to ever grace a person's face—would love any excuse imaginable to just go ahead and kill each other right here at the bride and groom's dinner table, and it's my job to stop them.

The fathers are engaged in a deep discussion about the most challenging holes on the golf green where they intend to spend the rest of the day. They're itching for release from their wives' death grip, and they aren't doing anything to help mediate the argument over the dream catcher Evelyn wants hung above the bride and groom's table—a topic that has managed to derail our final walk-through of the rehearsal dinner setup and waylay me getting more ibuprofen.

"You can't possibly think this is appropriate," Blythe says, standing at the foot of the ladder with her arms crossed over her black tweed jacket. She's holding a half-empty mimosa in her prim, pink-oval-manicured hand, tapping her wedding band against the glass.

"I don't understand your aversion to keeping our children safe from bad wishes and intentions on their most special day," Evelyn replies, a doe blinking at a hunter. Her eyes trail back to Deanna, a Love, Always staff member who has unwittingly gotten in the middle of this mess. "To the left, use that second hook. We want it evenly hung."

"We don't want it at all," Blythe counters. "We're not Native American. This is appropriation."

"I'm one-sixteenth Chickasaw, Blythe."

"And the rest is white WASP."

"Takes one to know one," Evelyn retorts. She holds her phone up to snap a shot, and then frowns. "I wonder if we can hang flowers from it to make it more decorative."

"Edward, Jesus, will you please chime in." Blythe raises her voice toward the fathers, both of whom now have refreshed glasses of beer. Ten a.m. in wedding time is apparently five p.m. everywhere else. Both Edward—father of the groom—and Grant—father of the bride—look over. They are nearly identical in their pastel polos and dim expressions.

"Whatever you say, darling," Edward replies. When Blythe glares at the dream catcher with meaning, Edward's green eyes follow. But he doesn't *follow*. "Looks great." He nods.

"Millie's style," Grant responds.

Blythe fumes, just as Evelyn claps in approval. "It's perfect."

The dream catcher stays.

For now.

I press Blythe to turn her attention to the head table décor. "The only element not in place yet is the flowers—" I gesture toward the cart Deanna wheeled over before she got wrangled onto the ladder. "Which we wanted to show you before we return them to the refrigerator."

Blythe blinks her attention reluctantly over to the cart, casting one more stink eye toward the dream catcher and her future family member. The groom's family is taking on the traditional role, paying for the band, food, and all décor at the rehearsal dinner. (The exceptions being that scandalous dream catcher and, of course, Mystic Maven's services.)

We walk over to the cart for Blythe to get a closer look and hopefully sign off on the whole setup. It's the final step in the walk-through, which means I'm counting down to my release. God, my head is pounding. It's not a hangover, thankfully. I think the culprits are exhaustion and dehydration. So, my booze intake last night definitely didn't help. As she takes the arrangements in, cataloging every petal and leaf, I let my eyes drift closed.

I had asked Zoe to take the lead on getting the parents settled and overseeing Homebase until I was up and about. An extra hour of sleep would have been a game changer. But I woke up at my normal time, no alarm clock needed, and the first thing I did while I lay in bed half-awake was check out Kit's Instagram feed. I was too tired to give it a deep dive after I followed her back last night. It was causing enough of a spiral that she had been thinking about me at all, and that thinking prompted her to search for my account.

Let alone follow and like a post.

The one thing I surmised from her feed, before I finally got up to get coffee, was that she is definitely not dating women. A quick scroll revealed a handful of long-term boyfriends over the last few years, and no sign of a single female who could be more than just her friend. For a second I thought the girl she's photographed with all the time—going to the beach, hiking Runyon Canyon, brunching and snuggling close—could be a romantic partner, but a little more sleuthing revealed she's just her friend Nina, who is definitely queer but doesn't appear to be romantically involved with Kit.

And probably doesn't know anything about Kit's onetime dalliance with pussy.

I press my fingers against the point in my temple where most of my headache is localized, when I smell a familiar scent.

Bitter, herbal, and smokey.

Oh great.

"I just need to add some more rose quartz hearts to the tables," Healer Arynne says, huffing past me. I'm nearly knocked down by her beefy entourage, dressed in matching shorts and freshly oiled.

Zoe appears in a stunning twist of perfect timing, directing Healer Arynne and her band of merry men to a corner of the room that's out of earshot of the mothers. God, I hope she stays out of the way this time.

Blythe pinches her features like a dried prune, her focus trailing after Healer Arynne, but fortunately she's not given any more ammunition for her cannon of disdain.

One more careful redirect and I'm out of here.

"I've set you both up with a day at the spa, tailored to your individual preferences, to get you rested and relaxed for tonight's festivities."

That focuses Blythe, livening up her features. All distraction evaporating with the promise of a massage. She focuses back on the list.

I pull my walkie from my waistband, calling for one of the spa staff to come retrieve the mothers. Zoe steps back into my eyeline, giving me a meaningful glare and moving away from the guests.

"I need a dark room and a tranquilizer to get rid of this headache," I say when I reach her.

"That'll have to wait," she says, anxious energy emitting from her like a force field. "Millie has arrived safely at the picnic location ahead of the food. The staff set everything up to your specifications, it's gorgeous—we got some great shots for socials—"

"Why do I feel like you're burying the lead, Zoe?" My voice is sharp with agitation I shouldn't be directing at Zoe.

"Because I am." Zoe sucks in a deep breath like she's prepping to hold it underwater. "The groom and his groomsmen are a no-show."

"What do you mean they're a no-show? They were supposed to be picked up—" I twist my wrist to check the time on my watch. "Half an hour ago."

"The driver just called."

"To say he was on his way to the picnic site?"

"To say the dudes are passed out in their tents." She pauses, correcting. "Except for Cash Kim, who was vomiting into the firepit."

I quickly dispel that image from my brain. *Focus, Kelley.* A fuckup like this could have a domino effect.

I've seen it before. The groom and groomsmen miss a pivotal prewedding event. They make excuses, but the bride doesn't buy them. She starts to tug at the threads of their relationship, question the validity of his claim on her heart. The groom makes an offhand remark, she spirals it into more, and before we know it the wedding implodes.

I can't let that happen here.

"Cover Homebase," I say.

"Way ahead of you." She hands me my wallet and a bottle of water plus two ibuprofen. The essentials. Zoe never misses. "Got the valet to pull your car around already."

I ignore my pounding head and the rumble of hunger in my stomach, yanking my phone out of my back pocket to put the address of the bachelor party festivities into my GPS as I book it across the venue to my car.

Chapter Nineteen

Kit

I ate my bodyweight in homestyle potatoes and huevos rancheros. The tableside guac was to die for, but the real scene-stealer was the pineapple peach agua fresca. I do a quick check of my clothes to make sure nothing got on the white tank and cutoffs in my enthusiasm, before paying my bill and leaving through the side entrance. Stuffed, happy, ready for a relaxing day until the rehearsal dinner festivities.

A day *not* spent obsessing over the wedding planner.

"Oof!" I exclaim with a gasp.

Julia barrels into me. My hand reaches out in a reactive embrace. She yanks her giant black Versace shades off, pinning me in place with her eyes. They're makeup-free and alive with alarm.

"Whoa, who died?" I ask.

"This wedding might," she replies, her voice electric.

"That's ominous."

"The groom and his dudes are passed out at Bachelor Town when they're supposed to be presentable at a picnic brunch on

Skull Rock." She's in a hurry, but she's not tugging out of my grip. "I have to go." Her eyes drop to my hand. One of my fingers has slipped in between the buttons on her light green button-down, touching the skin on her abdomen. The baby hairs stand on end, and before I move my hand away, I let my finger brush back and forth over her skin.

"You need backup," I say, releasing her. I shove the hand that was just touching her into my hair, twisting a chunk between my fingers.

"No, I'm fine," she says, waving me off. "You should enjoy the facilities." She's moving away fast. But that wasn't a question.

"I'm coming with you," I say, gripping her by the wrist. Her eyes trip to my hand before coming back up to my face.

"Are you sure you want to do that? It's bound to be a shitshow."

"All the more reason you shouldn't tackle it alone." I'm just as shocked as she is by the words coming out of my mouth. I am supposed to be avoiding her, not trying to find more reasons to be close to her.

She considers me and my proposition for another beat. I consider recanting but can't make myself say it out loud. Finally, she nods, and I release my grip on her wrist. She launches back out, and I follow her, matching her brisk pace.

"They were supposed to be up by ten, over to the site by eleven, but everyone is passed out or throwing up—" She cuts herself off. We turn the corner into the lobby, which is full of people I assume are family and close friends who have been invited to the rehearsal dinner tonight. "This is why I always insist the bachelor/bachelorette festivities don't happen on the same weekend as the wedding." She's lowered her voice, painted on a fake smile.

"Millie probably thought they would be the exception to your warnings," I reply. She's shoved her dark sunglasses back over her eyes, but I can feel her confirming eye roll through the lenses.

"And *she* is," Julia replies. "Despite the shenanigans of last night, the bridal party is on-site, on time, and undoubtedly camera ready."

We reach her car idling in front of the lobby entrance, flanked by two of the Celestial Sands staff. I climb into the passenger seat, buckling, as she starts the engine. Sitting in the console between the two seats is a rental car packet. I pick it up, examining.

"I drive a Jag," she says, throwing the car into gear.

The word *Jag* hits me right in the stomach, making it twist. Julia Kelley *should* drive a Jag. She should wear sexy dark sunglasses and simmer with intensity. She should be pissed off and dry-witted, and she should definitely be beside me in the driver's seat.

I tighten my seat belt. *Universe, take the wheel.*

She peels out, tires spinning up gravel to smack against the car's undercarriage.

~

It's a ten-minute drive to reach the location of last night's bachelor excursions. As we pull onto the lonely desert road, the entrance sign stands overhead. They've hung a banner that reads *Bachelor Town, population: the Final Four* over the sign, blocking the Pioneer Town name from view. As we near the site, I see a faux street of frame buildings set up to look like a ghost town from the Wild West, complete with a saloon, a blacksmith, and a doctor. I am assuming each of these buildings also has different uses that loosely correspond to their historical purpose. To the left of the street are a few large glamping tents similar in style to the ones at the Glamp-Out—canvas, with a firepit in the center. Parked alongside those is a party bus, the front doors open, the engine off.

As we pull up to the site, I notice the hunched-over form of one of the bachelors, his shiny black hair absorbing the stark sunlight. He's wearing a pair of assless chaps, his athletic torso completely bare. His head rests on the metal edge of the firepit and his back is already tinted pink from sun exposure.

"Goddammit, I hope his forehead isn't crispy," Julia says, shutting off the engine. She unbuckles. "But a crispy groomsman really is the least of my concerns."

I cut my eyes at her. "Have you met Millie Morgan? Aesthetics are God."

"Fair," she replies. "Fuck." We climb from the car to get a closer look. She gingerly touches the guy's pink-tinted shoulder. "Cash, you lucid?" He stirs with a groan and then lifts his head to reveal a pink stripe across his forehead, but hopefully with time—and some ice and a little makeup—it won't show in photos.

"This is manageable," I say, bending down to peer at the mark. "It's fine as long as one of the bridesmaids has a matching foundation shade."

Julia nods. "Right, okay." Then she shakes him a little more vigorously. "Cash, you gotta get to the showers in the Saloon." Another groan.

I pull out my phone, opening the GarageBand app to quickly search for a siren sound. I turn the volume way up and put the phone right by his ear. Julia looks perplexed, brows flexing with her unspoken question.

"It'll work," I say, clicking the sound. A siren rises, growing in volume like the real thing.

Cash's head shoots back up from the firepit edge. "What the

fuck, no—" he exclaims, smacking his palms against the metal, then up to his ears. Julia grabs him under the arms and yanks him up, putting his double nipple piercings right in my line of sight.

Cash is sooo the kind of guy I would have fucked in a bathroom and ghosted when he invited me to take out the paddleboats in Echo Park.

"You have to get showered, come on—" She starts pulling him toward the Saloon but he's still a limp noodle in her hands. I rush forward to help shoulder some of his weight.

"He smells like rancid milk," I say, nearly gagging.

"They had a boozy shake truck and burgers on-site last night."

"So it's his breath."

"I think it's oozing from his pores."

When we reach the porch, a man rushes out, arms extended to take Cash off our hands. He must work here, because he doesn't look like one of the bachelors. Julia tugs her sunglasses down, cutting him a look that could kill.

"Let me help you out—" he starts, but she interrupts.

"You'll do more than help me out. The management was aware of their ten-a.m. pickup time. There were strict instructions to make sure they were up—"

"You try wrangling a bunch of drunk frat dudes."

"I'm about to do just that." We hand Cash over, the move drawing another sour-milk-and-meat burp into the air. "Get him in the facilities, and make sure he doesn't slip on suds or something." The guy seems rightfully terrified of the petite brunette barking orders his way.

"Where are the rest of the guys?" I ask, offering him a smile. His pale eyes widen and shift toward the center tent. The biggest.

The canvas door flapping in the wind. He shuffles off with Cash. We slow turn to look at the tent in question.

Julia inhales sharply. "Honest moment?"

"Of course."

"I'm scared of what I'll find."

I flick my eyes over to her. "You mean is this *Very Bad Things* or *The Hangover*?"

"Jesus, hopefully neither."

"*Very Bad Things* is so much worse."

"Nineties problematics all over the place."

"Deranged Cameron Diaz was a vibe, though."

We approach the tent in unison, and Julia gives one more sharp exhale before gripping the edge of the tent flap and yanking it up. We step inside and let it fall closed behind us.

Men's bodies litter the ground, halfway shoved into sleeping bags, a couple of them laid out on cots, hugging pillows and drooling over the edges. They all appear to be alive, with no dead sex workers or babies in the mix. It's more than four guys, which leads me to believe that—much like the bachelorettes—the extended close crew were invited to participate.

"It's definitely not as bad as it could be," she says, shoving her sunglasses into the back pocket of her jeans. "But six guys, not counting Cash, is a lot for the two of us to corral." She looks at me, and then her face drops into a small, grateful smile. "But at least I'm not on my own."

I quirk my lips into a smirk. "Are you trying to say *thank you* without saying thank you?"

She sticks out her tongue and my eyes immediately drop to the move.

"I'm waiting." I cock my hip, resting my hand in the crook and tapping my fingers in a rapid, impatient rhythm.

"You're going to make me say it."

"I think it's important that you do."

She squirms under the expectation for another couple of seconds before taking her lower lip between her teeth, grunting, and mumbling out the two all-important words. I snort into a cackle. We both turn our attention back to the sleeping pile of men.

"Try your siren trick again," she says, motioning to my ass, where my phone is stored in the back pocket of my jean shorts. I tug it out, walking over to the nearest passed-out guy. He's blond and tan, buff, and totally the type of guy I would normally find hot. Right now, with the peach fuzz on his upper lip and smelling of booze, I can't comprehend why.

He's not the groom, Sean—who I know from Millie's Instagram. I see he is passed out on the cot near the back of the tent. I press my phone speaker close to this guy's ear and blare the siren sound.

It gets some grunts of stirring, and one of them calls out for five more minutes, but it doesn't do the job here like it did on Cash. I try it a couple more times, but even with it not right up close to my own ear, my head is starting to ache. When I look back at Julia, I see she's got her hands covering her ears and a pained expression on her face. I stand, pocketing the phone again.

"We need a new plan," I say, walking back toward her as she drops her hands from her ears. She considers the room, eyes drifting over each sleeping form, warm and cozy in the already deepening morning heat. For November, even in the desert, the weather today is warm, bringing sweat to all clothing-covered crevices.

"Shock," she says, her face twisting, features brightening with the beginning of an idea.

"Wake them up with a start," I add on.

"It's beyond warm temps in here," she continues. "It's downright toasty."

We look at each other in unison. "Debate team trip." The words said in sync set off a chain reaction of laughter.

Junior year, our debate team made it to the state competition in Sacramento. The whole team drove up on a bus and stayed overnight at a Holiday Inn right off the Five freeway. Julia and I were both on the team, alternates for the main players, sure, but that didn't matter for this trip. Everyone was invited. The night before the final match, some of the seniors—mostly boys and, you guessed it, Karen MacMillan and her posse—got wasted and didn't show up for breakfast. Our coach, Mr. Dudley, used the showerheads in the bathrooms to shock them awake. They all got slaps on the wrist for conduct, and a couple of the boys were given suspensions for supplying the booze that got everyone drunk, but Coach Dudley's method worked to rouse them awake enough to participate in the match.

"There has to be a water hose on the property somewhere," I say, now that our laughter has died back.

"It's wholly unprofessional to spray my clients with a water hose to wake them up," she replies. She's second-guessing her instinct, a trait I'm noticing more and more—another trait that is so unlike the girl I used to know.

"Julia." I savor the taste of her name on my tongue. Our eyes lock. "I dare you to find a water hose and spray these dudes awake with it."

My mouth goes dry as she stares at me, contemplating the

dare, clearly weighing out her options. She wasn't reckless, not ever, but she *was* sure every time she decided to act, always relying on her gut to lead the way. I feel it with a pang, the desire to remind her that she can trust herself. She doesn't need someone to dare her to do what she already knows she desires.

"Triple. Dog. Dare." I raise my brow in a challenge.

"Let's go," she says, and I see the decision snap into place as a wave of certainty washes over her from crown to toes.

We shoot back through the tent flap and blinkingly look around for a hose. Nothing right up next to the tent, or the surrounding tents, but not too far off we spot a watering trough like you'd expect to see in a real Old West town for horses to get a drink after a long day carrying humans and cargo through the desert. As we near, I can tell by the remnants of a few unopened beer bottles that its use in Bachelor Town was for storing libations. Rolled up on the side of the trough is a green water hose that appears to be connected to a water source below. Julia grabs the hose, uncurling it so she has a good grip, before turning the nozzle to test if it actually works.

The hose quickly tenses up in her hands, and after a few seconds, a slow stream of water begins to pour out through the end. She grins. "I'll unroll it back toward the tent. Can you go ahead of me to secure the flap open?"

"Sure thing." I run ahead to follow her instructions. There are ties attached to both corners of the tent flap, so I roll the first up to its corresponding loop, securing the corner back. I repeat the motion on the other side, finishing just as she reaches the tent and shakes out a kink that's formed while unrolling the hose. Her eyes meet mine as she gets into position, bright with excitement. She lets a sharp puff of air out through her nostrils.

"I'll turn up the pressure." On my way past her, the instinct to brush her arm with the tips of my fingers is almost too strong to resist. Her skin is warm tan; the faint hairs on her arm are soft. I count down as I walk, trying to focus on anything but all these feelings.

Julia isn't the only woman I've had an intoxicating crush on, but she's been the only one who ever felt worth risking it all for. I fucked it up before, even with the heady desire to give her my all, and I can't do that to her again. This time, if I take the leap, I have to be sure I'm willing to go all in.

I curl my fingers around the nozzle and twist until it won't go any farther. I can see the water pressure turning the slack hose tight on its way to the end. I chase the water all the way back to Julia, reaching the entrance to the tent just as she lifts the hose, placing her finger into the flow to make it spray. She takes aim at the groom's exposed, taut torso. Spray from the hose splashes out over the body of one of the other guys, who is sleeping in a beanie, a pair of boxers, and nothing else on top of a sleeping bag.

The drops hit his stomach just as the harder pressure smacks against Sean.

The groom's eyes slice open, startled, as his guttural scream fills the tent. He shoots to his feet, stepping on the beanie guy, which sends him upright and directly into the flow of the water hose. Julia turns the spray on his chest for a second, before moving it around the tent. In a flurry of water and wails, the bachelors wake, jumping in panic to avoid the continued onslaught from the water weapon. I'm hiding behind her as the mayhem unfolds, but all I can think about is how close I'm standing to her body.

My eyes rake down her form, coursing over her hair tugged into a tight, low ponytail. They slip over her curves, noticing the way her button-down blouse hits the waistline of her jeans, how the minty color pops against her skin. I imagine wrapping my fingers around her waist and tugging her against me. Pressing my whole body into the length of hers, leaning my nose into the crown of her head to smell her.

Making her mine in every single sense of the word, no remorse, no holding back.

Chapter Twenty

Julia

They're going to riot over this, but I don't care. This isn't the way perfect planner Julia Kelley handles unforeseen bumps on the road to her clients' marital bliss. This is wild, reckless, former teenage rebel Julia Kelley.

How I've missed her.

"Holy balls, Julia, what the fuck did you do this for?" Sean sideswipes the spray of the hose on his way over to me.

"You and your bros are an hour late to the brunch picnic site. Millie may be a saint but she's not going to let a full no-show slide." I lower the hose. "I can't let this derail your rehearsal dinner or, worse, the actual wedding."

He rakes his fingers through his sandy brown hair, eyes widening in horror.

"You're one of the most chilled-out grooms I've worked with in a while. Easygoing almost to a fault. I need you to *not* be that right now."

"Millie will be cool," he says, but it's clear from his tone he knows that isn't true.

"She's poured her heart into this wedding weekend. Do you really think she'll be cool if you don't show up for the brunch she spent weeks planning?"

"Oh shit." Reality checks in. He spins around to address his crew. "We fucked up, you guys. We have ten minutes to get presentable—"

"Less," I interject.

"Fuck!" Sean yelps. "Fall out to the Saloon."

They scurry around the tent grabbing up duffle bags and backpacks full of their belongings, some of their eyes still bleary, with hideously grouchy expressions on their faces, but at least they're moving.

"Thankfully, the wardrobe for today is all denim and linen. Wrinkle-free isn't expected," I say, leaning back in relief. Kit is close enough that I can feel the warmth of her body against my back. It sends a pulse through my stomach that I try to keep from showing on my face as the guys file past in a blur.

I spin around, holding the hose away from my body and hers. She looks like a kid caught with her hand in the cookie jar as she darts her eyes away. The expression sends another jolt of nerves through my body.

"I should shut that off," Kit says, swiftly turning back toward the trough. Her shorts are frayed and fitted, with her cropped white tank top showing off a sliver of her stomach. I have the sudden compulsion to hose her down, and in a knee-jerk reaction that I don't let myself question, I spray the backs of her calves.

She stutters to a stop, screeches, "Oh my God!" before whirling around, her mouth open in alarm. My stoicism breaks, letting the barely contained glee I feel at the sight of her shock and awe seep out from the crevices of my smirk. I point the hose toward the sand, making a small muddy puddle beside my sneakers as laughter rumbles through me.

"What the hell was that?" she asks, shooting back over.

I reply with another lift of the hose, this time to pelt the front of her thighs and shorts. She's jolted again by the cold, but not thwarted this time. She grabs fast for the hose, blocking the next spray with her hand, which sends the water shooting out in all directions. It dampens the baby hairs around my face, splattering cold and sharp against my cheeks and down the front of my shirt. I let out an involuntary yelp.

"Stop! That's freezing," I say, shivering.

She guffaws, lurching forward to grab for the hose. Her hands tighten over mine as she tries to wrench the hose loose from my grip. I twist around, bending over to block her. The move sends a stream of water over the tops of her feet where the skin is exposed through her flip-flops.

As she's trying to pull the hose loose from my hands, I raise my arm, sending a spray of water back down on top of our heads. It hits dead center on my crown, trickling down my neck to wet the shoulders of my blouse and back.

We break apart, shaking out the cold wet like a pair of dogs who just got a bath.

I spin back around to face her. My shirt is wet, but Kit's is soaked. My gaze travels the landscape of her body; the white fabric tank top is now basically transparent, clinging to her ample breasts contained in a lavender t-shirt bra. Her waist is a voluptuous slope, soft and inviting. Goose bumps rise on her neck where water beads against her skin.

My brain gets all fuzzy with desire, dredging up memories from the depths. Hot summer nights in the hammock. Sleepovers in her bed, her curling her toes into my socks, shoving them all the way off my feet. The way our games of touch escalated until finally the only thing we could do was kiss.

Her lips pressed against mine. Tentative. Unsteady.

Then all-consuming, all in, all I could ever imagine wanting.

The memory sends a shock wave through me. The feelings I have now are somehow even more visceral. She's looking at me with the same raw desire; there's no denying it's true. Her eyes drift and stop on the place where my blouse clings, wet against my shape.

I feel reckless and alive for what feels like the very first time in a very long time.

She lunges for the hose, grabbing me firmly before yanking me back against her. Our skin is slick, but her grip is firm. I try to hold on to the hose, but I'm disoriented from the closeness and she manages to work it free from my hands. She jumps back, raising it like a weapon, a playfully mischievous smile dancing to life.

I raise my hands, mocking defeat.

She grins. "I know you, Julia. You'd never go down without a fight."

I know you. She did. Once.

Could she again?

I make a break for it, running diagonally away from her, but she sprays me hard across the left side of my body. I squeal as I maneuver back toward her, grabbing for the hose with one hand and gripping her waist with the other. My fingers slide under her cropped shirt, shoving the fabric up to reveal more of her stomach.

Every touch of skin feels charged. Dangerous with all this water.

She buckles against me, cackling, and manages to work the hose between us. The water soaks us both through—shirts, shorts, jeans, underwear, all the way to my socks—it's too much, I have to let go.

"Mercy," I manage to say.

But she presses her hand to my back, holding me in place. Her mouth hovers near mine, her breath heaves. This close, the ridge of cream lace around the cup of her bra is visible through her shirt.

She lets the hose go and it drops between us. Her hand raises, fingers touching lightly on the edge of my jaw.

Is it too much to hope that Kit Larson is going to kiss me again in this lifetime?

Her hand tenses to tug my chin closer.

The crash of footsteps on the Saloon's wood plank porch sends us shooting apart. Worry flashes in her eyes. She looks over to where the bachelor party emerges.

"Of course," I say, clipped, bitten off with disappointment but not surprise.

I yank the hose up from the ground and walk back to the trough to turn off the water.

It's definitely too much to hope for.

Chapter Twenty-One

Kit

The silence on the car ride back is the deafening kind.

Julia's eyes are lasers on the road away from Bachelor Town. Her teeth grit into a clench that looks like it could crack her jaw right at the joint. She smoothed her ponytail back into pristine order, patted herself dry with the towel the Saloon manager offered us both after the guys embarked on the bus, but it doesn't erase what almost happened.

I almost kissed her. I tugged and she leaned in. It was happening, and I know if we hadn't been interrupted, it would have. For real, not just in my head.

She smacks the knob on her radio and static shoots out of the speakers before she turns the station. After a few angry swipes past rock and country, over current pop beats, through commercial breaks, she lets it stop on an early-2010s pop hits station playing the beginning of Miley's "Wrecking Ball."

Her lips twitch. Miley purrs the iconic opening lyrics.

Julia knows exactly what she's doing, stopping on this song. I remember us in the hammock hanging on the trunks of two tall eucalyptus trees beside my parents' pool house. Our legs curled together as we shared a pair of headphones, *Bangerz* playing from top to bottom.

"You wre-e-eck me," she belted, and I knew already she meant it like a compliment. We were devastating each other's ideals of the perfect life, making each other the one and only, heart-eyes emoji forever, and in the bubble of that summer haze, it was easy to imagine nothing could ever tear us apart.

We weren't supposed to wreck each other. We didn't believe the cards when they said that Twin Flames tear each other apart as they make each other whole. Right then, how could that ever be so?

I blink back the stinging in my eyes.

I was the wrecking ball against the future I wanted, but was too afraid to have. *I* was crashing into the friendship that should have meant more to me than anything else, destroying it in a single blow.

The last bar of the song plays as we pull up to the entrance of Celestial Sands. She slams the car into park, not looking at me before she yanks the door open. I see the glint of moisture on her cheek, and I know it's not a remnant of our water hose battle. I know I can't just walk away this time. I can't let her close her eyes and swing. We have to talk about this. We have to give this another chance.

No matter how terrifying that is to me.

I chase her down through the lobby, out into the courtyard. She's fast even with her shorter legs, but when I catch her, right at the break in the path that leads away from the building to the Homebase bungalow, my fingers close around her wrist to hold her in place.

"Talk to me," I say, when she tries to tug free of my grip. She spins around to face me, pulling me forward when I don't let her go. I'm afraid she'll bolt if I do.

"There's nothing to talk about," she says, venomous.

"There's definitely stuff to talk about," I retort. "We almost kissed back there."

"*You* almost kissed *me*." She pauses. "Again."

I chew on my lip, stumped for a second with how I should rebuff her insinuation that this almost-kiss was the same bait and switch as the last time. I don't want that to be the case.

I didn't want that then, either.

"You're straight," she says, when my floundering for words doesn't end. "Last I checked, that hasn't changed."

"There's a difference between being *straight* and being *out*." I drop her wrist as my temper flares. "I'm not straight—clearly." I feel my cheeks warm.

"No shit," she says, her voice still hard, but her gaze has softened. "But I'm not interested in being with a woman who can't even hold my hand in public." Her jaw does that scary hard clench thing again. "Been there, done that, never want to do it again."

She whirls around, but we can't run away this time. *Neither of us.* I follow, my brain spinning out with all the things I want to say. All these wild feelings, all these words I never got to speak, everything she's assuming about me that isn't true, plus all the things she's getting right.

She's twisting the key to Homebase in the lock when I say, "I pulled the cards again, on the way up here."

She stops. "What do you mean?"

"The Two of Cups and the Wheel of Fortune. Tell me you remember those cards." She swallows, not making eye contact as I speak. I push forward. "Madame Moira, that weird neighborhood psychic from the Haunt O' Ween in Old Pas—the dare—"

"Of course I remember," she whispers. "She said we were Twin Flames." The words, her voice, my heart, skips. "Like, what a weird thing to say to two preteen girls."

The air between us is heavy, thick with heat that can't be attributed to the desert.

"She said we'd always find our way back to each other, and we did," I say.

Her eyes trip up to mine, shiny and bright with unshed tears. "Kit, you broke my heart."

"I know." Her eyes search my face, hopeful and hurt. "I'm so sorry, Julia. I should have tried to explain what I was feeling. I should have sat down with you, face-to-face. I should've done literally anything more than I did."

"Yeah, no shit," she replies. "Do you know how long it took me to try again with a girl?"

"Not as long as me," I say. She leans against the doorframe, understanding etching its way through her features.

"I didn't want to have to find my way back to you. I wanted you to stay with me." Tears prick from the corners of her eyes, trailing down her cheek. I want to kiss them away. To taste the salt on her skin, the bitterness, and turn it sweet.

"I wanted that, too."

"But you bailed. You didn't want your parents to know. You didn't want to talk about what happened, you acted weird and dismissive, so how was I supposed to feel?" Her voice cracks with emotion.

"I was fucking terrified, okay? I didn't think there was a way to be rom-com dream girl if I ended up with *another girl*. All I knew of girls falling in love with girls was like the OG *L Word* and some male-gazey porn." She can't hold in a laugh, but does try to cover it up with a grunt. "I didn't know what I was supposed to be if I wasn't some guy's whole world, like my mom was my dad's. The perfect manic pixie dream girl with the glorious happy ending."

"You could have told me—we could have talked about it. At the very fucking least I could have helped you find better comp titles." She almost smiles, but she still looks sad. "I was your best friend."

It feels like a punch to my gut to hear her say that, to know how right she is. I was the idiot, the *tool* in the rom-com, who ran away from their true love in the third act.

I just hope it's not too late for me to win her back.

"I was afraid it wouldn't matter," I say, my own voice wobbly, tears threatening. "If you had to wait, for who knows how long, I was afraid I'd lose you anyway and it would hurt a lot more the longer it took, the further in love we fell." The word *love* causes a little explosion of emotion in her features.

"So you ghosted me instead?" Her nostrils flare.

"I wanted you, us, but I also wanted the Ideal Rom-Com Life Path I'd always imagined. I didn't think I could have both. So I picked the one I had a framework for." My voice shakes. Saying it out loud is a weight off my heart, but somehow it hurts more, not less.

"You know that's outdated as hell, right?" She almost smirks.

I exhale a laugh but it's hollow. "Is it? Look around you, heteronormative ideals are alive and thriving."

"Even in this economy." The tremor of a smile. My walls, and hers, crumbling. I feel tears on my cheeks, hot and fresh, and I don't even bother wiping them away. "You really picked poorly." She grins through watery eyes.

"I'd like to try again," I say, locking eyes with her. I take a tentative step closer and she doesn't retreat. "Julia."

"Kit." She nearly growls my name. I want her to scream it.

"Do I need to say it?"

I triple-dog dare you to kiss me on the mouth.

I'm close enough now that I can taste her breath on the air. I can smell the sunlight on her skin. I can touch her waist with the tips of my fingers. I can, and I want to, and as terrifying as it still is to feel those feelings and not push them away, I also know that feelings won't kill me.

But not touching her might.

She lets out a sharp exhale when I do. The tip of her tongue slips out to wet her lips. I look deep into her eyes as I run my hand over her curves, cupping the nape of her neck.

I tip her chin up with my other hand.

"Do *I*?" she breathes.

I fit my lips over hers, soft, so slow at first. Like the first few licks of an ice cream cone.

I don't want to rush—afraid of freezing up. I want to make it count.

Every last taste.

I brace for how this feeling overloads my senses.

Firm, plump, and small—her mouth fits like a puzzle piece with mine. She reaches up, gripping the belt loops on my jean shorts and tugging me into her. Our hips bump before her hand trails around my back and her fingers graze skin where my crop top meets my shorts. All my measured moves, the careful contemplation of her lips and mine, now feel way too slow.

Not enough. Never enough.

I press my tongue to her lips, edging them open. The flesh tangles, breath slides back and forth, and all those years of confusion melt away with the heat of our kiss. I press her back against the doorframe, smoothing my hands over the mounds of her shoulders, the dip in her waist, to mold them around the curve of her ass.

She twists us inside, and her hands rove up my back, fingering the wild waves of my hair, before she breaks the kiss, peppering more down the line of my neck. It feels so good—different from before. *Better.* I don't care who might walk by the window and see us. I don't have to know what this means, where it's going. I lose myself in the moment and I've never felt more certain that this is what I want.

Her.

Tangled in her body, wrapped up in her arms.

My fingers are feverish to touch her skin, wanting to get under her fitted shirt, but I don't want to unbutton it without her permission.

And I'm still too nervous to ask.

I settle for roaming over her waist, around to her back, gripping, feeling, desperately yearning. She presses my thighs open with hers so I can straddle her, and I let out an exhale of relief. Warmth aches between my legs, ready to ignite, but I want to slow down, to savor.

I break the kiss and make eye contact. Hers are darkly dilated with desire—it's thrilling to see that reflected and know it's because of me.

She wants me just like I want her.

"You're still a really good kisser," I say, breathless.

"Takes one to know one." She presses her smile to mine, light and playful.

I'm ready to go in for another round when her ass begins buzzing. She reaches back to yank her phone out of her pocket.

"It's Zoe," she says. "Shit. I have to take this." We separate, and it's the first time it dawns on me that we were making out in her bungalow, of which the main living area doubles as the Homebase for wedding operations. Anyone on her staff with a key could have walked in on us.

The thought is more of a thrill than I expect.

"Hey, Zoe—just made it back to the venue—" She's cut off by whatever Zoe is saying. From this proximity it sounds *alarmed*. Julia's listening face is pinched and puckered, her brows cinched into squiggles. "Oh Jesus, I'm coming."

She hangs up, her eyes trailing apologetically to me.

"Wedding emergency?" I ask.

"Potential vegan catastrophe. We're supposed to have vegan empanadas for the rehearsal dinner cocktail hour"—she smiles—"during which I'm told you will be offering readings."

"*Oui, oui*," I quip.

"And all of them are beef and potato."

"Sounds perfect."

"Sounds like my head on a platter."

"I don't see how that would remedy the lack of a vegan dish."

Her laugh is a burst of joy that brightens her features. She grabs me by the waistband and tugs me into her. Her eyes fill with worry. "You're not gonna bolt, are you?"

I let my forehead rest against hers.

"You can't get rid of me that easily," I say, smirking. "Not this time."

She kisses me once more before we break apart. "I'll come find you when this is sorted."

"Can't wait," I reply.

And I really, really can't.

Chapter Twenty-Two

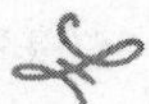

Julia

Focus is a fight when all I want is to lose myself in Kit.

I round the corner toward the restaurant and almost barrel bodily into Coco. She's talking on the phone, dressed in her brunch wear, and chewing on the earpiece of her sunglasses idly.

She smiles, holds up her finger in the universal *wait* gesture.

"We're not going to rush the process," she says into the phone. The person on the other end of the line must not agree, because I hear a garbled, but adamant-sounding, response. Coco shushes it. "It's the weekend, babe, just let it sit for two days. She's going to sign on, I can feel it." She hangs up.

"Aren't you all still supposed to be brunching?" I ask as soon as the call has ended.

"I had a meeting with a very important celeb collab for Coco's Intimates, couldn't reschedule." She waves the phone. "And then a call with one of my employees right after because it didn't go as planned."

"Oh, gotcha," I say. "You motioned for me to hold on, so I assumed you needed help with something."

She nods, twirling her phone. "You have lip gloss smudged on your neck and collar." She points her long red nail to the upturned, and now sullied, collar of my shirt. Fuck, I left my emergency bag at Homebase. I never do that.

I can't believe I did that.

She flicks her eyes behind me. "And there goes the tarot reader coming out of Homebase." She waggles her brow. "Mission Sexy Times, *success*."

My blush is immediate. "Oh my God, please stop." I wet the tips of my fingers, trying to wipe away Kit's lip gloss. To no avail. "Not Sexy Times."

"Evidence proves otherwise." She smirks.

I give up my futile wiping. The stain is staying.

I launch out. She follows.

"I don't have time for this," I say, speed-walking. "I'm in crisis maintenance mode."

"Always," she says, keeping my pace easily.

"You say that like it's a bad thing." Her hand drops to my shoulder, holding firm. I root in place, huffing.

"Make room for play."

It's not what I expect her to say, so it catches me off guard. "I'm on the job, on the clock, on someone else's dime. I can't make room for play if circumstances don't allow it."

"Circumstances will never allow it," she says, smiling. "Can I give you a piece of advice?"

I brace for something totally batshit, as is her typical MO.

"When I started Coco's Intimates, I was terrified to delegate any responsibilities to my team. I wanted to be cc'd on every email, called in to look at every swatch, meet every shipment, oversee wholesale orders, manually check online orders." She makes a *what the fuck* face, totally embarrassed by past Coco's failings. "It was a mess—I was a mess. I had a small team, all women, everything made in LA, and I could see it unraveling under all the pressure I was putting on it—on them. I wanted it to grow, but I didn't want to let go."

There's that phrase again. *Let go.* Like it's the first step in a wellness program.

I roll my eyes and she releases one hand to smack me on the ass. I sidestep the move but she doesn't give up, getting me on her second try. "I am offering pearls, and you're acting like a swine."

"Sorry," I snort. "It's just, letting go—come on, that's just slowly losing." Her face drops into a frown.

"You can't control everything." She winks. "Make room for play. It's the Coco's Intimates office motto for a reason."

She turns down the path that leads back toward the bachelorette party bungalows.

And I'm left wondering if for once I should listen when someone tells me to *let go.*

~

I arrive at the kitchen to find that the chef has locked himself in the dry pantry, refusing to come out.

I rap my knuckles on the door. "Javier." *Rap.* "This is Julia Kelley. We've been corresponding through emails." He's a new vendor for Love, Always, but he came highly recommended.

Zoe hands me one of the *offensive to vegans* empanadas.

"What's this?"

"Delicious," she says, biting into another one. "Maybe a few compliments will get him out of the pantry and back to work."

"Does he even have time to start over from scratch?" I ask, sniffing the crusty dough parcel. It smells spicy, with just the right amount of cumin. Zoe shrugs.

"T-minus six hours," she says. "Tight, but plausible."

I bite into the empanada and my taste buds are immediately flooded with flavor. The beef is tender, mixed with tiny russet potatoes and cilantro, seasoned with spicy chilis. I roll my eyes in ecstasy. "Yum."

"I know," Zoe replies, shoving the rest of the empanada in her mouth.

I turn back to the pantry door. "Javier, we understand the freak-out. But we can't let that stop us from problem-solving." I hear him whimper through the door. "I mean, have you met the groom and his merry men? They could clear a hundred of these babies easy and still have room for more." I pause. "They won't go to waste."

"But they only ordered three batches of the potato and beef, and explicitly wanted a vegan option. I had one all prepared," he cries.

"Correct."

"And when I left the bakery this morning, I was certain I had grabbed the cart of black bean and corn. I don't know how I did this!"

I turn to Zoe. "Why can't he just go back to LA and get the vegan dish?"

"They've been sold as beef and potato to unsuspecting buyers at The Grove kiosk."

I stifle a laugh. *Oh dear.* I turn back to the door. "Javier, the kitchen here at Celestial Sands is equipped with most of the items you need to make something just as spectacular, if a little more rustic."

"Corn?"

"Uh, I believe—"

"Cilantro, black beans, serrano peppers?" he lists.

"I can't be certain of the exact ingredients," I say. Zoe steps away again, walking back through the archway that leads into the kitchen. "But you should come out and try to turn this situation around." I don't want to be a dick, but this is his mistake—he needs to find a fix.

Zoe is back. "The kitchen staff I spoke with thinks they have everything he needs to redo the empanadas."

"Javier," I say, elevating my voice through the door. My tone is firm. "There's still time to fix this if you get cracking."

There are a few beats of quiet in which, with an extraclose lean, I can ascertain that Javier is moving around inside, likely searching for beans. Then there's the click of the lock and the twist of the door handle to reveal the disheveled-haired, red-rimmed-eyed Javier. He's a young entrepreneur whose family owns a well-known restaurant in West Hollywood. He's trying to make a name for himself, so a screwup on a big wedding account with an influencer like Millie would understandably freak him out.

"We have less than six hours until the cocktail hour," I say, as we all walk back over to the main kitchen area. The chef has given him a small space near the back door to work.

"Chef Dorian has agreed to allot room in the oven for up to three pans," Zoe says, setting two bags of black beans on the counter space. "And they have a pressure cooker for these."

I make a mental note to send Chef Dorian a flower arrangement. Her reputation for being a team player wasn't a fallacy, but this is really above and beyond.

Javier begins setting out his needed ingredients from the kitchen's supplies, and I let out a deep exhale of relief. It took every ounce of my training—all my impeccably honed willpower and self-control—to focus on the crisis when I could still taste Kit's tongue. I want to get back to her. Not solely to hook up, but definitely hoping that's still in the cards. I have to internally snarl at my own use of a term with such a literal meaning in our case.

I'd be lying if I said I wasn't at least moderately nervous she's going to pull the same disappearing act as she did that summer after high school if I ask her what this whole heavy petting, steamy kissing thing means for us when we get back to LA. Hell, I'm half expecting her to play down any connection here at Celestial Sands.

The second one might be for the best, actually, considering my brooding ex-girlfriend is on-site and trying to get me alone so she can mindfuck me into taking her back.

I motion for Zoe to follow me out of the kitchen. We're standing in the main dining room of the restaurant, where some of the extended family are enjoying lunch. Fortunately, the mothers are both still at the spa. I had Zoe schedule them lunch inside the facility as a precaution. Those two roaming the grounds unattended presents too many unknown variables, the mental flexibility for which I do not possess right now.

"Update on the fathers?" I ask Zoe, as we walk through the dining room to the courtyard. The sun shoots through the bright, multicolored lanterns hanging from the pergola that shades the area, casting Zoe in a rainbow of color.

"Still golfing. We sent a lunch cart out to the ninth hole, so my guess is they won't return until their barbershop cleanup." The groom's party, including both fathers and the two Connecticut uncles who flew in for the rehearsal to play ushers, are all getting a classically masculine (barf) treatment at the barber before tonight's events. Their version of a spa day.

"Bless the golf course gods for keeping them occupied," I say, steepling my fingers in mock prayer.

"They are the laziest of the gods, so I am told. Glad they came through," she deadpans. I let out an exhausted but genuine laugh. My mind is already moving away from wedding checkups and trailing back through the paths of Celestial Sands to Kit's Airstream trailer. "I'm totally rank after no sleep and bachelor wrangling. I have to go freshen up."

"Of course, boss," she says.

"I'm not your boss, Zoe. You work for Love, Always, not me."

Something like disappointment slinks through her giant, dark eyes. It's gone in a heartbeat, but I notice it, and I feel like I am inadvertently the one responsible for it.

I turn to leave the courtyard, planning to meander toward Homebase before DMing Kit to find out where she's landed. Just thinking the words brings the fresh memory back up in my head, sending shoots of heat through my body—my cheeks, my chest, between my legs.

As I pass in front of Homebase, I see the bridal party returning to Millie's bungalow after their morning of brunching. Right on schedule, as I would expect from the impeccable Millie Morgan. Millie waves me over as she unlocks her door, letting the other women funnel in around her. Piper, unsurprisingly, lingers outside to listen in.

"I know I have you to thank for getting the boys there in one piece," she says, and then restates, her nose scrunching, playful, "Mostly one piece."

"I have some ideas about how to remedy the Cash Kim forehead situation."

"He suggested I let him wear his trucker hat." She raises her brows in a *hell no* face.

"Oh God no." I laugh. "I was thinking strategic hairstyling plus a little concealer."

"Much better," Millie says. Her eyes drift to the hovering Piper. "Come on, sis, we have slippers and a plush robe waiting at the spa."

Piper feigns a smile. "Just need to steal Julia away for a quick sec." She winks, indicating the *sec* she needs is for some sort of supersecret wedding special and not another attempt to reel me back into her clutches.

"Okay, but make it snappy," Millie says, her tone playful. She moves inside the bungalow, letting the door close behind her.

I cut Piper a hard look and she flashes me a smirk, leaning close.

"I get bimonthly spa treatments at the Waldorf. I could skip out on these if you're free."

"I'm the planner of a destination wedding, my freedom is never guaranteed," I say, turning. She steps deftly into my path, all long legs, taut arms, soft flowing hair.

"One drink," she says. Leans, running the curved edges of her nails down my arm to my hand. "I'll even let you leave the walkie-talkie on."

"Not thirsty," I say, turning my face so it's tauntingly close to hers. "Enjoy the spa."

I step around her, and this time, she doesn't get in my way.

"I came out to my family over the Fourth of July." Her words hit their mark. I'm stunned into stopping, turning, unable to hide the surprise on my face. "It went wretchedly, as I knew it would."

"I'm sorry they didn't support you." I'm torn between giving her a queer woman hug of solidarity and bolting before she can interpret my empathy as something more. "At the Vineyard?" No hug, just polite questions allowing her to share her experience.

"On the deck before fireworks," she says. "Dad was mixing juleps. Mom was pretending to read her Nora Roberts. The nephews ran around the pool shooting water guns, Gavin and Helena were in floats in the deep end, and I just blurted it out." She's breathless, her cheeks flushed.

"I bet William flipped," I say. Her dad is a staunch conservative WASP type. Old money, and even older ideals. "Well, as much as a man who tucks his shirt into his swim trunks can *flip*."

"He didn't speak. Not through dinner or fireworks, not until Pamela brought out the cake and started to cut. And then he burst out with 'Lesbians aren't Presbyterian!'" She laughs, but the crack tells me she still doesn't think it was funny.

"Anyone can be Presbyterian," I say.

"I told him I only go to church on Easter and Christmas, so maybe my religion shouldn't decide my sexuality," Piper says. I let a laugh slip out and she smiles, pleased.

"Have things gotten any easier since?"

She half shrugs. "A lunch with Mom, which unraveled into her trying to set me up with *Diane at the club's* lawyer *son*."

"So, they're in denial."

"But I'm not anymore and that's what matters," she says, her voice going soft. "Right?"

Oh no, she's looking at me with hazel eyes of yearning, totally misreading my camaraderie as romantic interest. I have to shut this down.

"I'm happy for you, Piper, but you being out doesn't change anything where we're concerned." I motion to the space between us. I know I sound harsh, but my voice just takes on this stern tone in her presence. I had to adopt it to ever land an argument. Now that she's looking at me like that—all wispy and misty with hope—I just want to crush the dream. Not crushing it, not closing the door completely, scares me more than I like to admit.

Once, Piper had all the power and I had none. You don't forget that feeling easily.

"Julia, would it kill you to give me another chance?" She huffs, her nostrils flaring with annoyance. She's not getting what she wants, which is basically torture to a princess like Piper.

I give an almost imperceptible shake of my head. There's only one person I'm willing to give a second chance to, and it's not her.

"I'm interested in someone else right now," I say, turning to leave, but then quickly adding, "Really happy for you, though. Enjoy the spa."

When I'm far enough away from Piper, I tug my phone from my pocket, making quick work of going into Kit's DMs.

> Fire extinguished. Ready to start another one?

I hit send and immediately blush all over. It's too forward. I'm assuming too much about what Kit will want right now, when we haven't even talked about what this means in the bigger scope of our lives. I should follow up with something neutral. Ask if she wants to meet me at the restaurant. We can hang in public where we don't have to make out. My mind glitches back over the frenzied kissing session at Homebase. Her wandering hands and hungry lips. Hungry *for me*. I feel warm in one very specific place now, and it's making me lightheaded.

My phone *zzztt*s with a DM.

> I'll bring the matches if you bring the kindling.

I smirk with pleasure. Flirting, even over text, feels natural with Kit.

> . . . to my airstream trailer. In case that wasn't clear.

I launch out on the path, all reservations about how fast or slow this is moving forgotten.

Chapter Twenty-Three

Kit

After one more quick check in the mirror to make sure I look dewy, sun-kissed, and not deranged from all the sand and water that got stuck in my hair out at Bachelor Town, I remove the bottle of rosé from the fridge, uncorking it and placing it on the table with two wineglasses. I am one hundred percent certain I want to see where this kissing thing might lead, but I am also nervous as hell. *Rosé all day*, not so much, but a little definitely can't hurt. As someone with all the feelings, sometimes all zooming to the surface at the same time, it can't hurt to have a little depressant in my veins when I'm in a high-stimulation situation.

I pour a glass and take a gulp. I need to stop spiraling over the word *stimulation* and the way it immediately brings Julia's hands into sharp focus in my imagination. Since high school, there have been so many times I've wanted to just *kiss the girl*, but I've always chickened out because kissing leads to questions of meaning, it opens up doors to closed closets, and then it leads to *more*.

There's nothing linear about going from best friends to kissing. I don't know exactly when it became clear to me that I wanted to, and I never got to ask Julia how long she'd been wishing things would change.

They just did, slowly, and then all at once.

I knew, and so did she. And all those sensations and feelings and new, ferocious wants exploded all over my body, firing all through my brain. Then it wasn't just kissing, and what that meant wasn't a question we could leave unanswered. And all those feelings merged into a single, overwhelming one.

Fear.

I don't know how to do this coming out thing. I don't know what it will feel like when other people are let in on that secret. I don't know how to say it out loud.

I don't know who I will become on the other side of it.

I just know that I'm ready to *know.*

My phone starts to buzz in the back pocket of my jean shorts, and I yank it out, but my smile fades fast when I see who's calling.

Mom. Big white FaceTime letters.

I've been trying to ignore her texts, since, so far, all of them have been about packing up my childhood bedroom, or thinly veiled attempts to get me to talk to her about her new romance. I know it isn't fair to give her the cold shoulder while I talk Dad down from his merlot ledge, but I don't feel ready to face her yet.

She's bi, and she's further along in her coming out than I am.

But she's also my mom, who always preached the Ideal Rom-Com Life Path. She's also my mom, who used to be desperately in love with my dad. And even though I know she'd understand my fears about coming out, she still cheated on Dad.

And I'm not ready to let her off the hook for that just yet.

I feel around inside my body. My heart and emotions, my

instincts and gut feelings. The compass that spins, spins, spins, and the true north I'm not sure I've ever actually found.

A thought sharpens into focus.

I don't want to waste my chance.

No matter how happy Mom was at times. No matter how much she loved Dad. She was still playing a role, one I understand playing, one I can even understand her keeping from me when I was a kid, but I haven't been a kid for a long time. I can't help but wonder, if Mom had let me in on her journey, would it have helped me with mine? Could her honesty have been a push to propel me here sooner, with so much less yearning and time wasted hiding?

I want to blame her, blame Dad, for how long I've stubbornly barreled forward on the Ideal Rom-Com Life Path. Always looking for the end with boyfriends, keeping my career in motion but not really knowing where I hope that motion leads; short-term rentals, suitcases of belongings, daydreams of a time when I'll feel secure in myself, when I'll be fulfilled, when I'll actually be the *ideal*.

Mom coming out to me lifted the curtain, showed me the Wizard. My compass has been spinning out because I was chasing a phantom destination. The ideal of my perfect Nancy Meyers parents and the ingenue I was playing weren't real.

In the Larson family we all have our roles, and we're all really good at them.

Until we aren't.

My heart rate blasts off, a rocket on a crash course. I search the room for my cards, finding them on the nightstand. I grab up the deck in my left hand, gulping the last of the little bit of wine I poured myself, setting the glass down on the table.

I exhale a sharp breath, close my eyes, and shuffle.

Swish swish swish. The cards' weight grounds me and I open my eyes again, watching the shuffle. I feel rooted, secure in my body, every feeling coursing through me but not shaking me up. After another few swishes I don't feel so lightheaded. I don't feel so much like I want to pummel my parents with one of their vinyl records. I don't feel so much like screaming at myself in the mirror. I don't feel like I have to run away, even though it would definitely make all of these revelations stop revealing themselves.

I cut the deck just as there's a knock on the door.

Julia.

The whirring inside my heart stops.

Cards still in hand, I walk over to open the door. She's standing on the step. She's taken her hair out of her ponytail. The hair tie is around her wrist like a bracelet.

I'm overcome with how beautiful she is.

Her snatched waist, the sleek line of her collarbone, her curvy hips and plump apple bottom fitted in her jeans. The way the corners of her mouth tick up even when she isn't smiling. The three little freckles on her neck in the shape of a triangle.

I'm overcome with how very, very certain I am that I want her.

She moves up to the next step, but not inside. I could lose myself in her eyes, like they're the real sea and I am a sailor following a siren's call.

"Hey," she says, smirking.

"Hey," I reply, moving out of the doorway to let her inside. She steps up, kicking off her sneakers before walking farther into the trailer.

"This is such a vibe." It's clear she's impersonating me, or Millie, or some other LA influencer hot girl.

"It totally is," I say, exaggerating my voice and sticking my tongue out at her. She laughs and I am sure it's my favorite sound in the world.

I spin back to the table to pour her a glass of wine, setting the cards down so I can have both hands free. She unclips her walkie-talkie from the waistband of her jeans and sets it on the table before lifting my empty glass in the air, watching the remnant of liquid swirl.

"You caught me," I say, handing over her drink. Her fingertips graze mine when she gives back my glass for me to refill. Even this tiny touch is electric. "I was freaking out," I continue. "I started early." I tip some more pink liquid into the glass.

"Did it help?" She sips.

"You don't see a Kit-shaped hole in the side of this trailer, do you?" I take a drink that is decidedly larger than a sip.

"So what you're saying is, if you'd had some wine back then you might not have run off?"

I nibble my lip, catching her eyes with mine.

"I think I still would have," I say, walking over to the bed and dropping down to sit on the edge. She takes a drink, but otherwise looks like she's afraid to move. "What do we do now?"

"It's like you said: A lot has changed in ten years. So we get to know each other again," she says. She gives the spot next to me a pointed look.

"All yours," I reply, taking another sip of wine to quell the quiver of nerves fluttering around in my stomach.

"It's been a while," she says, sitting beside me. She smells like citrus soap and the sunny outdoors. Her denim-covered knee brushes against my bare one. My thoughts keep time with my heartbeat. *This is it, this is it.* "I'm Julia. Wedding planner, control freak."

"Is that what all the buttons are about?" I ask, motioning to her minty-green blouse and letting my eyes linger for a second on the mound of her breasts in the fitted fabric.

"You should see me on weekends," she says, grinning. "I roll up the sleeves."

I giggle at the image. She extends her hand for me to shake, clearly taking this whole introducing herself thing quite seriously. I fit my hand in hers and a new feeling, like a lump of hot coal in my stomach, threatens to make me squirm.

Loving her will be the most dangerously wonderful adventure of my life so far.

"Kit." I whisper my own name. She doesn't let go of my hand right away. "Tarot mystic. High-end party entertainment." I pause to force myself to breathe. "Panic attacks."

"Medicated?"

"Therapy and hypnotherapy."

She takes a sip, releasing my hand. Hers drops down to rest on her thigh, the edges of her fingers tantalizingly close to my bare knee. "Still a rom-com fan?"

"Die-hard," I reply.

"That's a Christmas movie."

I roll my eyes. "What about you?"

"I haven't seen one in a while." She doesn't say it, but I can deduce that it's because of me. Of what happened with me. Julia and I watched so many rom-coms together in the course of our friendship. She went right along with my movie-obsessed family, fit right in on Friday Movie Nights. She went to opening days and she could recite dialog back to me almost as well as Dad.

"I'll have to catch you up," I say. "Some people would say we are in a new golden era of rom-coms. There's even some queer ones." *I've seen them all.* "We should start with one of those."

She lifts her brows, shifts her glass toward mine and clinks. "It's a date."

It occurs to me suddenly that it really could be. "And dinner."

"At a restaurant with fabric napkins." She smiles, and it doesn't look sad. The memory may never totally stop stinging, but we can—and will—make new ones.

Together.

I'm hit with the urge to hold her close. I don't fight it. I skate my hand over her jawline, to the nape of her neck. There's no resistance as I tug her in for a kiss. My eyes close as she deepens the kiss, her lashes fluttering against my cheek as her tongue slips into my mouth.

It's almost wild how right it feels to get all tangled up in her.

When I pull back after a few intense seconds, I see that she's searching my face with her eyes.

"Piper's my ex," she blurts. "Full transparency."

"I know," I reply. I brush my thumb over her jaw before letting my hand drop back to my lap.

"Did she tell you?" She's gearing up to get pissed. "That would be so like her—"

"The cards—her reading last night indicated a breakup and *feelings* about it. Plus just every interaction I've observed between you two. It was easy to connect the dots." I brush her fingers with mine, gentle, what I hope is also reassuring.

"She knows about us." Julia sighs.

"Fuck." I exhale, blinking. "How?"

Julia scrubs her hands over her face anxiously. "I told her about you when we were dating and she'd pieced together your identity when she met you here." She looks at me, clearly nervous. "I'm sorry, Kit."

"It actually tracks that she'd figure it out. She's certainly cunning." I keep my voice light, trying to assuage her concern. I cup her hand in mine, rubbing my thumb along the knuckles. "I'm not intimidated by her. I can handle her death glares and shit talk." But there's more weighing on her than just this bombshell, I can see it tugging her shoulders down. "Her reading yesterday—she wants you back, doesn't she?"

"She does—not that it'll ever happen." Her eyes drop to my hand over hers. "Being with her changed me. It was subtle at first, just critiques, little tweaks of my every move and thought. Then way less subtle, glaring, suffocating. But I probably would have endured it forever if she'd been willing to be come out, especially to her family." She shakes her head, letting her eyes float back up to focus on mine. "I don't know what's happening here, but I don't want to be a secret just to have you."

Here it is. *Don't back away. Don't retreat.*

"I don't know what this is either. I'm not out," I say. She starts to pull her hand away. I clutch it, can't let it go. "I want to be." I fit my fingers through hers. "I might need some help from my friend."

She closes her hand, twining our fingers in unbreakable knots. Something like trust—that soft, safe, sure warmth in the pit of your stomach when you know, no question, you're right where you need to be—passes between us.

"About that," she continues. "Coco saw you leave Homebase earlier. She also noticed this." She reaches up to point at her collar. It takes me a second to figure out what the smudge is.

"Oh my God," I say, a laugh caught in my throat. "My lip gloss is that color."

"She also *connected some dots.*" Julia doesn't look as amused as I feel. "I didn't confirm, but she's . . ."

"A force to be reckoned with," I fill in for her.

"Exactly." She holds my gaze, hope mixing with fear in her eyes. I brush my finger over her knuckles again to reassure her that I'm okay. This is *okay*. Coco knowing something happened between us is *okay*.

Julia looks away after another beat, a blush forming on the apples of her cheeks. Her eyes land on the table.

"Those cards are different." She's looking at my tarot deck. "From the ones I saw yesterday." I take another sip of wine, untangling my fingers to retrieve the deck.

"I have this superstition about my decks," I say, setting my glass down before coming back to sit beside her with the cards. "The ones I use for clients, or to film YouTube videos, are only used for that purpose. And then I have my personal collection." I lift the deck in my hands, letting her get a good look. "This one, and an oracle deck that I don't have with me right now. I don't let clients pull from those."

Her eyes drop to the top of the deck.

"Not even me?" she asks. When she looks back at me, I hear that siren call to lose myself in her ocean eyes and I can't, don't want to, *won't* resist.

"Break the deck with your left hand."

This is how it all started.

With one card, then another, then a promise that we would always find each other.

She breaks the deck into two piles, handing the cards back to me.

"Which pile?" I ask. We're so close that I can feel her breath on my cheek; it smells of the wine, fruity and herbal and bright.

"Don't you have a thing you do?" She hovers her hand over the piles, mimicking what she must have noticed me do when I appeased Healer Arynne's meltdown.

"I can do that, or we can choose together." I take my lower lip between my teeth for a nibble.

She drops her eyes back to the two stacks in my hands.

"Okay. Together."

"On the count of three?" I ask. She nods. "One, two, three."

"Left hand," she says.

"My left," I say.

We grin up at each other.

I reintegrate the stack, putting the one in my right hand below the left. I wiggle my body, pushing my shoulders back to sit up straighter. I notice her glance at my neckline clinging to the edge of my bra.

"You're totally checking out my boobs while I'm trying to be a serious tarot reader," I scold, but it's flirtatious, playful.

"Sorry not sorry," she says, looking back at the card.

I brush my fingers around the edge before flipping it toward her.

My gasp hangs in my throat.

Chapter Twenty-Four

Julia

As my fingers brush the edge of the card, energy shoots into my heart, my pulse quickening.

The Lovers.

Two people stand naked facing each other. Behind them is a tree with intricate woven vines covered in crimson, orange, and fuchsia blossoms. The dark background of the card contrasts with the metallic strip that creates a border around the edge.

I don't know what to say. This card is intense. Bright and full of love, but it also makes me feel like the wind has been knocked out of me. It makes me feel like fighting. It makes me want to reach out and hold on for dear life.

"The Lovers card is the more intense version of the Two of Cups," she finally says, and she actually sounds like she's struggling to breathe.

"From our reading with Madame Moira."

She nods, holding eye contact. "Showing up in a reading between us is significant just because of all the *stuff*." She pauses, letting the full weight of that normally unimportant word settle between us. "But our history with the cards makes this feel like more of a sign."

I gave up on believing in signs before I ever really tried.

This weekend with Kit Larson has me questioning that steadfast lack of faith.

"What does it mean?" My throat is tight; my voice is breathy.

"Conscious connection, meaningful relationships. Some tarot readers describe it as the soulmate card—when it represents a relationship, it's usually not casual." She looks it over thoughtfully, as if this is the first time she's ever really seen the card, like she needs to take in all the details again just in case she's missed something. "There's a lot to say here about vulnerability and raw honesty, opening your heart to someone else to let them see your truest self."

"Family." The word comes in a burst, surprising me. She searches my face. "I always thought that was the closest you could get to real security. Finding someone who you trust like family."

I've looked for that in every romantic relationship I've ever embarked on.

I've never found it.

Her eyes drop back to the card. "At its heart, the card is about choice, so actually, you're right on." She smiles, soft. "The choice of who you love. What you want. How you connect and how much you trust."

Trust. The scariest word in the English language.

"It's also a sexy card," she says, her voice sly.

Heat pulses between my legs, an ache hot and fast.

"Like, go forth and fuck?" I ask; the word *fuck* is loaded. Ready to bang.

"I think the exact wording from one of my guidebooks is

sexual gratification beyond basic lust and longing; deeper, soul touching, tantric." Each word drips with desire.

Mine and hers—I feel the need open up between us.

"Lust and longing," I say, watching her face. She goes still. "Is a good place to start." I reach up to tuck a strand of hair behind her ear, running my hand over her cheek, to her chin. She melts into my touch; I can smell the faint hint of cherry in her lip gloss. "I'd like to kiss you now."

"Go ahead," she breathes.

I crush my lips against hers. Every reservation and all my lingering questions evaporate.

I pull her in so that our breasts press together as my tongue slips inside. Her mouth is the most delicious dessert, sweet and soft and warm, lusciously tinged with fruity rosé. I want to touch her everywhere, I want to make her scream my name, and when her hands clutch my hips, and the cards fall to the ground between us, I know she wants the same thing.

I tilt her head back so I can pepper kisses over her neck, breathing out the question, "Is this okay?" I need her to say yes. I need to know she wants this—wants me.

"Fuck yes," she gasps. One hand running up my waist to cup my breast over the shirt. "Can I please"—she tightens the grip her other hand has on my ass—"unbutton your shirt?"

I chuckle against her neck, flicking my tongue on the tender skin behind her earlobe.

"Go right ahead," I affirm.

She makes fast work of the buttons. "So tiny, so many," she grunts as she unhooks them one by one. I feel them spring open, revealing my uninteresting, basic black bra. It's got a little padding because Mother Nature did not endow me with much up top, helped even more by the racerback design.

She pushes back to get a look.

Her lips are swollen from kissing, her eyes delirious.

All pupils, all want.

She scoots closer, lifting her leg to fit around me and tug me in. Her eyes eat up the sight, and with her finger she traces the line of my collarbone, touching my heart pendant, down to the spot where the clasp holds the bra in place. Her eyes trek back up to mine, a question reflected in her dark pupils. I nod, fighting the urge to touch myself as heat pools between my legs. The ache to release that growing pressure is overwhelming, but in the best way.

She flicks the edge of the clasp with her fingernail and the bra pops open. It slides away from the little mounds of my breasts, revealing my nipples. She touches them with her eyes first. Her mouth drops open, hungry and eager. After a few seconds, she gently, almost cautiously, cups my breast in her palm, grazing the nipple with her thumb. It tightens beneath her touch, and she leans forward to kiss me.

Her thumb works over the ridge as my hands wind up beneath her shirt until they meet the resistance of her underwire. I trek beneath, lifting the bra up and touching her nipples. They're already alert, but she lets out a moan into my mouth, a *yes, more please,* and I am so ready to comply. Anxious to give her exactly what she wants.

My fingers slow their pace as they brush across the mound of her nipple, feeling the soft curve of her breast, heavy in the palm of my hand. She's full busted, something I've always been attracted to, and something she used to hate about herself because it got her all kinds of gross attention from guys—men, teachers, literally anyone with a Y chromosome.

I gently fondle her before snaking my hand out from under the bra and traveling around to the clasp in the back. She twists out of the straps, pulling back to let the bra fall to the floor, and I grip the small of her waist to tug her into me. My exposed breasts brush the thin layer of fabric between us. Her lips twitch into a smile beneath mine.

We're moving fast, though, maybe too fast. I want this, and so does she—I can tell—but I also want to savor this moment. I want to know her better.

I don't want to skip over important parts just because we have a history together.

Ten years have passed. *So much has changed.*

"Is it okay if we slow down a little?" I ask, pulling back to look her in the eyes. She presses her forehead to mine as her breathing downshifts. Her eyes are dilated with desire I *know* is about me. She runs her hand up into my hair, and twines a loose strand around her pointer finger.

"Tell me something about Kit Larson now." I speak it soft, but it's an order.

"A truth?" she questions, as that finger uncurls from my hair to lightly trek over my breasts. Her eyes stay on mine.

"Yeah, a truth." I grin at her reference to our favorite game from our youth.

She considers the question as her fingers consider the lines of my waist.

"I have no apartment, no furniture, just a few boxes of things that are all my own," she says, her mouth still tantalizingly close to mine.

"Why is that?" I ask, impressed I can focus as her finger taunts the waistband of my jeans on her journey over my torso. I'm not entirely surprised by her answer.

It's very manic pixie dream girl of her.

"I always thought I liked it that way—the impermanence of my existence. It gave me freedom to not get too tied down." She pauses, brushing my hair away from my neck and touching the mini red heart on my necklace. "I could pick up and leave when I was ready. And I was always ready sooner than I thought."

"Have you ever lived alone?" I ask, leaning, pressing a light kiss to the line of her neck. Two can play this game. Tiny touches tantalize. Women's skin is full of nerve endings, in all sorts of places you wouldn't expect, wouldn't know, if you aren't a woman yourself.

"Not alone," she says, leaning up to let me pepper kisses all the way to her ear. A gasp escapes her lips and her eyes roll closed. I smile against her neck.

"Do you want your own place?" I brush my nose over hers and lean back again. She fondles my hand, spreading the fingers wide and fitting hers between them before she answers.

"I think I'd like to own a couch. Pick out a bed frame and research mattresses." Her eyes open now, and have a sheen. "Maybe get a potted plant or two."

It's clear to me this means more to her than filling an apartment with furniture. This is a signal. A flare up in the air that she is ready to leave the manic pixie dream girl behind.

"Something to work on when you get back," I say, tucking her hair behind her ear. "I have some great recommendations for where to start. If you'd like some help."

She presses her lips to mine in a soft kiss. "I bet you have whole binders of research."

I tug her against me, running my hands up beneath her shirt. "I even used my label maker." I flick her nipple with the pad of my thumb. "Color-coded the folders." Our mouths meld into each other's and we get lost.

Tongues and hands and hair.

We spin around on top of the quilt, roughing it up with our movement. My head rests against a pillow and she fits her body next to mine, wrapping one of her languid, shapely legs over my hip and curling it to draw me closer.

I stare into her eyes as she lays her head on the opposite pillow.

"Now you," she says, pecking me fast as punctuation. "Truth."

"I'm starting my own business," I say. "Still weddings. All me, though."

"So that other account I saw on Insta *is* you?" She chuckles. "It wasn't set up with much, so I thought it might be a fake."

It occurs to me that others who have searched for my Instagram might have also seen this account. Maybe Zoe or my boss.

"I haven't told anyone at work yet," I say, pushing the anxiety about that possibility down with my reply.

"Not even Zoe?"

"Why would I tell Zoe?" I'm surprised by the suggestion.

"She just seems dedicated—and, like, to you. I feel like she'd want to know."

"*Feel* feel, like Mystic Maven feel?" I ask, biting my lip as a laugh rumbles up my throat. She shoves at my shoulder and I drag her on top of me.

"You can't build an empire alone," she grunts, straightening as she works my arms over my head and pins them to the pillows.

"Might be worth gauging her interest in joining forces. Venus in Libra vibes."

I wrangle free of her grip, twisting her around to the bottom again. Chest to chest, my thigh tucked in between hers, I kiss her full-on, working my tongue into her mouth slowly and feeling around.

Her hand trails open-palmed over my ass until she clenches the bottom of the cheek, getting a fistful before she nudges the curve of my thigh. I feel her warmth and return her nudge with my own. She giggles against my lips.

"This is fun," she says.

And it really is.

~

I never want this game of truth to end, but after another half hour of rolling around in her sheets, making out and telling secrets, the angle of the sun as it hits her face signals just how much time has passed since I first arrived.

"What time is it?" I ask. She can see the clock in the kitchen better than I can from where she's lying.

"Almost five," she says.

"Ugh, that's an hour till the rehearsal," I say, sitting upright and tugging my bra closed. We didn't rush to sex, staying mostly in the feeling and kissing stage of foreplay, and the fact that we are taking our time encourages me to believe we don't expect to run out of it.

She might not run away *this time.*

I stand, buttoning my shirt. "I have to get cleaned up before tonight." I have a duty to my clients, and unfortunately that means not languishing any longer in her bed. My eyes drop to her, still curled up and cozy, but tugging her tank top down. I can faintly see her nipples through her shirt, and it makes me ache between my legs.

I pop another kiss on her lips and walk over to the table where I left my walkie-talkie when I arrived. I pick it up, clicking it once.

It beeps, a double *blip blip* sound, and goes quiet.

My heart rate shoots up.

I click it again. *Blip blip.*

"Fuck," I exhale.

Kit's up, twisting her hair into a bun as she approaches.

"Fuck, fuck," I exclaim again. Clicking the button on the walkie-talkie. *Blip blip. Blip blip.* "It's dead. Zoe has no idea where I am—and it's not Homebase, which is where I said I'd be."

Kit's eyes go wide. "Okay, don't freak out. I'm sure it's fine."

"I gotta go," I say. Definitely freaking out. I shove on my tennis shoes and yank open the door.

I can't believe I did this.

I can't believe I was away for almost two hours, out of contact, the day of the rehearsal dinner.

I can't believe I let myself get so lost in the moment.

Her hands grip my waist, holding me in place. She spins me around.

And then as soon as our eyes meet, I can believe it all.

"Look." She points in the direction of the rehearsal dinner tent, which is barely visible from this vantage. "No fires. No floods. You are allowed to let go a little. Others can pick up the slack when you do."

I'm panicking, but it doesn't stop me from planting another kiss on her lips.

"See you tonight."

I run from the Airstream trailer in the direction of Homebase. Winding through the paths and still stupidly clicking my walkie-talkie as if it's going to magically have charge from just my sheer will.

That's when I see Zoe, standing outside Homebase with one of Healer Arynne's entourage. I rush up just in time to hear the tail end of their conversation.

"Just try to keep her phone away from her," Zoe says. "Whatever you have to do."

"Is everything okay?" I ask, breathless, probably looking mildly deranged. Zoe's massive eyes grow wider, and the shorts-clad man saunters away with little more than a side glance in my direction.

"No," she says, her face still alarmed. "But it will be."

I internally scream *fuuuucccckkkk* and externally straighten my posture under the weight of Zoe's glare.

"I walkied you and got no response. You weren't at Homebase when I came here," she explains, her voice more neutral than her confused expression. I try to tamp down my wild flyaways, not that I expect it to help at all. "Where were you—"

"What happened?" I ask, my mind racing with scenarios. And, yes, I'm avoiding her question with one of my own. She doesn't miss it, and I can tell by the look on her face that she is not planning on letting it slide forever.

"Someone on TikTok claimed one of Healer Arynne's crystals gave them a rash—"

"I can't comprehend substantiating such a claim," I interject.

"It doesn't matter to someone like her," Zoe says, no less annoyed. "The video had enough views that it sent Healer Arynne into a frenzied spiral fearing she was about to get canceled and for some reason that meant she should barricade herself in her room making response videos to the comments." She walks back inside Homebase.

My skin is clammy and my brain spins out at the word *barricade*.

"The rehearsal is in one hour." I follow her inside. I now sound like the panicked one.

"And until five minutes ago, I wasn't sure it would happen," Zoe replies. She reaches out a hand for my walkie. When I hand it over, she shoves it into the dock to charge with a little too much force. "I kept trying to get you on the walkie, but couldn't, and at the same time I was trying to convince her entourage to let me inside her room *and* trying to get the hotel manager to come open the door with the master key—which he didn't want to do, by the way."

"But he did?" I ask. She shakes her head.

"Bruno, the burly dude who just left, had a flash of awareness that if Arynne fucked herself over, he could be out of a job, so he let me in."

"Amazing luck," I say.

"I calmed her down and—for now—she's agreed to abstain from replying and checking socials, but I've got Bruno on phone watch." She crosses her fingers.

This could have been a massive disaster, and I would have been nowhere near the scene because I was off feeling up my former best friend.

I can't believe I was this irresponsible. It's not like me, buttoned-up, Julia-control-is-my-middle-name-Kelley. But at the same time, I don't regret losing myself in the moment with Kit.

I just wish I had lost myself in the moment at a better moment.

Thank God Zoe was here.

"You handled this with grace," I say, halfway thinking out loud. "A real pro."

"Duh," she says, but she's blushing hard enough that I can see the pink in her tan cheeks.

"My hat is totally off to you." I feign tipping a hat and she curtsies, her eyes sparking with pride.

"All part of the job."

"Not usually, but you didn't let that stop you from acting like it was."

"Because it could be." She gives me a big, confident smile, and I don't shoot the gesture down. "See you at the rehearsal," she says, walking to the front door of Homebase. But then she pauses, turning to add, "Boss."

I can't fight the grin that forms on my lips. And I don't correct her.

Maybe Mystic Maven is right about Zoe.

Chapter Twenty-Five

Kit

It took me a solid hour to recover from making out with the wedding planner.

The playfulness and ease were almost as incredible as all the other sensations: the heat of arousal radiating through my abdomen, thawing out forgotten and ignored parts of my soul, reminding me how easy it is for my body to respond to attraction when I'm not trying to tamp down the reaction.

I thought about digging in the Sexy Times bag and utilizing that oh-so-portable, perfectly pocket-sized gadget, but as much as I love—and advocate for—self pleasure, I also know how good it will feel when I get there with Julia.

Again.

And not in the fumbling, terrified, *can we really do this* way we did when we were eighteen. Not just with our hands. Not with my fear of what it meant hanging over our heads, coloring the experience with shame and confusion. I can't change how I felt then, or what those feelings led me to do after, but I don't have to repeat those missteps now.

I don't have to be afraid of my queerness.

I don't have to hide my desire for women.

I don't have to be the mysterious manic pixie dream girl whose purpose in the story is to teach the male protagonist the meaning of life. I don't have to fall in love with a guy and hope he'll chase me through the airport as I board my flight home.

I don't have to want a guy at all.

I drop down on the couch and hit the FaceTime icon under Nina's name.

When the call connects, I see that Nina is sitting on her balcony in a swimsuit with some kind of tropical cocktail in her hand.

"Ask me what I did today," she says, shades still up so I can't see her eyes.

"What did you do today?" I say with a smile.

"I landed the fucking girlfriend role on *Companion Report*—six episodes recurring with potential for MORE!" She squeals and I scream and she stands up to dance around the balcony. I join in, swaying on the couch and cheering until she drops back down in her chair.

"This could be it," I say. "The moment you look back on in ten years as the one that changed it all."

"Fuck yeah," she cheers. "Bring on those starring roles, Universe."

"Netflix, Hulu, Amazon Originals—" I list her favorite streamers, all of which she put on her vision board at spring equinox. "You call, she'll answer."

She hoots one more time, gulping her tiki drink with a satisfied smack of her lips.

"Now," she says, shoving her sunglasses down her nose so I can see her eye me in the FaceTime camera. "Give me all the updates on your re-meeting with the ex-bestie."

This is it. This is the moment.

"So, here's the thing," I say. God, why am I so nervous? This is Nina, my queer best friend. The closest person to me in the world. Basically my sister. I've described the shape of dudes' dicks to her, given her every glorious detail of the few spectacular fucks I've had in my life. She is my rock. She is a safe place.

"Dude, did you glitch? Is the call dropped?" Nina questions. I snap out of it.

"I'm queer." I spit it out like it's a piece of sour candy. Too tart to hold on my tongue anymore. "I like both women and guys. I always have."

She sits up straight in her chair.

"I know it's shocking," I say.

She pulls her shades off completely.

"I haven't told anyone, ever, except Julia."

Her face screws up. "Okay, we're gonna come back to that tidbit in a second, but, holy fuck, wow, amazing! And, I mean, also, that connects a lot of dots for me."

"What do you mean?" I'm affronted. "I gave you dots?"

"Just saying, there have been some moments where I was like, *maybe she doesn't just want dick*." She shrugs, scrunching her nose. "Pretty much ever since the Phi Beta Kappa party junior year. That girl . . . Maia—do you remember her? She was *fine*."

Awe shakes my features loose and I nod.

"She was totally into you and asked if you liked girls, too, and I—of course—had no reason to say yes so I didn't, but I pressed her on why she wanted to know and she said she just got a feeling from you."

Maia. The girl in Western Civ that I totally *did* have a crush on.

She was not only *gay*. But was also into *me*.

"Oh man, missed opportunity," I say, to which Nina chortles.

"For sure," she says, nodding.

I exhale a laugh but it feels more like a cry. And then it really *is* going to turn into tears. Big, real, impossible-to-hide tears. Her laughter dies back fast and she puts her face close to the camera.

"Hey."

My eyes well up.

"Hey, babe, look at me." Her voice is soft, reassuring, full of so much love.

When I finally do look into her eyes, the tears start to fall.

"I know it's scary to let things change. But it's also so incredibly good." Her voice is like a warm blanket, cozy and comforting. "This is it." She restates my thought from earlier. My chest gets tight and hot; my cheeks blaze as more tears flow. "This is the day you'll look back on as *the moment* when you chose to love yourself no matter what. It will be so fucking worth it."

I break down.

All the walls I've kept up, all the years I've stayed quiet. All the times I pushed away yearning, ignored my true feelings, minimized every desire just to preserve an ideal I let define me and confine me. All of that secrecy, running, hiding, being too afraid to seek, it all melts away under the light of truth.

I wipe my eyes as Nina wipes hers. She tells me to get a glass of wine so we can toast, and I dutifully—but still soggily—follow her orders.

"To your coming out," she says, lifting her tiki drink toward my screen. I cheers the camera. I'm surprised by the waves of relief and fear, peace and excitement that wash over me as I come down from the moment.

"Circle back time," Nina finally says. "You told Julia about this?"

I fill her in on the Epic History of Julia and Kit, hitting all the highs and lows of the five years we were inseparable: the tarot reading promising we were Twin Flames, falling in love slowly but completely, hooking up and freaking out, the way I tried to erase my feelings for her, the way I ghosted on my way out of town for Berkeley.

"And we kissed again," I say. "Today."

"Oh my God, when? Where?" She leans forward in her chair, waiting with bated breath.

"In here and in her room." I blush. "It was . . . really hot."

Nina squeals, "No fucking kidding. She's a fox."

"We pulled a card."

"Tell me it's a good one or I swear to God I'm gonna do a spell. Keep this shit on track," she threatens with tigerlike strength. I giggle, marveling at how easy it is to talk to her about this. How normal and good it feels.

"No spell needed." I exhale a sharp breath before saying it out loud. "The Lovers."

Her eyes get massive as the meaning dawns on her. "That's some soulmate shit right there—your psychic was right."

And I guess she was, but it doesn't change that Julia and I still have a lot to figure out. We still have a long way to go before we can know if this time of finding our way back to each other will be the last time.

"So, hate to bring this moment down with reality, but I have one more question," Nina says, brows drawing together to emphasize her seriousness.

"I know what you're going to ask, and the answer is no. I'm not telling them."

"I get it." But her face drops into a baby frown. "As a counterpoint, you will have to tell them—it's important that you do."

"And I will." I groan, gulp some wine. "I just want it to be my thing without them putting their expectations on it. Just for a little longer."

"Fair. One hundred percent fair," she agrees. "Clearly you should focus on the legit second-chance romance happening right now, in real life." She shakes the phone in excited agony.

"Oh my God," I say, laughing. "I'm hanging up."

"Rom-com gold, baby," she says. "This is the dream."

"*You* are the dream."

"I *am* the dream," she says with a pleased wiggle, and then exclaims, "Oh! Forced proximity! Friends to Lovers! Look at the trope candy."

"Goodbye, Nina," I singsong.

"Love you," she says. Kisses at the screen.

"Love you more," I reply, hanging up the call.

I fall back against the couch, letting the now empty wineglass slip to the seat beside me. I feel emptied out in the best possible way and grateful that I told her. Getting it out there—even if it's to someone I trust and love as much as Nina—feels like ripping the Band-Aid. Necessary, a little painful, bracing, but also like your skin can finally breathe.

She's right about my parents. At some point I will have to tell them if I intend to make a real go of this thing with Julia. The idea of that sends a thrill up the length of my spine.

If she wants me, if she wants to try, then there's nothing standing in the way.

Not even the past.

Chapter Twenty-Six

Julia

The bride and groom stand at the altar, where Healer Arynne walks them through the vow portion of the ceremony. We're t-minus seventeen minutes until the rehearsal party portion kicks off, and there haven't been any more disasters. Major or minor. Zoe comes up behind me, dressed in a pair of slacks and a tangerine button-down, her hair neatly arranged in a chignon.

She always manages to add personal flair to her mandatory dress code outfits.

During my rise in the ranks at Love, Always, I started requiring my wedding staff to wear professional dress for the main events. Slacks, clean lines, hair secured so it can't get untidy. It set our team apart in the crowd, and also helped signal we were officially in business mode.

I've changed into pin-striped slacks and a white button-down.

Classic. Boring. Exactly the kind of ensemble you'd expect, but that deep down makes me chafe.

I flit my eyes away from Healer Arynne's still-red-rimmed-from-crying eyes to glance over the rest of the wedding party. All present and accounted for, all mostly presentable. Cash still has the scabbing burn on his forehead, but he is expected to allow us to cover it by whatever means necessary (besides trucker hat) tomorrow for the ceremony. No protests.

When my eyes land on Piper, it's no surprise to me that she's checking me out. Her expression is equal parts guarded attraction and outfit scrutiny.

Part of the transformation I went through while dating Piper was a massive wardrobe makeover that struck as much Julia Kelley flair from my closet as humanly possible. I kept telling myself it was for the good of my career—no bride wants a wedding planner who stands out in the crowd. Draws attention.

I convinced myself that imposing that same dress code on everyone around me was the way to ensure I stood out as a leader. But anyone who knew me before will remember how decidedly more punk rock I once was. Not unprofessional, but always with an edge. A dagger earring. A pair of studded leather booties. More unexpected patterns, way less beige.

When I was working my way to a lead planner position—first pick of weddings, access to more resources—my overall vibe was a deterrent for some of the more vanilla clientele. Beverly Hills elite aren't exactly the most open-minded of individuals. I wasn't keen on changing to suit their comfort levels, and wouldn't have without the subtle, steady encouragement of my girlfriend.

Why don't we go shopping? Piper would ask, and then every item I picked would get feedback to push it in the direction she felt I needed to go. My success at Love, Always wasn't just a reflection on me. Piper was quietly out among her main circle of associates, but not anyone with ties back to her family. She was happy to wield her queer card when it would get her entry into circles that didn't trust her Connecticut Elite pedigree and the hefty dose of privilege that came with it. And turning us into a power couple was a means to at least one of her ends.

"Apparently, the video is losing traction already," Zoe says, drawing me out of my stewing revelry. "I had to ply her with dark chocolate to get her onstage."

"How's the social media ban going?" I say between gritted teeth. "Any updates from Bruno?" Her nostrils flare in amusement.

"He hid her phone," she replies. "I didn't ask how he pried it from her grip."

"I don't want to know." We both chuckle.

Kit suggested that Zoe might know I'm starting my own agency, and a part of me is dying to ask her.

To see how she reacts.

She's smart, probably much better at social media than me, and it's more than plausible that she figured out why I created the second account.

Even if Zoe wanted to come with me, I wouldn't be able to hire her right away. Even though the six-month noncompete in my contract is difficult to enforce in California, I am still planning to take that time to get all my ducks in a row. I've been saving for years to get to the point where I can quit, invest in the start-up, and also not go totally broke and have to move back in with my dad and stepmom.

There's no real wedding season in LA, but winter is the slowest time of the year by far, which is why the Morgan-Hayden wedding is so important. It's my last wedding before I give notice, but also it's the perfect inroad to influencers and young LA talent because of Millie's brand. When I'm up and running, this last wedding will be a great jumping-off point to gain new clients.

I look from the altar to movement at the entrance on the other side. Kit isn't obligated to arrive until the cocktail hour. I hate to admit there's still a part of me that worries she's going to bail.

But there she is, eyes searching the room until they land right on me.

And all my fears fall quiet.

The sherbet sky has turned the inside of the tent into a glowing poppy-orange hue. The colorful light dancing over her soft creamy skin makes her look even more ethereal. She's changed into a champagne pink dress that hits at the knees, coupled with a warm-toffee blazer. Her sleeves are casually rolled up to reveal a satin pink pin-striped lining that matches the color of the dress, and on her feet she's wearing Tory Burch ballet flats. She's got a few pieces of gold and crystal jewelry strung around her neck, dipping toward her full chest; her hair is wavy and loose, touchable.

Her eyes search the tent. God, I hope she's searching for me.

"You may now kiss your almost bride," Healer Arynne says, as cheers erupt from around the tent. I look back just in time to see her stifle a hiccup, her face an accordion of barely contained emotion.

Zoe steps into action, crossing behind the altar and up to Healer Arynne in a blur of tangerine, fitting her arm around the folds of her brightly colored caftan and pulling her briskly away.

Millie and Sean pass me on the river rock–covered aisle walkway; her blissful grin is all the assurance I need that this wedding will be a success.

I'm further gratified when I notice that Blythe and Evelyn are huddled together near their chairs in a joyous, tear-filled display. Blythe offers Evelyn a hanky and Evelyn lets her head drop to

Blythe's shoulder as she sobs. They approach, leaning on one another for support.

"You know, I think B was right about the dream catcher," Evelyn says. "Can we have it removed?"

"Already on it," I reply. I walkie over to the Love, Always staff member—Ben—who is overseeing the rehearsal dinner space right now, and tell him to nix the dream catcher above the bride and groom's table.

I watch them walk away, relief flooding my senses, and let my eyes trail over the faces of the bridesmaids and groomsmen, catching only briefly on Piper, who is stretching her head into an awkward position that takes up my whole view. But just past her, I see Kit moving through the chairs toward me.

Her face comes into sharp focus.

Everyone else in the room drifts to the edges of my vision, blurry, just shapes.

Kit is all I see.

The pink sheen of her gloss reflects light as she smiles. A row of earrings sparkles up the ridge of her left ear. She drops her eyes down the length of my body. They drift over my curves, tripping up to my lips and then settling into my gaze. There's no mistaking the want.

Me. Kit Larson wants *me*.

Make room for play. I hear Coco's voice in my head, her prompting that I let go. Then I see Kit standing at the entrance to her Airstream trailer, saying the same thing. They were both right; I got lost in the moment with Kit, and the whole wedding didn't fall apart.

I don't have to hold on so tight to make it happen.

When I look at Kit, I know every cell in my body wants to take the advice and run with it. I want the risk that leads to a rush. The adrenaline of jumping without overthinking. When we were friends before, our friendship showed me that letting go didn't have to mean losing. It's why I didn't question it when she kissed me, even though she had never told me she was into girls. It's why I believed it would be forever. It's why I was crushed when she ghosted.

Letting go led to loss.

The thought makes my stomach twist. The next time I fell hard was with Piper. And giving her an inch led to the biggest loss of self I've ever felt.

Kit and I meet at the end of the procession.

"Hey," she says, in what is the dictionary definition of *bedroom voice*.

"Hey," I reply, and I feel myself blushing.

I have the instinct to touch her hand and see if she pulls away. It's been a long time since I let go and let God. It's hard to know for sure if that's what I'm really feeling. Or if it's just hunger, or nerves, or a wish. My fingers flex before I stretch my arm out, touch her wrist, and tug her in.

There's no resistance.

She even smirks, bending against me to whisper right in my ear, "You look like a hot librarian."

I turn so that the edge of my mouth touches her cheek.

"So are we talking Rachel Weisz in *The Mummy*?"

"Take me on an adventure, madame," she quips.

I meet her eyes, asking with mine if it's okay to kiss her here. She turns her face until our lips graze. I close the gap, absorbing the moan on her breath. It's quicker than I want, but the fact that she lets it happen at all is something.

"I have to get set up for the readings," she says, her body leaning on mine. "You have to stop distracting me so I can intuit the cards." She presses her hips against me.

"You probably shouldn't let me do this then." I grab her by the hand, twisting away so I have a clear path outside the tent.

"Where are we going?" she asks, laughing but letting me drag her along. My fingers brush over her knuckles, creating tiny electric sparks.

I wind us back through the path until there's a break. It leads to one of the covered cabana seating areas. I spin, gripping her by the waist with both hands and pulling her against me. Our curves meld, all space disappearing between us. We kiss in a fever, nothing but tongues and breath and want. My hands tug her dress up until I can get them under. The tips of my fingers taunt the lace edges of her panties, brushing against the mound of her want.

"Fuck me," she exhales against my mouth.

"With pleasure," I reply. My fingers test her longing. She clenches my hand between her thighs and I feel her quiver the whole length of her body.

"I have to get to the rehearsal table tent," she says, pushing back to look me in the eye. Hers are bleary, her lip gloss smudged. "Damn." She kisses me again with fresh desperation and I let my finger flatten to apply pressure right where she's wettest.

Her growl is ravenous. "Hold that thought." She bites off the order. I pull my hand from between her legs and twine it in her hair.

"Tonight's festivities can't end fast enough." I kiss her again, this time with even more fervor.

With a squeeze of my ass, she lets me go. "It'll be over before you know it."

I watch her walk away. My body is screaming for her touch, the feeling so intense that I have to burst into a manic dance to try to expel some of the pent-up energy from my limbs, turning in a semicircle as I shake my body out.

"I saw you." Piper's voice comes from behind me. "Groping the tarot hottie." Sharp pricks of dread shoot through my body, hitting nerves and sending heat into my fingertips, quickening the rate of my pulse.

"And?" I spin to face her off. I haven't done anything wrong, so why do I feel like I need to prepare a defense?

"The least you could do is not flaunt it right in front of me." Her brown eyes simmer with hurt.

"Why is that the least I could do? You and I have been broken up for over a year. No one here even knows we used to date," I say, chewing on my lower lip. "Except for Kit."

Her face drops, and I already know before she says a word that her voice will be tinged with a wobble. The only time Piper Cunningham ever shows a modicum of weakness is when she thinks it will get her what she wants.

"It's pretty heartless that you aren't even considering my feelings." Wobble right on cue. "I came out to my family for you—"

"No—look, I am happy that you came out. I'm proud of you for taking that step. But you didn't do it for me." I feel my throat tighten as tears threaten, hot and thick in the corners of my eyes. "We haven't spoken since I got my stuff out of your apartment a year ago. And then you come here, what, expecting I'll just fall all over myself to get back together with you?"

Her nostrils flare. "We were good together."

"I was a pawn on your twisted Piper chessboard. You used me, you molded me, and anytime I pushed for my own desires, you shot me down or made me feel foolish for wanting them at all."

"I only did what I thought was best for us."

"You did what you thought was best for *you*."

Piper tightens her jaw, her body rigid. She sweeps the length of her red waves over her shoulder like it's a shield. "Are you in love with her?"

I divert my gaze away, but it doesn't do anything to stop the blush creeping into my cheeks. *Do I love Kit?* I probably always have. I probably never stopped. With all this want and years of wondering finally materializing between us, the idea that love could be our endgame seems almost too good to be true.

The Lovers.

Could it be us forever?

"You do," she whispers. Her face twists, contorting, but it's an expression that's much more than hurt or longing. It's broken glass, all sharp edges, a dangerous weapon.

I push past her without another word.

Chapter Twenty-Seven

Kit

Normally, I would be much better at spinning the appearance of the Tower and the Devil—two major arcana cards that when placed one after the other almost never forbode a period of ease—but I'll admit my head is not in the game. Especially after Julia passes by looking like a fever dream I never want to wake up from.

"You're saying this is serious," Sean's grandmother, Patrice, says. She's a tiny woman with immaculately set silver hair and a small gold cross dangling at her neck, which she clutches like it will protect her from the cards. "You look worried."

I blink, focusing on the cards again. I did say that, and I can feel the way my face has gotten stuck in a furrow of features that probably looks like someone trying to shit out a brick. These cards could very well be the harbinger of immense struggle, but I should not have said that out loud.

Think fast, Kit.

"The Devil and the Tower are not always a bad or difficult

combination, but they almost always signal a time of change on the horizon."

"I'm eighty-three," Patrice replies. "At my age, the only change I have to look forward to is death."

My eyes flicker wide. This combination can indicate a sudden or jarring change that forces us to confront our deepest, darkest fears. I resist the urge to ask if there is anyone in her life that she would be shocked to lose, but I happen to know she's happily married to Sean's grandfather so my guess is that would get an enthusiastic yes. I decide to spin my interpretation in a different direction.

"This combination isn't all negative," I begin. Her eyes narrow in suspicion. "It encourages us to confront our fears in order to live a fuller life."

"I'm not afraid of dying," she says, her voice tinged with resignation.

"That's very evolved of you."

"Horseshit," she spits. It genuinely shocks me and a laugh I'm trying to stifle barks out instead.

Millie, who is passing behind Patrice, stops short—champagne flute in hand—to eye me over her future grandmother-in-law's head.

"This looks like some big calamity," Patrice says, pointing to the burning building of doom. Millie's brows quirk in curiosity; I bite back a grin. "And this is the greatest trickster there ever was." She points to the Devil.

"In Christianity, sure, the Devil is a symbol for carnal sins, but in tarot he represents the need for shadow work—"

"Black magic?" Patrice's voice is gritty with surprise. Millie cackles, walking up and placing her champagne-free hand on Patrice's shoulder.

"Hey, Granny Hayden," Millie says with the voice of a benevolent angel. "I think Bob is looking for you by the photo booth." Bob, her beloved husband. I will the Universe to cut them some slack. Patrice gives the cards, then me, another once-over before huffing away.

Millie and I lock eyes, hers full of mirth, pupils dilated from the champagne haze. She scrunches her nose, smirking. "She's an old-school hell-and-brimstone type, but she's a firecracker."

"A truly bright light," I reply. I start to pick up the cards and reintegrate them into the deck, shuffling swiftly. I've been at it for a couple hours, which is almost the allotted time we agreed to for this event. My brain is in countdown mode.

"I'm so happy," Millie says wistfully, drawing my attention up to her face. "Thank you for coming all the way out here." She looks around, eyes misty.

I shuffle the cards.

"Break the deck," I say. She does, into three stacks, and then she points to the middle. More confident than she was last night in her choice.

"My instinct, too." She beams with pride. I flip it over.

Ten of Cups, upright. *Oh thank God.* I breathe a sigh, and when I look back at Millie, I can tell that—even before I explain the card—its meaning is seeping into her bones. She embodies the energy of this Ten.

"Long-lasting love. A home, a family, a life together." I list off words that come to mind when I look at the card. Words I know are associated, but feel more intrinsically linked to Millie and her near future.

"This is the dream, right?" Millie says, touching the children on the card. "I don't know how I got so lucky this early in my life." She looks up to me.

"It's not a dream. This is your life, and it's beautiful and complex, but it's not luck. It's fate." She beams at my use of the word.

"Fate," she repeats, her face aglow. It's not just the candlelight making her shimmer. It's coming from within.

It's been a long time since I've said the word *fate* with conviction, not just because the word itself holds so much weight to those who want to believe in it, but because I myself had lost the certainty that it was something worth believing in. Fate felt like a passive ideal. Like an excuse to be disappointed. Like a reason to hold on to past ways of thinking just because at some point they had felt soul-aligned or brought success.

But this weekend has made me hope that fate could be working with me.

Sean swoops up and clutches Millie around the middle, peppering her cheek and neck with kisses. She giggles, letting him practically carry her off in his arms. They spin around in a dizzying display of affection—one that would definitely have once made my heart clench with jealousy.

Millie's Happily Ever After looks exactly the way I always expected my own would, but now that I'm in this *thing* with Julia—coming out slowly, coming more into my true desires—I'm beginning to see how there are a lot of ways to live that fairy tale in real life and how important it is to make those expressions of this romantic ideal just as relevant as the more conventional ones.

I search the crowd of family and friends for Julia. The countdown clock fires through me, an alarm signaling it's time to go.

When I find Julia standing off to the side of the space surveying her success, my stomach fills with butterflies.

Julia Kelley gives me butterflies.

Kissing her turns my body to putty and my insides to molten lava. Touching her is addictive, a craving I don't ever want to get rid of.

I am about to pack up my cards when someone says, "Closing shop?"

Coco, holding a wineglass, looking camera ready as ever. I should ask her for an on-camera reading. I need something more tangible to show for this weekend—something that gets my videos in front of the kind of clientele I can demand a higher wage from.

"I'm pretty spent." I should, but I don't.

"Plus, you know, you have other plans." She winks at me. Her default expression, as Julia said. But this time it feels laced with specific meaning. And I'm pleased to discover that I don't mind at all.

"Important plans," I say, a giddy smile spreading across my cheeks. I break away to wind through the crowd.

And right into Piper.

"Shit," I say under my breath.

"Careful there, you almost groped me," she says, standing too close for comfort. I take a generous step back. "I would hate if it got out that you get fresh with your clients."

Heat prickles the skin on the nape of my neck, making the tiny hairs stand on end.

"What would all your exes think?" she continues. "Especially David, the freshest body."

"How do you—"

Her eyes drift over my head and she raises her hand to wave. "Just steer clear. You're not my type."

She presses past me and I get the distinct feeling that she was trying to threaten me. I shake it off—as much as I can. I didn't do anything inappropriate. I don't have anything to be worried about.

It's an empty threat from a bitchy bully.

As I make my way through the crowd looking for Julia, I notice Zoe talking to one of the kitchen staff, pointing authoritatively toward the head table. It makes me hopeful that maybe Julia has already given her marching orders so we can get the hell out of here.

My brain is a haze; my heart taps a beat against my ribs. This is going to happen.

When I find Julia in the crowd, nothing else matters. Her eyes trek down the length of my body, heat gathers between my legs, and I almost buckle with want. I rush to reach her—not even thinking. I tuck my hand around her waist and kiss her, working my tongue gently into her mouth. It doesn't bother me that anyone could look over here and see us. That then they would know I don't just think she's the coolest girl alive. I think she's the hottest. I don't just want to be best friends.

I want her, body and soul.

I pull back. "What do you say we get out of here?"

Her smile is sorcery. Her "yes" is a taunt against my lips.

Chapter Twenty-Eight

Julia

We didn't stop touching the whole walk back to Kit's Airstream trailer.

Not when we passed Natalie doing shots of mezcal with a few of the guys from the groom's party, or passed the mothers of the bride and groom locked in a warm embrace, sobbing about becoming a family. We didn't let our fingers disconnect when we opened doors or moved through tight corners on dimly lit paths or while I shot off a quick text to let Zoe know I was going off duty for the night.

Kit isn't out yet, but she isn't hiding either. Here, she doesn't have to explain her sexuality to the people who might observe us. No one *here* is invested in a past version of her that makes them feel comfortable. But that doesn't mean this is easy for her, and it doesn't make her openness any less comforting to me.

When we reach the gate to her accommodations, I tug her to a stop. She turns, still not releasing my hand, and at this angle the moonlight touches the top of her head like a halo.

"What's up?" she asks. "The other side of this gate is paradise."

"Are you saying your pussy is a wonderland?" I reply with a smirk, referencing the queer love Halsey anthem. She tugs me in, her grip on my hand pulling mine between us so it presses between her thighs. She's hot; I can feel it through the thin fabric of her dress.

"You're not having second thoughts?" I ask. I can't be distracted by her magical sex before asking at least one of the most important questions.

"I want this, Julia," she whispers, then kisses me. "I want *you*." She moves her hips until my hand is firmly between her legs. "I've never been more certain of anything in my life."

She kisses me, all intoxicating, and as our mouths meld together, our breasts touch. I run my hand up her body to brush her nipple through the thin fabric of her dress. She clenches her thighs, using the hand I'd left there to apply pressure.

"Noted." I tug back. "But not out here."

Her eyes are dark with her dilated pupils. She fixes them on mine.

"I have an idea," she says, flipping the lock up on the gate and pulling me to the other side.

To paradise.

~

"You better not be peeking," she scolds. I can hear glasses clinking as she walks back toward me from inside the trailer, then her motion pauses and there's some kind of shuffle before she commences her approach. I'm sitting on the outdoor bed curled underneath a heavy patterned blanket. She wanted to set the scene, to show me she wasn't just looking for some quickie thing in the bed of an Airstream trailer. She can provide foreplay. She isn't trying to rush us through this.

I hear her steps halt and then her breathing quiver a little before she says, "Okay, you can look."

She's brought out a bottle of wine, glasses, and a small charcuterie board, probably utilizing the overpriced hotel-supplied items in her fridge. She's removed her professional jacket and wrapped another dusty rose blanket around her shoulders.

"I'm guessing you're like me and you didn't get to eat at the thing," she says. "Not even one of those extra beef empanadas."

"The groomsmen eviscerated the excess."

"I'm deeply bummed out," she replies.

"You should be," I say, my mouth watering at the doughy memory. "I had one earlier and it was a pouch of pure heaven."

"And you couldn't save me one?" She fakes being offended, puffing out her lip in a pout, but she still approaches with her tray of goodies. She sets it on the bed, picking up a lighter she brought from inside and using it to light the firepit beside the bed. She grins, pleased, as soon as the flames catch. I watch her shadow against the dark copper fence line that surrounds the whole space. I guess if someone really wanted to see inside, they could, but they'd have to be willing to get branded a total perv in the process.

You couldn't accidentally peep; you'd have to *mean* it.

Kit sits on the other side of the tray, wrapping her blanket tighter around her shoulders and slipping her foot beneath her. I'm transfixed, watching her every move. The way she tucks her hair behind her ear, letting her row of earrings catch the light of the fire. The way she wets her lips before she untwists the wine cap. She's always been this way—soft and sensual. Graceful and sure.

She hands me a glass, raising hers toward mine.

"I feel like we should do a cheers." She looks nervous to suggest it. Like she expects me to shoot her down. My heart does a flip because I can't believe she wants to impress me. She never needed to do that, never had to try—just her existence was enough for me.

"To finding our way back," I say, tipping my glass toward hers. The glass doesn't quite touch.

"To each other," she adds. *Clink.* She sips and then gulps down some wine. "Okay, total transparency, I'm terrified."

"We don't have to do anything that scares you."

She grips my hand, squeezing. "That's just it." She gulps more wine. "I want to do what scares me."

"We're not sixteen anymore. We can just do things because we want to, not because we want a thrill."

"I'm not looking for an adrenaline rush," she says, and then with nervous, shaky hands she stacks a cracker with salami and cheese. "Maybe an endorphin rush." She fills her mouth with the cracker and I let out a laugh before joining her in the charcuterie. She's smiling when she speaks again. "I've been scared my whole life of acting on the things I really want."

"Like *life* life, or just sex life?" Confusion pings through me. She seems built for her career, actively trying to expand it, successful and happy.

"All of it," she says. "Can your life really be what you want if you are denying a truth about yourself?"

I reach across the charcuterie to touch the curve of her exposed knee with my hand.

I don't want her to think that just because this version of me looks perfect, polished, and pristine, that I'm not still the live wire desperate for connection that I always was.

"I don't have everything—" I cut myself off, rethinking. "Anything together, either." She's looking into my eyes and it's like she knows, without me even saying it out loud, just how out of control this control freak feels. She pops a grape into her mouth, chewing, wheels turning as she gears up to speak.

"It's like the whole left side of my body was numb—and I made it that way. I ignored it long enough that it just went dormant, and on the rare occasion when I did notice it, instead of nurturing it, I let it starve. Watched it wither. And now that I can feel its hunger again, all I want to do is feed it."

I set my glass on the platform by the bed.

She pops another grape between her teeth and bites. The juice dampens the corner of her mouth, glistening in the light. All I want to do is lick it off. All I'm hungry for now is her.

I fit my fingers around the handles of the tray. "This is in the way."

Her eyes lock with mine. *This is really going to happen?* they seem to ask.

I set the tray out of the way, taking the few seconds of privacy as my face is turned away from her freak-out. This *is* really about to happen. I am going to have sex with Kit Larson. Real, grown-up sex. This must be what people who get to sleep with celebrities feel like—bewildered glee mixed with apprehension that they'll screw something up and squander their chance.

When I turn around, the edges of her blanket shawl have slipped down to reveal her shoulders. Her skin absorbs moonlight like a sponge. Stars spray out in all directions behind her. The fire's flames flicker and dance, making a movie along the fence backdrop.

She's looking at me with so much love, expectation and longing all wrapped up in her beautiful face. I close the distance between us in a rush, crashing my lips into hers, ravenous and feral, a wild, untamed thing in search of a brand-new adventure. Tongue and teeth clash; my hands roam into her hair and get buried. My mouth searches her neck like it's the X on a treasure map. I want to taste the dip in her collarbone. I want to uncover her breasts and tantalize her nipples with my tongue. I want to make it goddamn clear that she is the most beautiful person to me.

Perfect in all imperfection.

Perfectly, wholly, my Twin Flame.

Chapter Twenty-Nine

Kit

Lust ripples over me.

What if I tear the buttons of her pressed white blouse and watch them spray across the bed? What if I nibble her earlobe and fist her hair?

My hands grapple for a hold on every tiny curve of her body. She tongues between my collarbone and then down, down, until she's between my cleavage. Her hand on my shoulder tugs at the strap of my dress, pulling it loose from its place until it makes space between my breast and the fabric.

"Can I?" she breathes, the act of questioning just as titillating as the suggestion. I nod, unable to speak, my words trapped by the grip of desire. She pulls my dress away and my breast slips out. I watch her eyes widen, desire written in her aqua irises, before she flicks my nipple with her tongue, taking it entirely into her mouth.

My blood pulses into every hidden crevice. The sensation of her tongue swirling over my nipple is madness I want to give all the way in to, but then her hand sweeps up my thigh, gripping my ass over the skirt of my dress, and my hips buck up like a bronco. She releases my breast from her mouth, catching it with her hand and sweeping her thumb over the nipple. My body screams and I tip my head back.

"You're right," she says as she exposes my other breast. "Your tits are paradise." She raises her hand to cup it, smiling at the already hard nipple.

I want to reciprocate, to feel her skin on my skin. "Unbutton your shirt."

She leans up, and I can tell by her smirk that she's pleased to take my order seriously. She makes quick work of the buttons, exposing her simple nude bra. I reach out, taking the edges of the shirt in hand and shoving it off her shoulders. I reach behind to unclip the bra clasp and let it fall between us. When I lean back, her tan nipples, edged in the faintest hint of pink, small and perky, wink back. I can't control myself; I don't even try. I take one in my hand, tweaking the nipple, and then cover it with my mouth. I spin my tongue around it, grabbing at Julia's thighs, her hips. Wanting to climb on top of her, wanting to strip her thighs bare, rip her panties off and cast them in the fire, spread her lips and taste.

It's too much feeling, too much want—*too much too much too much*—exploding all over my skin, through my limbs, directly into my veins. I'm going to shatter and then I won't be able to have her, and all I want is to have her.

I wrap my arms around her, holding her against me, and we drift to lie down against the mattress. Our kisses slow, turning soft, and she tugs the blanket up over our bodies. I pull away, pressing my forehead to hers and breathing out heavily, so full of meaning. I try not to spiral over her breasts and mine brushing, naked. I want to feel this and not feel the need to run away. I want to be in this, completely, for real.

"Are you okay?" she asks, breathless herself.

"I feel like my insides are going to burst out," I say, but my hands have a mind of their own. They trek over her rib cage and draw a line down the smooth, taut expanse of her stomach. She brushes the hair off my face, pressing the tip of her nose to mine.

"I'm scared, too," she whispers, her breath grazing across my cheek. "I haven't felt this free in a long time. I forgot what it was like to unclench."

I kiss her softly. "I wanna make a pact."

"Like a blood oath," she quips, grinning. "I'm afraid I don't have my pocketknife."

"We can find another way to seal the deal," I reply, feeling naughty. I nudge my hips closer.

"I'm listening," she says, and now her hands are the restless ones. They draw circles on my thigh, getting higher and higher with every swirl.

"No more denying. No more pretending. No more playing roles." Her eyes widen and fix on mine, and I think that even without me saying it aloud she knows that I see her denial of self runs deeper than just her clothes, the missing piercings, the shaved head. "We be us."

Just like we always were when we were together. Back then, we knew we had each other's back, and it made everything—all the hard things and all the good ones, too—so much easier, sweeter, better.

"Us," she says.

"Us." I kiss her with everything in me.

All the feelings that make me afraid I'll implode.

All the want, the need I haven't dared acknowledge my whole life.

It all floods to the surface of my skin.

As the kiss deepens, we begin to move. Twisting together until Julia is on top of me, working my dress over my head and surveying the spoils of her efforts. Her eyes drop to my light pink underwear, her lips falling open, her tongue practically wagging. Her hands glide over my thighs and hips, fingers delicate as they tempt the edges of my underwear. Her face is close to my pussy; the only thing between her tongue and my pleasure is a thin barrier of fabric.

"Can I?" she asks.

"Anything," I breathe.

She inches my panties *down down down*, kissing my thighs, touching the tender skin gently with her fingers, sending shivers of pleasure through me. When she returns her attention between my legs, she takes her time to learn the curves of my body all over again.

I've never had a woman go down on me. I don't know what to expect.

She gently spreads my folds with her fingers, using her thumb to apply pressure to my clit. I clutch my breast, undulating toward the pressure, feeling on the edge but not wanting to tip over just yet. Then her mouth takes over, kissing and licking, taking liberties with every crevice until the only thing I can do is gasp.

Her tongue dips inside and her fingers follow.

My body lets go as I tumble over the edge, buckling against her skin. The orgasm crashes through every remaining wall I tried to keep up, like my body wants to confirm every salacious thought and filthy, beautiful desire I've kept locked inside for so long.

When I finish, she drifts up to kiss my neck, touching my breasts, painting circles in the crevices of my elbows. She presses against my thigh with her pleasure. I'm shaking, untethered, but still I want to touch every part of her. Make her lose herself in the moment.

Show her it's safe to let go.

I tug at the button on her pants and she lets me slip it open.

Down, off, revealing simple white cotton undies and a dark, delicious bush showing through the fabric. I pull them down, taking in the sight of her. She's perfect. Her hair a supple brown, her skin tan. I use my fingers at first, slipping them between the folds until I can see her flower. She's deliciously wet; it takes very little urging before her moans grow hot and heavy. Her hips pulse in a rhythm with my fingers and I slip one inside her.

Then another.

I kiss her clit before flicking it with my tongue. Her hips buck, affirming that's the spot.

She knows this is my first time, but she trusts me, and that trust is a boost to my self-confidence. I can make her scream.

I want to.

My tongue touches her clit. She squeezes her legs in and a heady moan releases from her mouth. I'm lost in her taste, like it's the most delicious, decadent dessert, and with every stroke of my fingers and every press of my tongue, I can feel her getting closer.

She slams her hands to the bed, her fists clenching, yanking, her body shaking.

And when she comes against my tongue, I feel it ripple

through my own body—the most powerful, magnificent ocean wave.

She tugs me up to kiss her, and I taste the salt of tears on her skin. Her lips quake and she turns her face to bury it in my neck. I pull the blanket up around us, my own tears threatening to fall.

Her eyes find mine. "I missed you." She brushes a tear from my cheek.

"Now you don't have to."

Ever again.

Chapter Thirty

Julia

I've already spilled two cups of coffee this morning and it's not even ten a.m. My brain is a puddle of memory, reliving last night, wishing to go back in time and do it all over again.

Not to change anything.

Just to be there.

This second cup of coffee is spilling over a table on the restaurant patio where a massive breakfast buffet has been set up for all the guests, Love, Always staff, and other support staff—including Healer Arynne; the caterer, Javier; and everyone from Desert Roses, the floral designer for the whole event. Millie wanted to make sure the staff was feeling appreciated. I'm just grateful they'll at least be fed before all the intensity of final-day prep gets underway. Hangry employees and romantic bliss do not mix.

Zoe rescues my Wedding Day binder from the pool of brown liquid as I jolt up, grabbing napkins from the buffet table to blot it. Fortunately this cup was less than halfway full and most of the caffeine now courses through my veins. Zoe returns with a plate, gesturing for me to drop the soaked napkins on top.

"Thank you," I say. "Again."

She chuckles. "I should probably not comment on your dreamy-eyed, head-in-the-clouds energy since you're my boss—" She stutters at the word. A word I have scolded her for using many times before. I resist the urge, and she carries on. "But what the hell is going on? You're acting like you took a Xanax."

My shoulders shake as I chuckle, leaning back against the frame of the door. I can't sit back down because I'm too restless. Like there are ants in my pants, or maybe it's just that I want more of Kit in there.

"I don't know what you mean," I say with a sneaky quirk of my lips. Her face scrunches in disgust.

"Liar," she says, shoving the napkin plate into the hands of a passing waiter. "You're acting like a woman in love, and that is something I honestly never thought I would say to you." She stands beside me, surveying the patio. "No offense."

I'm a little taken aback that Zoe ever thought about my lack of a love life, but my endorphin-filled brain is too happy to dwell on it.

"Maybe I'm just feeling like I can finally ease up tension on the reins," I say, flicking my eyes to view her reaction in my peripheral vision. Her curtain of dark lashes pinches, just like her thick eyebrows.

"You've suggested this before and never followed through," Zoe replies.

"There's a first time for everything," I say.

Right then, there's an energy shift on the patio, and my eyes shoot in the direction I feel it coming from. Kit's presence is the dawn breaking pink and purple against a clear blue sky. Her hair is tucked into a messy bun on top of her head; a few spiraling waves dangle to brush the edge of her jawline. She's wearing a loose, pastel pink cropped sweatshirt and some tie-dye leggings, tennis shoes and no makeup.

I left her in bed this morning and it was the hardest thing I've done all year.

After we had sex last night, we stayed on the outdoor bed until the cold air became more than we could take and we had to move inside. But we didn't go straight to sleep. We talked like we'd never stopped talking, like time had folded in on itself and we were getting a do-over. The more I learned about her life since I'd last known her, the more I wanted to hold her close.

She told me about her parents splitting up, and how it felt like a cruel joke of fate when she first saw me here. She'd come to escape and instead she was given a karmic reunion.

She knows she's good at what she does and she loves helping people feel like they are in control of their destiny. Even if all she is doing is confirming a truth that they already know. If she could get higher-end clients, she'd be able to turn that into more lucrative jobs, which would give her more time to develop ideas for static income. *Maybe a tarot deck*, she said, *or a course for manifesting.*

Do you remember the lake house? she asked, her voice raspy, her eyes drooping. I spent a few summer weeks with her out there, sunbathing on the sand and using a beat-up red canoe to explore in the deeper waters. *I go there in my mind when I start to feel the grip of anxiety. That spot where the beach curved out of view of the house.*

Her eyes blinked closed.

You were the only one I ever trusted enough to take there in real life.

After hours of talking, I still feel like there's so much to learn.

Now, she's working her way around the buffet in Zoe's and my direction, and I'm not paying attention to what my face is doing, but Zoe certainly is. She's openly staring at me staring at Kit, mouth agape.

"Why are you making that face?" I ask under my breath.

"No way," she hisses. She looks from me to Kit and back. "You and Mystic Maven."

"That's not her name."

"Oh. My. God."

Kit approaches with her plate piled high. Eggs, bacon, a croissant, and a "breakfast salad," which is just salad at a different time of day. Our eyes connect and suddenly I don't care if Zoe sees me blush and therefore knows I'm acting a fool all because of Kit.

"Good morning," she says. She smiles and light catches on her translucent lip gloss. She flicks her gaze to Zoe, who does not fix her face. Kit's brows quirk. "Hello, Zoe, ready for the big day?"

I elbow Zoe. She's too busy staring to notice.

"She's had one too many espressos," I say.

"It's going to be a gorgeous day," Zoe chimes in. Finally.

Kit looks between us. I know she knows. I pray to any god who will listen that she doesn't make this a thing. Kit nibbles on her lip, but it's clearly just to bite back her growing smirk.

"See you ladies in a bit," she says. I don't exhale relief, but I sure as hell feel it.

As soon as Kit is gone, I turn to Zoe. I really can't believe I'm about to do this, but I am. I motion for her to follow me through the restaurant, through the lobby, and out in front of the hotel entrance. The fountain bubbles behind me when I turn to face her.

"Yes, Kit and I are a thing," I say. "We have a history, like, ancient history, and seeing her this weekend has totally thrown me for a loop and sent me spiraling down memory lane and made me realize I still have feelings for her, and it turns out she's into me, too."

Phew. It feels surprisingly good to say it out loud.

Zoe squeals and wriggles, reminding me of a seal who found the perfect sunny spot on the shore. She grips my hands and bounces up and down. She's genuine. She's happy for me. Warmth spreads across my chest as I watch her face break into the biggest, brightest smile. What the fuck is this feeling? It's a little like nausea, but a lot like drinking hot cocoa by a fire—comforting and sweet.

"Julia, this is incredible. I'm so happy to see you happy—and distracted." She adds the last bit with a shy smile. "You left the rehearsal and didn't have your walkie on last night. When you texted me that I was in charge until morning, I fully expected you to recant, show up at the takedown, or text me at three a.m. with a list of things I'd done incorrectly."

I want to be offended but I can't be. Everything she just said is one hundred percent something I would do (or have done).

"I don't want to be disrespectful," she adds, but I can feel the *but* in there. "I think you make it harder on yourself when you insist on retaining control. There's a cost, and despite your ability to deliver on your superhigh standards, I don't see how that will be sustainable when you're running your own business."

She braces for her words to sink in.

I lock her in my sights. "How long have you known?"

"Pretty much since you started the Instagram."

"Okay, wow, I'm just gonna blow past that." I suck in air through my nostrils and let it out in a meditative huff. "What's your honest opinion?" Zoe's expression sharpens; she clears her throat. Every move lets me know that this is the opportunity she has been waiting for.

"You're the best, and not just that I've worked for at the agency. I follow all the wedding TikToks, am up on the goings-on in the LA scene and beyond, and your work is impeccable. And I think that's because you get that what makes a good wedding isn't delivering on some laundry list of moments. It's not following trends or being ahead of them, even." Her eyes get cloudy and I wish I could look away from the display of emotion, but Zoe's vulnerability makes me respect her more. "What makes a good wedding is the people at the heart of it. The two people choosing each other, hoping it will be forever."

"Turning two into a family," I reply with the words I've held secret in my heart for so long about why I want to branch out on my own. Yes, it's for more control, but it's not the kind of control that can't let anyone help. It's the kind that creates such a strong vision that others want to help make it a reality.

"I'm just saying, if you want a right-hand woman, I'd like to be that."

I can't promise her a job but I want to. I think back to my oath with Kit. If I'm not pretending, holding back from who I am or what I want, then I shouldn't ignore this feeling. I have to be honest with Zoe, but that doesn't mean I can't give her hope.

"It's gonna be rocky and unpredictable for who knows how long, but there's no one I'd want as my right-hand woman more than you."

Her smile is a bright beacon of joy. "Then when you call me, I'll come."

It's starting to feel possible that everything I want for myself, my *life* life and my sex life, could actually fall into place. That the whole picture could be beautiful. That Kit was right when she asked if you can really be happy when one part of your life is cut off and withering. Even when things inevitably fall apart, and what's out of our control stays that way.

We be us through it all.

Chapter Thirty-One

Kit

Thank Spirit I'm not booked for anything until after the wedding ceremony, because my brain—and also my intuition—are mush. The soft mashed potatoes you get at a Golden Corral. I am playing a steady repeat of all my favorite tracks from last night.

The way Julia smiled, with her whole body and all her feelings, when she talked about her dad and stepmom, Ana. Who never had more kids but did adopt a menagerie of pets including chickens, a tortoise named Ted, three ball pythons, and "the most hideous dog to ever grace the planet Earth." Literally. She showed me the awards.

The way she got passionate about her desire to build an agency on her own, to provide not only a place for diverse couples to feel safe to express their wildest wedding fantasies, but a place for her to help couples see this new beginning is about more than the party. It's about choosing each other and making that choice count.

The smell of her neck, the taste of her sex, the way her eyes get a little hooded with sleep, and how her hair is wild when she wakes up in the morning.

I don't know exactly who she is, or what happened between high school and today, but the mystery of Julia Kelley is the most exciting one I've yet to unravel.

I flip my hair back and turn off the blow-dryer. I have about an hour to get ready and get centered before the ceremony begins. I don't have to be on duty for the ceremony, but Millie asked if I would come and contribute good energy to the vibes. And of course I will, but also any excuse to be in the same room as Julia is one I will gladly take.

I set the dryer back on the vanity, using my fingers to brush through the gentle waves. I usually add in some texture with an iron. I know it's not the TikTok way, but I tried those no-heat curlers and didn't find them reliable to use for an event where my hair has to actually be photo ready without fail.

While the iron heats, I put on my primer, my mind wandering. This wedding is over tomorrow, which means we leave the desert *tomorrow*, back to LA, back to real life. Back to my divorcing parents who are selling my childhood home. Back to a world where the only people who know I'm queer are my best friend and the girl I'm dating—oh my God. Back to figuring my shit out, but now with this new, scary, exciting thing in play.

Julia and I live in the same city. Tomorrow we have to leave this oasis, but we don't have to go our separate ways. Her life and mine could intertwine. We could go on dates and get to know each other as who we are now. Memorize each other's coffee orders and figure out sides of the bed. We could go on vacations and sneak off to see matinees on a weekday. We could fall asleep in front of the TV and buy each other lingerie.

When she starts her business, I could help her set up the space, and after time has passed—once we've gotten tired of keeping a toothbrush and toiletries at each other's places, when a drawer isn't enough to fit all our clothes, when we're not just falling in love but deep in it, all the way—we could find a place we both call home. Somewhere I can grow herbs in the window and she can have a little home office. We could adopt a dog and fight about what to name them.

Then she could get on one knee and I could meet her down there because I was thinking the same thing. The *I want you forever* thing. And we wouldn't want to wait another second to get started building the rest of our life together.

We could have a life together.

A whole life.

Two of us making it up, together. Whatever we want it to be.

If Julia were one of my exes, I'd call Nina right about now to get her to talk me out of these daydreams. They're just the product of the Ideal Rom-Com Life Path, and expecting that from another person is foolish. Asking for it is childish. Hoping for it is how you get your heart broken.

I close my eyes, trying to tune in to the compass. That spinning, off-kilter inner guide that I've been forcing to point me down a path I didn't even really want—or at least, I didn't want in the narrow, ultraspecific way I was going after it. I want to believe it's stopped swirling because I've finally given up pretending, and not only because I found Julia again.

My phone buzzes, dragging me out of my inner world.

It's a text from Dad. *Oh shit.* I swipe the notification open. He's sent me a screenshot of my mom's Facebook status.

In a relationship

Then another screenshot. This one is of her and the woman. Willa.

Pretty, extremely fit, and openly snuggling with my mom on my parents' front porch. The front porch that leads inside the house. The house that leads to the backyard where the pool house is situated. The pool house where my dad is currently shacked up.

I'm typing a reply when the phone starts to buzz with an incoming FaceTime.

Dad, of course.

I answer, fully expecting his breakdown mode to be in high gear. Weepy eyes, glasses off, probably a glass of merlot in hand. He's all those things, plus a sun hat because he's sitting in a float in the dead center of the swimming pool.

"Dad, what are you doing using your phone in the pool?" iPhones can handle getting dropped in water, sure, but even the newest ones have limits. And I know for a fact Dad has already dropped his in the toilet and the birdbath twice. Each.

"They are Facebook official now!" he exclaims, ignoring my warnings.

"Dad, nobody cares about Facebook anymore," I reply, rolling my eyes.

"Well I do!" he cries. "All our friends do. The guys at the club do—she's brought her to the club. They golfed ten holes and then did the sauna before taking a photo together in front of everyone right there on the veranda."

"I know this is hard, but you two are breaking up. You had to expect that she would bring her out and about. You had to expect she would introduce her to your friends."

"I did, I did, but now that it's all happening, I just want it to be over."

I know he means the meet and greets and not his life, but I make a mental note to see if Nina can go over and check on him this afternoon.

"She served me papers."

"Divorce papers?" Now, this does surprise me.

"It's over and I don't know what to do without her," he says, his face breaking down as tears well in his eyes. "It's just happening so fast."

It hurts to see Dad in this state. It makes me angry again at Mom for making choices that put him here. And that thought makes me a whole different kind of angry. I want to put all of this on Mom, but I'm leaving out a crucial part in the narrative. Dad is a hopeless romantic who has built his happiness on someone else, and as he did, she felt trapped, went behind his back, just because she wanted something different for herself. Just because she wanted to look out for herself and her own happiness for once.

I'm afraid of being like him in a relationship. Of someone else's love defining my joy.

But there is an even deeper fear buried under the surface. Scarier for me to consider.

I'm afraid of becoming like my mom. Following my heart and breaking someone else's in the process.

As much as I want Julia to be my true north, I don't know if making her that is fair. To her, or to me. I don't know yet if I can let my intuition lead without a point I've designated as the end. If

I can see life as a joyous adventure and not worry so much about reaching a certain outcome.

An ideal outcome. A Happily Ever After.

I want to believe that the more I trust my inner truth, the more that truth will set my path free. I want to believe that even if Julia chose to walk away, I wouldn't crumble without her. No matter how much I want the life we might build together or how much I'd miss her if she were gone.

My mind conjures an image of the World tarot card, the meaning rising to the surface.

Life is more than just a *The End*.

The End is really only the beginning.

I look back into the FaceTime camera and talk Dad down from yet another wine and social media ledge. I promise him when I'm home tomorrow I will help him sort all this out. He's not alone. And then as soon as I hang up, I text Nina to do some stand-in-daughter recon, which she's happy to do after her dog-walking gig.

I want to be with Julia. For now, that's the only part I need figured out.

Chapter Thirty-Two

Julia

Most people know at least a few wedding day superstitions.

Rain is a good omen, despite how it can royally fuck with anything from the venue to the bride's updo.

Borrowing an item from a happily married woman and wearing it the day of is good luck.

Finding a spider in your clothing, while totally creepy if you aren't into arachnids, is supposed to be a portent of good health and happiness.

You're not supposed to see your betrothed before the ceremony.

You get it. You know.

The truth I've learned from working countless weddings over the last five years, is that every single thing can go right on the big day and the marriage can still fall apart after. Maybe weeks, months, years, it doesn't matter. The only omen that truly makes a difference is the love that passes between the couple.

Marriage isn't luck.

It's meaningful work.

Millie's eyes tell me she's ready. Sean's tears are a display incongruent with the jock I know he likes to play, since he isn't one deep down inside. Cash Kim, whose hair has been carefully styled to cover the patch of raw, blistered skin on his forehead, openly weeps, and both Banks and Tucker hold on for dear life as they all turn to man puddles right in front of my eyes.

Natalie is pristine, holding the bridesmaids' line at attention. They are all gorgeous—way less weepy than the dudes. Coco is the only one with a lip wobble. Piper, stoic as ever in the face of true love, hasn't flinched since she took her place. But when the bride and groom begin their vows, there's not a dry eye in the house. I'm overwhelmed with confidence that these two—with the support of the family and friends who found their way out to this desert oasis to bear witness—will have a life full of love and a marriage that stands the tests time always offers.

My eyes drift to the back row, where Kit sits. From here, I can't see her face or tell if she's tearing up. All I can see are her shoulders, bare in her strapless jumpsuit. All I can think about is the way her face would look up close to mine as she said the words *I do*.

A future with anyone didn't always feel like a safe bet.

First, because—though I do experience the occasional attraction toward someone of the nonfemme variety—the vast majority of my relationships are with women. When I came out, I had a feeling that my preference would be for women. Most of the people I liked were female identifying. At the time, same-sex marriage wasn't recognized nationwide. The happily ever after Kit is always going on about wasn't for everyone.

It's outdated now, like I said to Kit before we kissed yesterday, but back then I wasn't sure how I could have the family I longed for if I loved a woman and wanted to spend the rest of my life with her.

The norm made my desires seem unattainable.

Later on, after a few relationships—and subsequent breakups—I started to lose hope that I would ever find someone I wanted to make a go of it with. My eyes drift momentarily back to Piper, and I let myself cringe at past me for her foolishness. I wanted Piper to love me the way I loved her, and once I gave that up it became impossible to imagine a future together.

I want to believe that with time, Kit and I can create the kind of relationship that weathers storms, wants the best, embodies more than the vows couples say on their wedding day—embodies the two of us with all our imperfections and scars.

I want to believe it. I'm just not sure yet that I can trust that and just let go.

Let it happen.

The recessional begins to play and the whole audience rises to their feet to observe Millie and Sean as they leave. Healer Arynne stands at the geometric altar, her giant eyes misty, her job completed without any final obstructions to the wedding weekend. I should be watching, looking out for possible missteps. I should have gone ahead of them to the staging room, checked the champagne was chilled to perfection and had it ready and waiting for when they arrived. Those few minutes of alone time after the ceremony are critical to most brides and grooms.

I should be doing a lot of things, but instead I'm watching Kit press the back of her hand to her tearstained cheek, dabbing gently. I'm walking over to tuck up behind her chair. I'm relieved when she leans into me, tilting her head to rest against mine.

"Nothing but good vibes for these two," she says.

"For us, too," I reply. It's almost a question.

She doesn't say no. She just squeezes tighter, leans a little harder, says yes with her body, and I trust that her heart will follow.

~

Kit is fully in her element.

The showmanship is the best of the weekend so far. I haven't watched any of her YouTube videos yet, or googled that Kardashian episode Zoe informed me was "a big deal" in gaining her followers. I don't know if she's at her best, or if she can do better, but I don't want to miss a moment.

She gives Healer Arynne a three-card reading that makes my stomach hurt from holding in a deep belly laugh. There's a story playing out in the cards that Healer Arynne can't stand seeing in such exact terms. The Five of Swords followed by the Five of Pentacles and then the Hierophant (also a five), which even I know can't be good.

"Well, fives are curveballs. Where normally reversals are read more negatively, fives flip that on its head." All of her fives are upright. My skin sizzles with satisfaction as I watch Healer Arynne rebuke Kit's reading.

"Energetically this isn't feeling right to me," she spits. "Your deck needs a cleanse."

"I cleansed it before you stepped up," Kit says, calm and cool, but her smile threatens to crack and ruin it all.

"It didn't work, now did it?" Healer Arynne replies, shoving the cards out of order and turning away from Kit's table. I don't know, it seems pretty damn accurate to me.

I chuckle, grabbing a champagne flute from one of the passing trays.

Then Piper steps into my path.

Blocking out my view of Kit. Blocking my way forward.

Cunt-blocking me, hopefully for the last time.

She's got two glasses of champagne in hand. "I was going to offer—"

"I'm covered," I say, trying to step past her. She moves into my way.

"Truce, please," she says. She places one glass on the nearby table, and raises the other in surrender. "Just want to chat and then I swear, you can go back to . . ." She clears her throat. "Whatever it is that you're doing."

I should not take her up on the offer. Even just a chat with Piper can turn into a mindfuck of labyrinthine design. Our last few months together felt like being in an endless bad dream. Like following the exit signs in a parking garage but never getting out. We would have the same fights over and over, just with different set dressing, and every time I would walk out of them thinking that *this time* would be *the time* she finally understood my perspective. *This time* she would choose to respect me.

That time never came.

"Fine," I say, because I would rather keep her placated with a few minutes of my time than have to keep dodging her all night. "Let's chat."

I follow her out of the reception, winding back toward the main building.

I don't owe her anything, and in a few hours, I will no longer be working the Hayden-Morgan wedding. I will be off duty, and hopefully getting up to something naughty with Kit in her outdoor bathtub. In a few hours, I will not have to think about what Piper Cunningham wants from me again.

"Are you taking me off somewhere to murder me?" I quip,

making sure to add a chuckle to keep the mood light—if you can ever really keep it light when murder is mentioned.

She walks us into one of the alcove seating areas. This one has an outdoor couch and a few funky bamboo chairs all situated beside a mini bocce ball court. She stops beside one of the stray balls, picking it up with her free hand.

Okay, so, murder isn't totally off the table, I see.

"The wedding was beautiful," she begins. Mundane small talk. Piper is great at it. She's had years of practicing surface-level chitchat. "Every detail felt tailored to the two of them."

"That's usually the goal of a wedding planner," I reply, defenses up. Her eyes land on mine, steady and serious. I control my urge to swallow, but not the way my nerves spike, making the thrum of my pulse pound in my ears.

"This is my first chance to see one of your weddings in real time," she says, rolling the ball in the palm of her hand. "It makes me proud."

"Pride that is totally unwarranted."

She rolls her eyes, her Cheshire-Cat smile faltering. "Come on, I can take a little credit." She looks me up and down. I'm wearing a suit vest and pants that she bought me. Dark green Versace. One of the most expensive items I own and a gift from *her*. I packed in a robotic state. Checking off items on my list and not really thinking about choices.

I can't believe I picked this ensemble when I already knew she would be here.

Fuck my overextended brain.

"I'm donating this as soon as I get back to LA," I reply. I wish I could rend it to rags right here, but that would probably cross a professional boundary. Nudity at work is definitely frowned upon.

"It's designer. At least sell it on Poshmark or something." She's smirking.

"And what, send you half the profits?" I reply, trying not to smile. Never smile. Never show weakness or compassion or care with her.

"I'd settle for a dinner," she says. "On you."

My stomach sours. "I've made my position clear this whole weekend. I've told you I want nothing but the best for you, but that doesn't include having me in your life." Fuck my wobbling chin and my feelings.

"The tarot hottie isn't a reason to cut me out—"

Tarot hottie. She uses her nickname for Kit as a way to undercut her as a valid choice. My temper flares. "You're a narcissistic prick!" The words burst from me like an explosion. "*That's* why I am cutting you out. *That's* why I don't want anything to do with you."

Her jaw clenches. She steps forward, whipping out her phone.

I refuse to concede ground, so even though she's too close for comfort, I don't back up. She swipes the screen open to show me Kit's Instagram feed. In the corner, I see that she's signed in to one of her secret accounts. She's got a few, on all different platforms, that she uses to lurk / stalk everyone from potential interview subjects to friends she secretly hates.

"Do you follow her?" I ask, but I don't know why I would be surprised if she does. Keeping tabs on her competition is one of her trademarks. Her eyes darken, the color chilling. She's been caught and she hates that. I tense my jaw. "How long have you been following her?"

"That doesn't matter—" she starts.

"Since you got here? Since you saw her?" Her brow edges up

ever so slightly. Fuck. "Oh, no, you've been following her since I told you her name."

"I just wanted to know what was so special about her."

"You're deranged, you see that, right?"

She shoves her phone in my face, ignoring the accusation. "She just broke up with a *man* she'd been living with for months."

Admittedly, I hadn't given the dude much thought. Kit didn't seem very concerned about her breakup, so I wasn't too worried about fallout. Her freak-out that led her to bail to the desert for this job was her parents' split, not her own.

"And?" is the reply I go with.

"She's not out, Julia."

"You weren't out for years, that's not a reason to break up." I can tell this stings. In her mind that is the only valid point I made when I ended things. The rest of my argument, about how she treated me and how suffocatingly miserable my life had become with her, was debatable at best, inconsequential at worst.

"Admit it," she continues. "A part of you is afraid that this is nothing but a desert-induced, wedding-influenced *curiosity*." Her eyes blaze, a triumphant, prideful expression working its way across her face. This is her final flaming dart, but it doesn't hit its mark.

I know what I have with Kit is the beginning of something great. I know that because I feel more like myself than I have in a long time. Freer and ready for anything. Willing to let go. Trying to trust that I can.

I'm focusing on that. Not whatever her Instagram feed would have me believe.

"I don't have to explain myself to you," I say, ready to walk away. "You can't win 'em all, and you definitely aren't winning this one."

I turn to walk away, but she grabs my bicep to hold me in place.

"Don't," she pleads.

"Let go," I reply.

But she doesn't. Her grip tightens and I have to break it. I yank my arm away and hiss, "We are never, ever getting back together," storming off with Taylor Swift's iconic breakup song playing in my brain like a soundtrack.

Chapter Thirty-Three

Kit

Trying to wrap up a reading with one of Millie's high school friends who didn't make the wedding party cut isn't going all that well. She's pissed, mostly attending the wedding to shit on the whole affair, and her pettiness made an appearance in her spread.

"It's just like, who the hell even is Piper?" she asks me. I have some theories on the tip of my tongue, but not a single one of them is safe for work. "She just weaseled her way into the lineup as soon as Ellen was hospitalized." She raises her brows with meaning.

"Oh, well, the cards indicate that you need to release your judgments—"

"Or is it that I'm right?" She purses her lips, cocking out her hip in defiance.

"No, usually when Judgment appears it is a prompt for the querent"—I point to her—"to look inward and assess where they are not being fair and balanced."

She sucks through her straw, chewing on the end as she glares from me back to the cards.

"Whatever, I'm getting another piece of cake," she says. Gone before I can reply.

"Good riddance," I say under my breath, shaking my head as I clean up the spread. I spritz the air with my cleansing spray bottle, when my phone buzzes with a text from Nina. She's been asking me to send her a pic of Julia and me together since I came out to her over the phone yesterday.

by now, you two are probably all liquored up

loosened up

give me the goods

I snicker, responding with a selfie of me making a kissy face.

you are gorgeous but I know what you look like

I want to see what you + Julia looks like

"Hey," Julia says, coming up from behind me and nudging the palm of my hand with the tip of her finger. I lock my phone and set it on the table beside my cards before spinning around to grip Julia by the waist. Her face is close enough to kiss but she doesn't lean in, so I don't either.

"You okay?" I ask, when it takes her a second to meet my eyes.

"Yeah, yeah, just tired," she says. "Ready to get back to LA." Her lips quirk into a small smile when I press my forehead to hers.

"Same," I say. "But only because I want to get this thing out on the open road and see what it can do." I press against her, letting our curves meld and mold together so she gets my meaning. She fits her lips with mine, and when she pulls back I see the faintest hint of tears forming in her eyes.

"I'm not going anywhere," I say to reassure her. "We're having a date at a place with fabric napkins."

She looks me in the eyes. "Kit, will you dance with me?"

The words are weighted, hefty with meaning, tinged with hope. She wants to believe me when I say I want this, and I want it out *there*, and I want to be out; but also she still needs more proof. It doesn't hurt as much as I expect it to, to know she doesn't quite trust me. It lights a fire in the pit of my stomach, making me want to take action.

"Yes," I say. "I'd love to."

She runs her hand down my arm until she reaches mine. Her grip is sure and gentle. I let her lead me to the dance floor they've erected in the center of the space. The stars overhead and the glow of a waning full moon, serene in the indigo ink expanse of the night sky, set the scene. She twirls me out until her grip almost releases. Our eyes lock over the parquet floor. I feel attention shifting to us, interest drifting, but Julia is the only one I see.

She twirls me in, her left hand pressed to my lower back, her right twining our fingers and curving our arms, just as Taylor Swift's "This Love" begins to play over the sound system.

The tinny, dreamy melody. The winsome, willowy vocals.

The words catch in my ears, making this moment feel as fated as every other that led us back to each other. This song came out the same year we fell apart. It played on the radio and was all over playlists, at parties, for months. A taunt of the love we lost that I couldn't believe would ever come back to life. It's about that kind of soul-aching connection that can sometimes arrive when we aren't ready for it and then the only thing for us to do is let it go.

I tighten my hold on her waist. My chest is tight, my breath catches as I remember her absence from my arms, in my life. It stung like a scorpion and throbbed like an injury deep inside my bones.

And then here she was again, a force I couldn't ignore. Breaking down my walls, waking up all my senses. This love is alive because finally I am ready to let it thrive.

We kiss as the chorus rushes to a crescendo. Tongues tangle, her breath and mine becoming *ours*; her body softens against me and my closed eyes fill with tears. When I open them, the tears rolling down my cheek, she kisses once, twice, both cheeks.

"I don't want to struggle through the night with someone new," I say.

"I don't want to ever watch you leave again," she replies, her lips wobbling with tears she's holding back.

She is the one I need. No more running.

"You won't," I whisper against her cheek. She buries her face in my hair, tightening her grip around my waist. "This love is real."

When she looks at me again, her cheeks are wet with tears.

But she's smiling.

We sway together until the song drifts to the end and the mood on the dance floor shifts to something more upbeat. She draws back, laughing when I shimmy and twirl, but we don't stick around for more.

“I need to finish up my set,” I say, pointing to the tarot table.

“I’m thinking of getting Zoe to cover for me for the rest of the night—once you’re done?” she asks, sheepish, her cheeks flushed. I press a kiss to the constellation of freckles on her neck.

“I say *hell yes*,” I reply, kissing her one more time before letting her go. I watch her walk away to find Zoe.

I keep wanting to pinch myself to convince myself that this is real. Julia and I really found our way back to each other. The prophecy that we were Twin Flames destined to break apart, destined to wind up together, was true. It almost makes me want to go back to Old Pasadena and find Madame Moira just to say, *Hey, remember us? We’re the two twelve-year-olds you informed were meant for each other and, plot twist, you were right.*

When I reach my tarot table, I see the ghost of a notification darkening on my screen. I pick it up, absently swiping when I see it’s a few back-to-back texts from Nina. She’s probably berating me for that pic again.

But when my eyes focus on the texts, that is so not what it is.

The first comes directly after a FaceTime notification, reading: babe call me back immediately

The second and third are pleas for me to reply.

The fourth is a link to a TikTok and the preview image is of me.

Me and Julia.

Dancing.

My heart rate skyrockets. My mouth goes dry.

With a shaky hand I click on the link. It opens in the app, spinning for a second before fully loading.

It’s a video of us dancing. Kissing. Snuggling. Lost in the moment together.

It's a video of us, but it looks like a movie. Like we're at the earned romantic climax, and not the compulsory third act breakup, and as much as I want to believe we're ready to walk into the sunset together, I can't. Every pin holding up questions I have for myself and my future falls from the vision board of my life as I watch us spin around the dance floor.

My eyes drop to the text on the video.

> She wanted sympathy for her breakup but she was keeping a secret. #mysticmaven hooks up while on the job. Geez, let the sheets cool. Trying a woman this time, too??? Fast, even for a serial dater with no identity of her own. Being alone must be her kryptonite. #chooseyourowntarotadventure

My legs wobble as the words sink in. Whoever wrote this yanked my fears out in the open and posted about it on TikTok. They used my hashtags so all the people who follow those would see it as soon as it hit their feed. I tap over to Instagram and Twitter to see it has loaded up on each of the sites.

My followers are flipping out in the comments. They are sharing it, calling out the account that posted it while simultaneously spreading the fucking word like an unchecked California wildfire. My body reels and I fall against the table, bracing but not able to stay steady.

Coco is the one whose arms break my fall. She heaves me up, letting me sway against her as I try to keep my bones from going liquid.

"You okay, Kit?" she asks, and I can smell the alcohol on her breath. I wish I'd had one too many and that was why my head was swimming. I drop the phone to the table in front of me and I watch her gaze fall to the screen. The *mysticmaven* hashtag is alive with the video. Taking over my other content. Taking over everything.

Over and over and over.

Me sharing an intimate moment in what I thought was a safe space.

Me forced to come out.

This is not how I wanted to do it.

This is not how anyone wants to do it.

In a few hours it will be everywhere. My friends and fellow influencers will be coming into my DMs with all kinds of support and trios of hearts and GIFs of girls kissing and fuck fuck fuck I don't want that right now.

My haters will spew vitriol like Linda Blair in *The Exorcist*. Heads spinning around with gleeful possessed mania. I refuse to look at the comments to see how many of the trolls have already found their way in there or are the ones actively sharing it.

My mom—Mom will see this. There is no way Dad won't find out. And no matter how they react, I won't be the one who told them. It won't be coming from me, on my terms.

"Who did this?" Coco asks me, getting in my eyeline. "Do you recognize the account?"

"It's a fake account," I say.

"It has to be someone at the wedding." Coco stands up straight, looking around as if she'll be able to identify the culprit with just a glance.

"I know who it is," I say. Coco follows my gaze to the edge of the dance floor.

Piper stands beneath a lantern glowing red. The shimmer of a champagne flute in her hand. The glimmer of a malicious grin on her face.

"Why would she—"

"She's Julia's ex."

Coco's response is lost in the whir of blood rushing past my ears, the spinning dervish of my thoughts as I think back over the events of the evening. Before we danced, Julia's expression was pained. Her makeup muted. Her mascara-tinged lower lashes smudged. Could she have had an argument with Piper while I was distracted working? She told me Piper was vindictive; she told me she always gets what she wants. I know Piper wanted her back—her reading all but confirmed that for me.

"I have to get out of here," I say, gathering up my tarot deck. The cards spray out in my haste, dropping from my grip and falling all around the table. I frantically grab them up, while Coco tries to assist.

"We need to let Julia know," she says. "I think she'd want to help."

My eyes fly to hers. "And risk blowing up this wedding? No." I shove the cards in my bag and yank up my phone. Piper's *ideal* is me running scared and Julia broken, back in her arms. She knows about our history and she knows me bailing will trigger Julia's insecurity about what happened when we were teenagers. I know that no matter what I say, Julia will try to stop me from leaving.

But I have to get to my parents before they see this. If that's even possible.

I have to at least try to tell them on my own terms.

My heart slams rapidly, pumping me up with confidence, not sending me flying with fear.

I have to face this head-on.

"Going somewhere?" Piper asks as I near her. She takes a generous sip from her champagne flute.

"You know this is the kind of behavior you can get canceled for?"

"Like I care about a few snowflakes on the internet calling for my blood," she replies with a sneer. "Besides, they couldn't prove it was me."

I'm not dumb enough to engage her anymore. I swipe a champagne flute from a passing tray, lifting it toward her as if in cheers. Her brow rises.

I aim for her face and shoot.

Chapter Thirty-Four

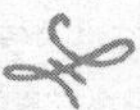

Julia

A piercing shriek from the other side of the reception area pulls me out of my conversation with Zoe. I turn around just in time to see the back of Kit's head walking away from a champagne-drenched Piper.

The shrieker.

My first thought is that Piper is taking a shot at Kit now that she can't get to me. My second thought is that Kit might think this is too much drama, and instead of dealing with it head-on, she'll run away. But that doesn't feel right, not now, not after everything we've been through this weekend. I'm stepping away from Zoe midexplanation of the end-of-event checklist when she clamps her hand around my forearm to stop me.

"You should see this," she says, handing over her phone.

It takes me a second to figure out what I'm looking at because it doesn't make logical sense in my brain. It shouldn't exist and it damn well shouldn't be on TikTok. It's a video of Kit and me dancing, kissing, twirling, and whoever posted it has cut themselves in reacting with a heart eyes filter.

"I don't get it," I say, trying to process it and failing. "How is this here?"

"The Mystic Maven hashtag has over a million followers. That's how it's spreading so fast—whoever uploaded this used it to get the attention of her following." Zoe looks practically ill as she relays this information. "From what I can tell, this is not the original video. That one went up maybe fifteen minutes ago, while you two were still dancing."

"This is outing her." I feel sick saying it out loud.

Zoe nods, solemn, and then swipes around until she gets to the original video, which was posted from an anonymous account. The same kind of profile picture–free, nonsensical handle type of account that Piper uses to stalk and lurk and fuck around with people she hates.

Rapidly, details drop into place with clarity.

After I shut her down, promising once and for all there was no hope of reconciling, Piper had nothing to lose. She filmed us dancing. She uploaded it. She got revenge.

She wants to drive Kit away. Even if it won't get me back.

She wants to make her suffer, out Kit in this horribly public way she did not consent to, simply because Piper can't stand losing.

I cross the dance floor in a fugue state of rage.

My fingernails dig into my palms but the pain only adds urgency to my movements. It's impossible to keep a lid on my anger even though I know that I should. Blowing up at Piper—a member of the wedding party and close personal friend of the bride—will surely have consequences. But I really don't care. I'm sick of keeping my cool just so I can be some perfect version of a professional woman.

You can be a pro and feel your fucking feelings all at once.

I whirl her around by the sticky, champagne-slick shoulder. Her mascara is running, but I can't tell if it's from crying or champagne or both.

"Kit hasn't even come out to her parents, and she definitely isn't out online." My voice is high-pitched, ripping through the sound of the music. "And you just posted a video of us kissing. You *outed* her." I show her Zoe's phone. She doesn't even look at it, refuses to make eye contact with her shameful act. "You did this!"

"I didn't do anyth—"

"Stop lying," I plead-scream. "Stop pretending to have changed, to care about anything or anyone but yourself." She balks at my words, putting on a disgusted, defensive scowl as a mask.

"I don't have to tolerate this treatment from the staff."

"Oh, so now I'm nothing but staff?" I shove her shoulders with both hands, but she tightens her core, holding her footing firmly in place. "Half an hour ago you were trying to win me back."

"Get over yourself." She swipes her hair over her shoulder, eyes rolling.

"I can't believe I ever cared about you," I say, shoving her again. This time she loses her balance enough to stumble back a couple of steps.

"You did more than care about me, Julia. You *loved* me. You told me all the goddamn time," she says, sneering down her perfect ski slope nose at me. "It was so pathetic."

Love isn't an everyday thing.

"Not being able to say the word. Not being able to show it—that's what's pathetic."

"Bet it feels pretty good getting to reject me," she replies wryly. "Even if your tarot hottie is a casualty of our little war."

I ball my hand into a fist. Someone grabs my wrist, stopping me before I can swing.

"Don't," Zoe says, pulling me back. Her dark, kind eyes search my face. "You do this, she wins." Zoe's appearance drags me back to reality and puts my body back in time and space. I'm working this wedding—this important wedding.

"Why don't we take this"—it's Millie's soft but commanding voice—"out of the view of the guests." I flick my attention over to see she's standing near Piper but looking out past the string lights that form the perimeter of the reception space.

Beside her, the rest of the bachelorette party crew begin to gather.

Jenni definitely has her phone up, poised to film, and I can tell by the glint of anger in her eyes she's hoping to catch Piper doing something malicious. Natalie's grin isn't subtle. Heather looks ready to throw her own punch, and Maddie and Lisa are on their phones typing like mad.

It's no surprise to me that the rest of Millie's friends hate Piper.

Just not as much as I do.

My eyes find hers. "No, there's no need to take it anywhere else. I'm done." I straighten and Zoe releases my wrist. "I'm done with you. I'm done with everything you made me and everything I never wanted to be because of you. I hope your bitterness rots you from the inside out. It's just too bad I won't be around to watch it."

I have to find Kit. I have to tell her that I'm all in, no matter what.

I have to tell her she's not alone in figuring this mess out.

I drag my eyes away from Piper's cold stare, softening my expression when it lands on Millie. "I'm sorry to have made a scene and I hope you won't hold it against me, but I really have to go."

My hopes of a stellar performance are dashed. I wouldn't blame Millie if she bad-mouths me all over town after this.

"Take care of her," Millie says, cutting Piper a withering stare as she steps around to face her. Piper flinches beneath it. "Lisa, Maddie?"

"We're trying," Lisa says.

"They never want to take anything down anymore," Maddie adds. Millie turns her attention back to Piper.

"I can't believe you begged to be a bridesmaid. For what? Because the wedding planner was your ex and you had some scheme to get her back? And then you outed Kit because you lost—it's just so petty and small." Millie shakes her head. "I really despise both of those things, Piper, and you know that."

Coco runs up, panting. "I followed Kit to her Airstream trailer trying to talk her into taking a beat before bailing, but she's frantic. I think you're about to lose your chance to stop her." She directs this last comment specifically to me.

I don't think. I just run.

"She's already getting her car pulled around by valet!" Coco calls after me.

Thank God I'm wearing close-toed, low-heeled shoes. It makes running along the paths that wind through the courtyards and into the main building easier. I wrench the doors open, stopping only momentarily when I enter the building to look around for any sign that Kit is waiting inside for her car. When I don't see her, I make a beeline to the double doors and shove out into the night.

Light bleeds down from the overhead lamp. On either side of

the doors they've set up heaters to stave off the cold. Her car idles as the valet attendant loads her bags.

"Don't go," I say. Her head whips around in my direction.

"Julia." She says only my name but it feels like a magic spell. Her eyes are red and puffy from crying. She's still the most beautiful woman in the world to me.

"I saw the video." I step closer. One step, nothing more—I'm afraid to spook her. "It's all my fault."

"It's Piper's fault—" She's shaking her head, but I interrupt.

"I should've known she'd do something like this after I told her there was no hope of us ever getting back together."

"Her going full villain is not on you." She slams the passenger door closed. The Sexy Times bag is in the front seat of the car, right next to her bag of tarot decks.

"I shouldn't have asked you to dance when I knew she might be watching. I wanted to prove to myself that you weren't afraid to be with me in front of a crowd of people." I am desperate to get the words out before I lose my chance, but my throat is tight, trying to swallow them back down. "That was wrong and selfish of me—I'm so sorry, Kit."

Every bit of control I thought I had was an illusion, and that makes my body feel off-balance. My head spins. I take another step closer but she doesn't. She's not moving toward me, and even though she isn't moving away either, it feels like a chasm is opening between us.

"I wanted to dance with you," she says, eyes trailing over my face like she's trying to memorize it. Hers are shot through with red from crying. "I made my own choice. I don't regret it." She sucks her lips between her teeth, her eyes watering. "I wish you would've let me in on your reason."

"I really screwed this up—" I reach, she doesn't.

"You helped, but Piper did *this*." She's got her phone in hand, and her fingers visibly tighten around it when she says "*this*." "Not you. Or me."

Her assertion that this isn't my fault, or hers, makes hope flicker to life in my gut.

"We can figure this out together," I start, desperation laced through my words. "I know we can—"

"I have to get back to my parents before this news reaches them," she says, just as the attendant closes the back door of her Jeep. "Everything is such a mess—Dad is already so raw from Mom leaving for another woman. Mom follows me on Instagram, she follows the hashtags, there's a real chance she will see this if I don't get home now—I have to try." I can tell she's trying not to spiral, but her urgency and adrenaline come off in waves of anxiety.

"Let me come with you," I say, my voice quivering. "Let me help you through this."

Her eyes soften, but she shakes her head once. "They might be glad to see you—really, I'm sure they would—but they'd *definitely* be embarrassed to have this conversation in front of you." She moves and the curves of her features find the lamplight over my head. "This has to be a just me thing."

Tears well in her eyes.

I want to take her in my arms. I want to take this pain away.

"I don't know how to be this true version of myself yet, Julia." She chews on her bottom lip. "I don't know who that girl was in that video, looking all sure of herself, so at ease."

"That video is intrusive and wrong—"

"No—I mean, *yes*—" She breaks off, blinking, tears dropping down her cheeks.

"There's a *but*," I break in. "There doesn't have to be."

"Yes, there does," she replies, inhaling deep to steady herself. She wipes at her cheeks. "The Kit in that video isn't scared. She's queer as hell and loving it. I want to be that Kit."

"You are." My voice is a plea.

"That Kit wouldn't let this video be the way her parents find out the truth. She wouldn't run from any of this. She'd stand on her own two feet, waving a metaphorical bi flag." Her smile is swift, real, even though her voice cracks and her cheeks shimmer with tears.

She's not backing down. She's not running away. As much as I want to hold on to her, she's asking me to let her go be brave. She's showing me she's ready for this.

This life filled to the brim with her truth; no more half a life, half a body awake.

"I have to do this part on my own." She pauses, the air heavy with the weight of her words. "Because *that* Kit is the closest I've felt to *me*." Her eyes pin me in place. "I don't want to hide this from my parents anymore. I don't want to pretend I'm some ideal that was never even real. I don't want to lose you again."

I shoot forward, gripping her hand, tugging her closer. My nose brushes over hers as a shiver of desperation surges in my chest. I love her, and she is asking me to let her go.

"I'm not going anywhere." I brush her cheek, tucking her hair behind her ear and letting my fingertips dance down her neck. She doesn't resist the affection, but instead, she drops her forehead against mine, holding my body to hers.

"Neither am I."

She gives me a soul-deep, world-bending kiss. My heart cracks open, all the tall, tall walls tumbling down. I brush my thumbs over her cheekbones and wind my fingers in her hair. My tongue searches her mouth as a cry rips from my throat.

I already pine for her and she's still right here.

She pulls away, keeping me held in her gaze. "I didn't regret falling for you that summer. I don't regret anything we did here."

She pulls away, turning to leave me behind.

"I gave up on psychics," I say, fighting the despair in my voice, but feeling it all the same. "I gave up on magic. I didn't believe there could be a power in the universe bigger than human will. I stopped thinking there was anything worth risking my heart for."

Our eyes lock across the expanse of her car hood. Across time and space and history and hurt. Over years spent searching for something that feels as real as each other.

"I'm glad I was wrong."

I know that no matter how hard I want to hold on, I can't. I have to let her go. I have to trust her to come back.

That's what love really is.

Not possession. Not control.

Love is letting go.

I watch her climb into her car and buckle up for the ride back to LA. She leaves me under the same constellations where last night we had sex, shared secrets, and fell in love like we'd never stopped. Where, tonight, I choose to trust the universe—her, me, whatever this tether between us truly is—for the first time.

This time, she will come back to me.

Chapter Thirty-Five

Kit

The desert turns to cityscape but I barely notice what's happening outside my car windows as I drive. Fear pings around my rib cage like a pinball. I let my heart pound and my skin slick with sweat. I let my tears fall and my brain play tricks on my body, convincing it that feeling this is the real danger, when it's really the opposite.

This is the most alive I've ever been.

The most in my body, the most in my intuition. As scary as going it alone to tell them is, it also makes me feel powerful. For so much of my life I've played the role I was cast in. It was so easy, the effort it took never really showing through the cracks. I did it because it felt safe, because it was expected, because it looked really great on paper.

Not doing that anymore is my compass finally pointing North.

I don't know what will happen with that video—how it will affect my online persona, what repercussions it might have for my hopes to reach higher-end clientele. I can only hope that once the dust settles, I'll find a way to reclaim this moment for myself.

I don't let myself think about what happens with Julia when this is all over, because I don't know yet how long it will take for me to be ready *for real*. The not knowing can't negate the rest. I meant what I said to her before I left. I don't regret her, and I'm not running away.

I'm taking my own path to get to her.

To us.

I wipe my eyes and turn the music up and somehow I make it all the way home.

I beat down on the horn as I pull into the driveway.

Mom swings open the front door, dressed in a nightgown and housecoat combo. Willa's sleek form makes an outline in the front window.

"Katherine?" Mom calls down from the porch. I'm sure she's squinting to make sure that it's me. "Is that you, Kitten?" I see a golf club in her hand, poised as a weapon.

"Yeah, Mom, can you come down here?" I stand with my car door open, blaring the horn a few more times. Mom covers her ears, abandoning her nine iron and stepping off the porch.

"Will you stop"—*honk*—"with that"—*honk*—"hideous noise?"

"Where's Dad?" I ask, honking again and drowning out her reply.

"Jesus Christ—stop that!" She's off the porch, a pair of Crocs on her feet, rushing around the front of my car. "He's in the pool house—you know he sleeps like the dead." She places her hand over the horn, blocking me from honking again. I shoot out of the car and down the driveway to where the gate sits open even though it's almost two a.m.

"I told you guys to lock the gate at night," I spit in her direction. "What is the point of having a security gate if you don't use it?"

Mom's shuffling behind me trying to keep up and she gasps for me to slow down.

"Please, my knees—Kitten, are you okay? You're acting very erratic right now—you didn't take drugs, did you? People are always taking drugs in the desert."

"I didn't take drugs," I say as I scale the steps to the pool house front door. I proceed to bang on the door with the force of an eager intruder.

"You haven't answered any calls or texts—is this about the bisexual thing?" Mom asks.

"Bisexual thing?" Stay calm. Stay in your body. Stay in this moment.

"You know . . ." She points toward the house where I assume her girlfriend is hiding from me and my car horn.

"Yes. It is." I beat on the door again, and finally see the bedroom light flick on. Dad must have had a good writing evening if he fell asleep before three a.m. "Also, it's not."

"That's so confusing," she whines, scrunching her face into a pout.

The door to the pool house bursts open to reveal Dad, glasses askew on his face, dressed in a t-shirt that says "Tom Hanks is my hero" and some plaid pajama pants.

"Cupcake?" His voice is thick with sleep. His eyes slowly travel from me to my mom, who is in a growing state of distress. "Camille, why are you over here? My side—" He walks out to the edge of the porch. "Your side."

Mom's eyebrow fishhooks and she points a long finger at me.

"Your daughter is melting down and likely any minute the cops with arrive. You know that busybody Missy Green has it out for me—"

"Oh please," Dad rebukes. "Like you haven't given her every reason to despise you. Case in point, you called animal control on her for having a pet opossum—"

"Opossums aren't pets and everyone knows tha—"

"Fuck me with a flamethrower, will you both please shut up?!"

That does it. Both of their mouths seal closed in shock.

"Please sit down," I say, lowering my voice. I motion to the rocking chairs sitting nearby. There are three. One for each of us. Will Dad take his in the divorce? I blink back the tears that immediately well in my eyes. "I have to tell you something."

They creep down into the two rockers farthest from each other. That never would have happened before. Before, they would have sat side by side, holding hands across the expanse between them.

I cannot fixate on this or I'm going to burst into tears.

The only solace I have is that Mom doesn't seem to have seen the video yet. It's a surprise that she hasn't, but she's never held anything in this long, so I'm guessing I'm in the clear. At least where coming out to my mom and dad are concerned.

"What's up?" Dad asks, rubbing his eye with the tip of his pointer finger underneath his glasses.

I clear my throat and wish I'd gotten a little bit drunk before I woke them both up to tell them I'm queer.

"I—well, here's the thing," I stammer, eloquence and resolve dissolving beneath their gaze. I close my eyes for a split second, seeing Julia's face first, and then the compass in my own soul.

Spinning, spinning, spinning.

It's not just about the gay. It's about so much more and that's why this is so hard.

"I can't even make a decision without touching a tarot deck."

I spit out the words like they're a spicy hot pepper my sweet little tongue can't take. When I open my eyes, it's to see the two bewildered faces of my two exhausted parents. "You smothered me with expectation—"

"I'm pretty sure we've been extremely supportive despite the fact that we do not understand how *tarot reader* is a real job," Mom says, batting her lashes and tensing up her face.

"No, you're right. No matter what job I had or what I studied in college, no matter how many guys I dated or lived with, you were always supportive." I direct this more to Mom, and I can feel Dad edging over, trying to get in my line of sight.

Dad was the one I was terrified to disappoint.

"You sold me on a life that was impossible to achieve. One you both knew wasn't even really the life you were leading." I look between them now and can feel the well of emotion ready to erupt within me.

Deep hurt and all this need, years of never feeling like enough.

"We didn't think it was important to tell you about your mother's history," Dad says with a sigh. "How was it relevant to you?"

"These things, no one gives you a guidebook to follow," Mom says, dropping all pretense in her voice for the first time in such a long time, I forgot what she sounds like without it. "I didn't think it mattered that I was bisexual, since I was married to a man."

The erasure of her own identity helped me be more afraid of mine.

"But you still tried to give me a guide with a really important chapter missing," I say, throttling my voice to try to control the waver. I swallow a lump in my throat but it bursts out, making my lips wobble.

"We were just trying to be aspirational," Dad replies, but his face shows the signs of breaking down. Tears threaten behind his thick glasses, big in the magnification.

"Aspirational, Dad, come on—the Ideal Rom-Com Life Path," I say, almost choking on the words before they come out.

"Oh, Kitten, no, that wasn't prescriptive—" Mom tries.

"Mom." It's all I say. It's all I need to. The look I give her lets her know the rest.

"You're right," she whispers. "She's right."

Every smile came with a story. Every moment of my life was a narrative he wanted to play out in a specific way. My life wasn't the messy, complicated existence of a young woman finding herself. It was a script with a specific, preplotted ending and any scenes that didn't fit were scrapped. Unimportant. Ignored on the cutting room floor.

"Dad." I crouch in front of him, gripping his hands in mine. "I shouldn't have listened to you." His brows are like caterpillars finding each other on his face. "I should've been listening to me."

"I never said I had all the answers—"

"Clint." Mom's voice is a low warning. "Life with you is a pressure cooker and you're the only one who can turn it off."

Mom and I meet eyes. She gets it, just like I thought she would. She hurts, probably more than I can even understand.

Dad's face creases, tears threatening to fall. "I'm sorry I made you feel that way—I didn't mean to." He grips my hands, worrying them between his own. "I didn't see it that way, I didn't—" His voice cracks.

"I know you didn't." I clutch his hands and now his tears make good on their threat. "I know you're not a villain." He was doing his best, even if it wasn't the best. "It was a lot easier to be what you expected, and Mom expected, and then what YouTube expected, and TikTok, and Instagram, and boyfriends, and friends, and—to make all that work I had to shove down my own truth."

I don't think I can look him in the face for this part. I rise from in front of him, dropping into the chair between him and Mom. I take a few measured breaths while they watch, but I can feel Mom revving up to fill the silence. I'm about to lose my window.

Now or never, Kit.

"I like women, too."

My voice is small but I'm proud there's no wobble in it. I close my eyes to shut out the world, to let them have their reaction and not feel like they have to hide it on their faces.

"You what?" Dad exclaims the question.

"She's bi, Clint," Mom says, like she's trying to shush him. "Or pan or queer or—"

"I don't need you to list every label in the sexual identity flag, Camille," Dad snips back.

My eyes still pinned closed, I snap, "I don't know how I'm labeling myself yet, so can we just *stop*?"

Silence stretches after my words. I feel them beside me, fumbling through this with me. I know they're looking at me and each other. I know they aren't sure what to say now. But in the quiet, my own thoughts whirl. The relief is bigger than I expected, like a bubble popped in my chest and now there's all this space to breathe. But there's also rawness. A sensitivity that makes me afraid to open my eyes, like I'm a person who's been in a dark room for too long emerging to blink into afternoon sun.

"Cupcake." Dad's voice. One of his hands grips one of mine.

"Kitten," Mom adds. Taking the other.

"We're not going anywhere." They say it together.

I blink my eyes open and turn to look at them. Dad's gazing at me with tears in his eyes, Mom's face is wet. My eyes fill up at the sight of both of my parents crying, with me, for me. Dad reaches over, brushing my cheek with his thumb.

"Well done."

"What do you mean?" I exhale, tears dripping into my mouth.

"For telling us." He tugs off his glasses to wipe at his eyes.

"You're not upset with me?" I ask, and I feel so small and scared. So much like a kid looking for their approval. "Disappointed?"

"No, never—"

"But Dad, you've been freaking out over Mom being bi. You've been heartbroken."

"I was heartbroken that she cheated on me," Dad says, with a small grunt of disdain.

"Cheating is an awfully strong word," Mom inserts.

"Not that she likes women, too," Dad adds before she can say more. "I don't fault her for that part."

Mom grips my other hand, patting emphatically. I whip my head around to look at her.

"He's surprised." She bends toward me, kissing my cheek. "I always knew deep down."

Our eyes connect. There are so many things I want to talk to her about now that all of this is out in the open.

"But the Ideal Rom-Com Life Path—"

"My Screenwriters of South Pasadena Reddit has a whole thread about the need for queer rom-coms in a largely cis-het space," Dad adds, a spark of humor in his voice. "Be the change, I suppose."

My life is still his favorite movie, but I guess as long as he is okay with whatever ending I want, that's good enough progress for now.

"You're not the one to write that movie, Clint," Mom chimes in.

"I'm not saying I am," Dad replies. "It's just interesting and I thought Kit might like to read it."

Mom winks at me. "I suppose you could share that Reddit thing to the Larson fam group chat."

"Oh, you suppose?" Dad replies with another grunt.

"Wait, so the group chat isn't going dormant?" I ask, and I don't know why my lip wobbles and fresh tears prick at the corners of my eyes.

A look passes between them. It's the kind that comes with years together. A badge of being truly known, something you can never lose once you have it.

"Of course it isn't, silly," Mom says, nudging my shoulder with hers.

"Stuck with both of us forever, I'm afraid," Dad adds.

They both come in for cheek kisses and I scream like a kid trying to escape.

"I have to ask, why are you telling us now? At three a.m. instead of over coffee at a reasonable hour?" Mom feigns a yawn. "Not that I mind."

"I'm going viral," I say.

Mom blinks in surprise, going for her phone in the pocket of her robe. I press her hand away.

"It's a really long story, but I kind of fell in love with someone at the wedding I was working." I cringe, bracing for how the last part will hit them both. "You know her. Julia Kelley, from high school."

Mom screeches, gripping me by the shoulders and forcing a hug.

I'll have to tell them the whole story—or, like, the PG version of the story. But for now I settle on, "I may need to stay here for a while. I need to figure some stuff out."

Mom looks to Dad. "I'll get the air mattress from the garage."

Dad shuffles off toward the garage, Mom calling out orders to him to *watch out for black widows* and *while you're in there could you get my old aerobics videos down from the top shelf?*

I drop back into the rocker, leaning my head against the wood.

This is what it feels like to trust your gut and follow it. Feel the fear and do it anyway.

Being with Julia this weekend reminded me that I am a person capable of doing that. I need more of that in my life. I need more following my compass. I need more faith in myself.

Then I need to find my way back to her.

Chapter Thirty-Six

Julia

ONE MONTH LATER

It's been a dream of mine to have a space in the Arts District in downtown LA ever since I started working on Rodeo Drive at Love, Always. Most people would argue that reaching Rodeo Drive is a better life goal, but Angelenos know what's up. The Arts District is where innovators set up shop, and all kinds of people from all walks of life flock.

I check my phone to see if Zoe has replied to my text, but she hasn't. Probably driving. She is a stickler for the *no texting and driving* rule, and I am respecting her boundary about it.

I'm still at the beginning of my six-month noncompete clause after resigning from Love, Always on mostly amicable terms. My boss tried to keep me on by dangling carrots she hoped I'd chase. *Three more weeks of vacation time. A forty-five percent pay increase. A title change that allows you to have first pick of clients.* The job security and the money were hard to let go of, but I'm getting pretty good at relinquishing control. Not expert level yet, but learning fast.

The first thing I did when I got back from the desert was hand in my resignation.

The second thing I did was immediately donate half my wardrobe to charity, including the green Versace I wore to Millie's wedding. Piper's gift to me, now tainted not only with her touch, but also with the scent of that night's painful memories. It was a purge of more than just my work wardrobe and other morbidly meaningful items, and it's taken me a while to come to any kind of equilibrium with how this new, less buttoned-up Julia Kelley wants to look.

Today, for instance, I've paired some moto boots with belted pin-striped slacks and an old Fleetwood Mac t-shirt that used to be my stepmom's but was stolen by me one Christmas in college. It shrunk, and I cropped it, then added a fitted leather jacket since it's a little nippy in LA today. December usually is, and it's been uncharacteristically rainy already. No white Christmas is likely, but a wet one seems guaranteed.

I haven't minded the gloom. It's suited my mood a lot better.

The third thing I did when I got back to LA was send out emails to Piper's editors, letting them know about her behavior and threatening to expose it. The very real implied threat that the information would be used against her discouraged them from continuing to hire her. No one wants that kind of bad press. Not even the press.

I know it's vindictive as fuck, but it's also well-earned. My own "Vigilante Shit," and I believe Taylor would be pleased to know the day I hit send on those emails, I drew my cat eyes sharp enough to kill a man.

Or, in this case, a woman.

Millie, Coco, and Natalie made a group text that included me and was largely dedicated to keeping tabs on Piper. I think she most recently published an article in the Martha's Vineyard periodical all about their annual regatta gala. How the mighty have fallen.

The only thing I haven't done since I got back to LA—even though every day I consider taking the leap—is DM Kit.

I never got her phone number before she left the desert, and in the weeks since then she's been mostly MIA from all her social media accounts. The one exception was a post she made a couple days after she left Millie's wedding. It loaded on all her accounts and was just a simple text image saying she was taking a break from content creation. She gave no indication of when she would be back, and did not address the still heavily shared and commented-on viral video of us dancing.

For a few weeks, I gained new followers as her fans figured out who I was and came over to my Instagram to lurk. Many have since unfollowed me for lack of Mystic Maven sightings, but a hefty number remain and even engage with my content.

"Warmer, warmer." I hear Coco's voice from behind me. She's talking about my clothes. She's become a sounding board for my aesthetic evolution, weighing in on how to strike a balance between personal style and professional branding.

She dangles a set of keys in front of my face when I turn around.

I won't launch my agency for a few more months, but the space in which I will do the launching is still up in the air.

"My friend Hugo owns the space and he's not *technically* showing it for another month, but if you want to get it premarket price, he's willing to listen." The group text, aptly named *Desert Bitches* (by Coco, of course), also yielded some leads on studio spaces all over the city, but this is the first one in budget and in my ideal area.

My phone starts to buzz. *Zoe.*

"We're waiting," I say when I answer.

"I'm walking over from the parking garage now," Zoe says, out of breath. "Do not leave me behind." I hang up without confirmation.

Zoe won't quit Love, Always until a month before we launch, but I'm already paying her a small hourly rate to help facilitate all our pregaming. My hope is that by the end of Q2 I can make her salaried and give her a more fitting title than "assistant to the director."

"Did I tell you that Jenni is dating one of the dudes from *Selling Sunset*?"

"There are dudes on that show?" I quip.

She raises her brows. "Exactly."

"So you've officially given up then?" I ask. She doesn't reply to that, but I really hope—for both of their sakes—that she has. I don't know what kind of person would make Coco genuinely happy, but Jenni isn't the person.

"Jesus, she's going to get hit by a car." Coco completes her sidestep of my inquiry, focusing instead on watching Zoe dodge a Tesla in the pedestrian walkway.

Zoe has not developed chill even though she now no longer questions her value to me.

She whips an iPad out of her bag and illuminates it before shoving her sunglasses up to hold her hair back. They strain against the pressure.

"Okay, I have our specs for the studio space, so we can compare with this one." Zoe looks up to see we're both staring. "I'm here, let's go."

Coco chuckles as she opens the door, letting us into a tight stairwell with a large, bright window at the top. The stairs take us up to the studio, an open loft with windows on three sides. It's a blank canvas except for the functional and attractively designed kitchenette and bathroom. The lack of other walls or décor is both a pro (absolute freedom) and con (there's nothing existing to build off). I walk the floor as Zoe takes some measurements, dutifully inputting them into the iPad.

I step up to the window, taking in the view of the row of dining and shops on the street below. If I get this place, I'll have to live and work out of it. My budget does not allow for a separate apartment and my lease is up next month. My parents have agreed to house some of my furniture and extra belongings until I can get a more permanent living space.

"What do you think?" Coco asks. "Knee-jerk reactions only."

"I want it," I reply. "But you know Zoe won't swing for it if she thinks it's too small."

"It's massive," Coco replies. "You could roller-skate in here. Set up a dance floor and boogie." Coco does a disco jig to demonstrate.

My stomach twists.

The last time I danced was with Kit at Millie's wedding. My jaw clenches, but Coco doesn't seem to notice the tender spot she's inadvertently pushed on.

"Oh shit!" Zoe exclaims from the other side of the loft.

"Please tell me that's a good *oh shit*," I say, even though it sounds more like the disastrous kind.

Zoe looks like a kid who got her finger caught in the cookie jar. Not promising. She approaches, iPad out in front of her, and I can tell by her twitchy expression that she is about to launch into an overexplanation.

"What I'm about to tell you might piss you off," she says. Coco guffaws. "So bear that in mind and confirm you want to risk it but will not hold me accountable."

"Zoe, this, right here, is freaking me out," I reply. She blinks and stutters to a stop, waiting for me to respond to her request. "Okay, yes, I confirm."

She turns the iPad around to show us the screen. She has YouTube pulled up and the Mystic Maven main page open. It doesn't register with me for a second that the reason she's showing me this screen is because Kit has uploaded a new video.

"After she announced her hiatus, I set up alerts for new video postings in case she came back. I know you've been playing it cool since the wedding, but we can all tell you are hurting."

I can't feel my legs. I look to Coco, who is nodding in agreement. I can't breathe.

"This just hit my inbox." She walks closer so that I can easily read the title.

"Choose Your Own Way to Come Out," a play on her popular video series *Choose Your Own Tarot Adventure*. It's a little over four minutes long.

"Julia," Zoe says. "Say something."

The thumbnail image is her face, with a tastefully designed background in the colors of the bi flag. Her hair is tipped with fresh pink, her makeup is minimal.

"Play it," I breathe.

Zoe taps the button in the center of the video and we all huddle around to watch.

Chapter Thirty-Seven

Kit

EARLIER TODAY

"Are you ready?" Nina is behind the camera. The face of my best friend is the best possible prompt for total and complete honesty.

"No?" I say it like a question. She cackles.

"I have a shot of tequila waiting for you as soon as you're done."

I adjust in my chair, fluffing my hair and doing a few simple inhale/exhales to calm my nerves. I shake my body out and shuffle the deck of cards in front of me. The act has become more of a confirmation of my intentions, and less of a method to manage my mental health. But it's still reassuring no matter why I do it.

"Do you think she'll see it?" Nina asks.

"I can't think about that right now or I might throw up."

Swoosh swoosh swoosh. A card pops out. My hand hovers over it but I already know what it's going to be. Flip.

The Lovers.

I close my eyes, clutching the card.

"Ready."

"Three, two, one, rolling . . ."

I open my eyes, taking a beat before I start to speak.

"Hi, there, lights and loves," I say, impressed with the ease in my voice. "It's me, Mystic Maven, and I know it's been a while. I hope the universe has been treating you well and that karma is your friend. I've been quiet here—well, I've been quiet everywhere. Makes me think of that Taylor Swift lyric—*Nobody's heard from me for months. I'm doing better than I ever was.*"

I take a deep inhale. Fuck. This is harder than I thought it would be.

"But even Taylor had to come out of hiding, and if she can do it, so can I." I touch the ends of my hair, twisting them nervously. "I wanted to stay away at first because every time I saw the video—you all know which video I mean—my anxiety would spike, adrenaline would flood my system, my heart rate would shoot up so fast I got scared it would never settle back down. I've had panic attacks since my late teens, but they got really bad in college. That's actually how I got into tarot at first. It helped me understand my emotions and gave me a sense of control in a world where very little felt like it was happening on my terms."

My eyes drift away from the camera. "I guess that's a story for a different day.

"As you can tell from the title of this video, I'm here to tell you—this community of beautiful souls—a story. My story. My way. On my terms. No one should have the moment of coming out taken from their control. No one should have to see themselves all over social media sharing a moment they thought was private. The person who posted that video did so without my permission, but something that they meant to harm me—and, in no small way, harm her—"

Julia.

"—empowered me instead."

I look directly into the camera.

"So here it is. Here *I* am." I tighten my hand around the tarot card. "I'm happy to say, out loud, that I am bi."

There it is. Nina does a cheer off camera, waving a little bi flag I had no idea she brought with her. I feel the corner of my lip edge up.

Calling myself bi feels right, *right now*. The more I learn about my own sexuality, the more I see my own queerness through the lens of a rainbow spectrum.

The more I know that my experience is mine alone.

Mine to understand. Mine to approve. Mine to feel.

All mine.

"Wow, that feels so good to say. I know a lot of you will wonder how I knew, or when. I've always known on some level, but until recently, I was terrified to act on my feelings. And even when I did, I was mortified that someone would find out and it would change who I was to them. I wouldn't be able to get that back—I wouldn't be me anymore, even though my queerness is an integral part of what makes me *me*.

"When that video went viral, I didn't have a choice to keep it a secret anymore. But I wasn't going to let that define what I did next. I wasn't going to react. I wasn't going to hide. I wanted to listen to my own heart, get sure of what it wanted. Because no matter what you saw in that video, it wasn't the whole story, and it definitely wasn't my voice telling it."

Now for the scariest part.

This always works in the movies. The speech. We all know it well. Right now, a montage is playing in our heads of all our favorites. Adam on the plane in *The Wedding Singer.* Julia in the bookshop in *Notting Hill.*

And, of course, the original.

Harry Burns on New Year's Eve pouring out his heart to a weepy, permed-to-perfection Sally Albright.

It's iconic for a reason. Essential to the plot.

Only my love interest isn't here. So, yeah, I really hope she sees this.

"From here on out, I reclaim the narrative. My queerness isn't something I'm scared of anymore and I'm not hiding from it. That means that I have something I need to say to the woman who danced with me that night and who in every way is worth risking it all to be with."

I lock eyes with the camera, pretending I'm locking eyes with Julia.

"My Twin Flame, I'm done running. I'm done being a version of myself that isn't the whole picture. I miss you like mad. I want you so bad. I'm ready to find you again, if you're ready to find me."

Now my heart races for an entirely different reason.

Adrenaline I want. Hope that I believe in.

Chapter Thirty-Eight

Julia

We stand in a stunned silence, but my brain is loud, thoughts all crashing around in my head. Did she just give me a rom-com speech?

"I can see that you're losing grip," Coco says, dropping into my eyeline. "But yes, she did, in fact, declare her affection for you to her now"—Coco looks at the iPad again—"one point two million subscribers." Her hands cup my shoulders. "What are we thinking? What are we feeling?"

"She said she wanted me . . ."

Coco nods. "Umm, yes, important detail to focus on."

"I don't know if this will help or hurt, but I have one more secret I've been keeping," Zoe chimes in, locking the iPad screen and returning to her bag.

"Zoe, you're leaving us hanging in a crisis . . ." Coco says.

My eyes focus on Zoe as she approaches, clutching something in her hand.

Not just something.

A tarot card.

"When we were cleaning up after the wedding, one of the crewmembers found this." She hands it over, facedown. "It fell out of the deck she was using."

It's warm, even though that makes no logical sense. The warmth sends waves through me before I flip it over.

The Lovers.

The grown-up version of the Two of Cups. The Twin Flames in action. Us.

"Tell me everything you know about rom-com endings."

Chapter Thirty-Nine

Kit

It's been a week since the video posted to my YouTube channel. It wasn't the way I wanted it to happen, but Piper forcing me out on social media didn't hurt my channel at all. In fact, the viral explosion of it garnered me more followers, every day, for weeks.

But it's nothing compared to the reception of my own coming out.

That version has brought in interest from *Good Morning America* and the *Drew Barrymore Show* podcast. My channel is blowing up, and I am starting to see proof of my theory IRL. You can't truly have a whole, fulfilling life if you are denying a part of your identity.

Coming out changed my existence.

My life.

It's giving me the one that I want.

The response from friends and fellow creators has gone a long way to make this moment feel meaningful. They've shared the video so it eclipsed the original outing. They want me to succeed in this new era of my life, no judgments, no pile on.

After I posted the video, Mom got me a cake with rainbow layers to celebrate. Dad grilled out. Willa showed me and Nina how to work both our cores and pelvic floors while my parents argued about an offer that had come in for the house.

We were moving on, all of us, becoming fuller versions of ourselves.

But Julia still hasn't DMed, and that makes me worried that in the time it's taken me to figure my shit out, she's moved on for the last time. I believe in the magic of the universe, but maybe Madame Moira was wrong. Or maybe it doesn't matter what the universe wants if the people don't anymore.

I want to spiral about it, but that's not productive, and it's definitely not going to change the outcome if I do. So I let the fears exist, but I don't let them shape my thinking. I get my head in the game. This is my first job since Millie's wedding. I need the money for a down payment on an apartment, since just this morning Mom and Dad accepted that offer on the house. In a few weeks, my childhood home will sell to a family moving in from Ohio. A little girl with blond hair will take over my room. Everything will change, and even though I'm almost thirty, it's going to take some adjusting.

Fortunately, I'm getting good at going with the flow and trusting my instincts to guide me.

I check that the address I have is correct. It's a studio space in the Arts District. The event is for a group of visual artists getting ready to launch a show next week. They want me to read the cards for their event.

I push the intercom button.

A woman's voice crackles through the speaker. "Welcome to Euphoria."

"Hi." I try not to sound weirded out. "This is Mystic Maven—Kit. I'm here for the tarot reading. I was hired by Zed."

"The Omega, yes." Ha, okay. Because Zed for Z, the end of the alphabet. Jesus, at least the pay is good.

They buzz me in. I take the staircase up to the second story, per the instructions.

But when I step into the loft, it's not anything like what I expected.

They've strung lanterns around the room, their golden light complementing the sunset that cuts through the windows on three sides of the space. The room is flooded with color and life. There are flower arrangements dotting the floors, paintings of desertscapes and night skies creating a story around the room.

It's an homage, perfectly designed, but it's not what I'm focusing on. My eyes have fixed on the woman standing at the center of the room.

Dressed in poppy orange.

Her fade shaved.

Her nose glinting with a piercing.

In her hand she holds a card. I recognize it immediately as one of my own from a deck I haven't touched since the desert. I didn't know it was missing, but somehow it makes sense that she has it.

"Are you doing what I think you're doing?"

She steps closer. I step closer, too.

"You got your speech," Julia says, her face coming into sharp clarity as she nears me. She's never looked more like herself. Her wild waves tossed to the side, her skin tan and glowing, her tiny waist snatched up with a belt. "Let me have mine."

I bite my bottom lip. Waiting.

"You're no one's manic pixie dream girl," she begins, catching my eyes in hers. Reeling me in with her gaze. "You're not the ingenue of a story someone else is writing. You're here for so much more than just to inspire a greater appreciation for life in the main character." She smiles with her whole body and it cracks me open. Feelings I've been holding in erupt all over my skin.

The sharpest of them being joy.

"You aren't for my benefit, but still, it's hard to believe that you might want me. I don't think I'll ever get over it, because in my wildest dreams I never expected I'd get to fall in love with a woman like you."

My heart races, but it's the kind of racing that makes you feel like you can fly.

"I don't know everything about you. You don't know everything about me. But I want to uncover every mystery that you want me to, and I want to be with you for every hard decision and scary moment. I don't want to own you or make you feel like you aren't your own person. I want you to be free and I want nothing more than to be by your side for a lifetime of unexpected adventure or just lying on the couch and watching Netflix." I laugh as tears break free from my eyes. "I'll take anything, really, I'm way less picky than I used to be."

Somehow as she's been speaking, we've kept moving, like at the centers of our bodies are magnets that draw us into each other.

From somewhere in the room, music begins to play.

The song.

The one we last danced to. The one Piper tried to steal from us.

But this love is good. It is alive, back from the dead.

"I triple-dog dare you to dance every dance with me." Her voice quivers as she extends her hand to me.

"Do I need to say yes?" I reply, taking her hand and pulling her into me.

"I wouldn't mind hearing it," she says, tucking her free hand into my hair and running it over my earlobe to my chin, where she holds on. Ready to kiss me. "Just one more time."

"Yes." I let my forehead fall against hers. "Forever, a million times, yes."

When our lips touch

two flames, broken apart, mended together, become finally, forever

one.

Next Halloween

Kit

It's steamy, the air tacky with humidity.

A heat wave at Halloween, a true Los Angeles classic. I'm sitting on a small plaid picnic blanket saving our spot while Julia gets us bratwursts. Kids run around blowing bubbles, dressed up as Buzz and Woody, Mario, Luigi, and Peach—any character you can imagine. Parents sip beer and fish through Halloween candy bags as the band sets up for the show.

It's the first Haunt O' Ween I've attended since I left middle school, but I'm not here just to eat a food truck dinner and listen to a queer girl cover band known for their stellar renditions of '90s and early aughts hits. Although, I'm hoping they bring out the Alanis tonight, and I can tell from the beleaguered parental crowd gathering in anticipation that I'm not the only one.

I smooth out the pleats of my hot pink skirt, adjust the barrette in my hair.

First Halloween together as a couple, we had to choose a queer iconic pair to portray together. No surprise there were a lot of important gaps in my gay cinema knowledge—an offense that we have been working to remedy. I had the rom-coms covered since I'd watched them all as part of my lifelong obsession, and since there weren't that many to begin with.

Not nearly enough.

Julia has made it her mission to transform my family's tradition of Friday Movie Nights into a new couples' ritual. It's your basic Netflix and chill situation—on the couch I bought myself, in the apartment I rented all on my own—but with a deep dive into queer stories that graced the big and small screens over the last ten years.

We debated our gay couple costume of choice. Listing out all the possible combinations until we landed on one we both loved.

Megan and Graham from *But I'm a Cheerleader.* A game changer in queer media. And a pretty easy costume to put together. We've been surprised how many Gen Zers are familiar with the pair, calling us out in admiration, applauding our attention to detail.

We came to the Haunt O' Ween festival to have some fun, but we also had a plan. Or, I had a plan and Julia went along with it because she loves me.

Find Madame Moira, tell her she was right about us. The final button on this part of our story. The World card to end one chapter and begin the next.

My own closing scene from the rom-com I no longer need to play a role in.

Madame Moira was advertised on the website, her booth number listed, but when we got there tonight, we found the booth filled by an antiques dealer claiming all his items are haunted.

No mysterious tarot reader to be found. Just a lot of creepy-ass dolls.

Julia drops down beside me, crossing her legs in her long pink skirt.

"I got us extra sauerkraut," she says. "Despite the fact that it will ruin our breath for the rest of the night."

"At least we'll be foul together," I reply, leaning over to nuzzle her and plant a kiss on her neck. When I sit back up, I can feel her eyes searching my face. Reading it, gathering information, trying to suss out my thoughts.

Trying and succeeding.

"You're disappointed we didn't find the psychic," Julia says.

"I know what you're going to say," I reply, cutting her off before she can get there. "*This isn't a movie.* But wouldn't it have been perfect?" I don't want to sulk, so I bite into my brat and look away from her toward the stage.

"It's still pretty perfect to me." She touches my hand, brushing the knuckles with her thumb before locking our fingers together.

I melt. She's right. Of course she is. An open-air concert at the Halloween festival where our epic love story technically began—iconic. I tug her up from the ground and bump her hip with my own.

"You're right," I say, pressing my lips to her ear to make sure she can hear me over the first chords of "Don't Speak." "You make everything pretty perfect."

As I'm leaning into her, my eyes catch on something over her shoulder.

No, *someone.*

A swath of raven-black hair. A cape of midnight purple.

Our gazes lock across the expanse, and I can feel that she's not just looking through me, at the band or the food trucks, the families or the kids in costume.

I see her see us.

And then I see her smile.

Acknowledgments

Writing *The Lovers* was the culmination of a many-years-long journey to leave behind the confines of a life that didn't serve my true identity. If you had told me all those years ago that *this* would happen, that I would be writing a sapphic rom-com as my romance debut, I probably wouldn't have believed you. Not because I wouldn't have wanted it to be true, but because for that to happen, so much would have to change.

Kit and Julia's story is a testament to my determination to live authentically and love myself enough to honor my own true north. To become my own *ideal*, fabulously flawed in all my realness.

Without that journey, this book wouldn't be here. But nothing in life is accomplished alone.

The first person who believed in *The Lovers* was my agent, Katie Shea Boutillier. From my off-the-cuff pitch to the final pages, you were all in. Your genius, your guidance, and your belief in my ability to tell this story fueled its wild ride to publication. You are lightning in a bottle. Thank you for lighting my way. Working with you has changed my life—let's keep making magic together for years to come.

My editor superstar, Kristine Swartz. You gave me the note that unlocked this whole story, and showed me that not only did you get what I was trying to do, but you saw me, the author in the making and human being writing the words. I love that we get to make beautiful books together, but I also love that we are BTS ARMY cohorts. You are truly a kindred spirit in all the most important ways.

Without BTS, this book would not exist. I found BTS when I needed them most. I will never forget sitting in the dark, watching Namjoon deliver the "Speak Yourself" speech at the UN, because it was then—that moment, crying into my pillow—that I promised myself not only would I love all the colors of my identity, but I would let those colors shine bright and loud. In some of the hardest moments, BTS gave me strength to keep loving myself and keep telling my truth. Kim Namjoon, Kim Seokjin, Min Yoongi, Jung Hoseok, Park Jimin, Kim Taehyung, and Jeon Jungkook: You are more than seven to me.

Berkley team extraordinaire! Mary Baker, Caitlyn Kenny, Christine Legon, Tara O'Connor, Anika Bates, Sarah Maxwell, Vikki Chu, Hannah Gramson, Alicia Hyman, and Lindsey Tulloch—there is no home I'd rather have for my adult romances, and no better team. Thank you for the work you put into making this book such a beauty.

To my longtime CPs and dearest friends, Tracey Neithercott and Sara Biren, you two have seen all the ups and downs, given countless notes, shared tears and cheers, and never once stopped believing I could make my dreams come true. I am so glad I chose you both from that blog hop years ago and made you become my forever friends.

Liz Parker: You get a paragraph all to yourself, because you gave me my first tarot deck since I was too superstitious to buy one for myself. Without that gift, I wouldn't have been able to write *The Lovers*. Somehow you always know what to say to elevate my writing, but you also always have the best advice for anything from herbal remedies for my uterus to what to do when one of my plants is looking poorly. You are a friend who became real family, and I am thankful every day that we met, but I am even more thankful that you moved to LA.

Emily Wibberley, my agent sis who has become a most valued ally and friend. You are the smartest person I know (don't tell Austin). Thank you for being someone this secretive Scorpio can truly trust. Austin Siegemund-Broka, Bridget Morrissey, and Farrah Penn, y'all are the coolest. We should really check on our garage ghost, don't you think? Gretchen Schreiber, thank you for listening to me spiral over everything from publishing to BTS.

Courtney Kae and Falon Ballard, I am so happy I met-cute (see what I did there?) you two. Your warmth and kindness welcoming me into the LA author community has truly been a bright light, and I am so incredibly grateful. To the Solvang Boozy Book Babes: Kate Spencer, Erin La Rosa, Alexandria Bellefleur, Evelyn Skye, Sonia Hartl, Carlyn Greenwald, Susan Lee, Lacie Waldon, Holly James, and S.L. Astor, when are we writing that wine-themed anthology together?

My agent bro Matthew Hubbard: Getting to know you has brought so much joy into my DMs and texts. Your encouragement and enthusiasm acts as a jolt of energy to my cranky Scorpio soul.

My BTS ARMY leaders, Alice and Catherine: If BTS gets

credit, you should, too. All the spirals in hotel rooms, all the photocards, and all the no-sleep nights blossomed into friendships that run deep and give abundantly. Thank you for teaching me to be ARMY *and* for introducing me to Nina, Reera, Loni, and Sherry, the BTS Crew. I love all you weirdos.

To all the bookstagrammers/booktokers/podcasters who have been cheering for *The Lovers* since the announcement, thank you for being excited for this book and sharing it proudly. Your support means the world to me. And to my fellow queer authors: Thank you for your bravery, your honesty, and your stories.

My *The Lovers* playlist was an anthem built by queer musicians. Reneé Rapp, Halsey, Hayley Kiyoko, Demi Lovato, boygenius—your music was my companion in the solitude of creating this story. I learned so much more about my own queerness by listening to your words. And to Taylor Swift—without "The Very First Night (Taylor's Version)," I would not have unlocked the plot.

Mom, you taught me to be strong by showing me every day how to persevere. You were my first-ever favorite storyteller; thank you for teaching me the ropes. Dad, thank you for introducing me to rom-coms and being proud of me even if my life doesn't look at all like how you imagined it would. To Samantha, your love and support for my writing is an act of bravery. I am honored to call you friend and family.

To my hypnotherapist, Jenn Levin, thank you for helping me heal. Tarot, astrology, and sound baths play a role in *The Lovers*, but they also have served as tools in my journey of self-love. These nonreligious spiritual practices have helped me connect with my own intuition in the most intrinsic ways.

To every reader who picks up this book: I hope you find joy

when you read, and I hope you know you are beautiful, worthy of love and the life of your dreams.

Sam, my son, my favorite human. All those hours you spend hanging out with me watching *Modern Family* or playing *Mario Party* or listening to music tell me how much you love me. You are growing up well, and I am ever so proud to be your mom. Samson, you are my soulmate dog, and your love has helped me through deep darkness. James, you're a very good boy. Zuko the dragon, I don't care what Sam says, you do like when I pet your beard.

Finally, last and greatest, Nathan. Your love created a safe place for me to become *me*. You are endlessly fascinating, you are kind, you make the best cocktails, and you hold me gently, lift me bravely, love to watch me soar. Thank you for doing this life with me.

Photo courtesy of the author

Rebekah Faubion is the author of queer rom-coms with tons of heart and more than a little steam. She is also the author of the young adult horror novel *Lost Girls*, from Delacorte Press. When she isn't writing books that make her bi soul sing, she enjoys watching anything romantic or scary (or, better yet, *both*), hiking in the Hollywood Hills, and reading tarot by candlelight.

VISIT REBEKAH FAUBION ONLINE

RebekahFaubion.com

RFFaubion

AuthorRFFaubion